COUNTRY LIVING: THE HOMESTEADER'S BIBLE

Other TAB books by the author:

Dedication:

With love and thanks to Caroline for her patience, proofreading and personal caring.

Acknowledgements:

I would like to thank the following manufacturers and organizations for supplying illustrations and information for this book: W. Atlee Burpee Company, Hand Tool Institute, Chrysler Corporation, Koppers Company, Majestic Company, Teco Products and Testing Corporation, Jer Manufacturing Inc., Homelite and Sears, Roebuck and Company. Their help is greatly appreciated.

No. 1301
$21.95

COUNTRY LIVING: THE HOMESTEADER'S BIBLE

BY CHARLES R. SELF

TAB BOOKS Inc.

BLUE RIDGE SUMMIT, PA. 17214

FIRST EDITION

FIRST PRINTING

JANUARY—1981

Copyright © 1981 by TAB BOOKS, Inc.

Printed in the United States of America

Library of Congress Cataloging in Publication Data

Self, Charles R
    Country living.

    Includes index.
    1. Farmhouses—Design and construction—Handbooks, manuals, etc. 2. Agriculture—Handbooks, manuals, etc. 3. Rural conditions—Handbooks, manuals, etc.
I. Title.
TH4920.S44   690'.867   80-23583
ISBN 0-8306-9672-5
ISBN 0-8306-1301-3 (pbk.)

Contents

Introduction

Country living is something that all or a great many of us seem to want these days. Country living may be the answer for a few people, but far from as many people think it is, will be or can be. First, moving to the country is no longer as simple as it was back in the days my grandmother sold one 360-acre farm for less than $4,000, and bought another of about the same size for a similar price. Now you will be lucky to find land priced under $1,000 an acre in most areas of the United States, even rural areas.

Last year I missed a chance to buy a 169-acre place, with a livable but old 10-room house. The asking price was $65,000. There was no road frontage. The property was about two-thirds timberland, but remaining land was cleared and fenced (with barbed wire). There was lots of work to do, and not an outbuilding worth keeping. Still, with a 10½ percent mortgage, it would have been a superb buy for this decade. Unfortunately, the required down payment was out of my reach. Today, mortgage money is just about out of reach, with near 18 percent rates, when it is possible to find the money. That will change, of course, but we can all bet that if land prices come down, they won't come down very far. Population pressures assure, or should assure, a continuing rise in the price of land, if not building.

Locating land, and paying for it, are only two of the problems a person or family wishing to return to the country will encounter. If you're well off, these two problems don't need to concern you. But over the past decade, I've seen an awfully large number of people totally unsuited to country life take to the farms and small ranches in the countryside. A few of these people may make it but most will not. The reasons are not always simple.

7

For the blue collar worker who is used to hard physical labor and who hunts and cleans his or her own game, the chances are probably better. Then we run into one other problem—isolation. Country living doesn't have to be isolated, but cheaper land usually is pretty far from any center of what we call civilization, and sometimes quite a distance from other people. You may say that's fine. What you want is to get away from others. But have you ever tried it? You will likely have to miss not seeing a play at night, going out to a fancy restaurant, haunting museums and missing coffee with a group of friends. My advice is to try it first. Socialization is a fact of human life. Missing it too frequently can do some odd things to the average person's psyche.

Solitude may not be a problem for you. Hard physical labor may not be a bother, but other difficulties crop up, some because of lost conveniences, some for other reasons. It may not be possible any longer to zip over to the corner store and grab a loaf of bread or quart of milk. Sure, the country store is alive and well—very well, today, since the cost of fuel has risen. But the prices tend to be alive and well, too. Planning ahead for shopping trips becomes essential if the distance to a major shopping center is much over five miles.

In addition to such minor problems, consider that if you use electricity, when the power goes out it sometimes stays out for days. Last year I sat in my home in Virginia for 4½ days with no electricity. Fortunately, wood stoves are all I use for heat anyway, and I had more than enough kerosene lanterns around to give plenty of light. Others who needed electric stoves for cooking and furnaces for heat had to move to town. We were short of water, but we also always keep at least 10 gallons in reserve, though that's far from enough to do everything. It does keep the teeth brushed and the worst of the dishes washed, while a slit trench serves as a latrine. It beats $35 or more a night for a motel.

Country living also involves getting dirty in a way many city people can't imagine. We may not face the grit and grime of smoggy conditions or the effects of many chemicals in the air, but we do face getting down in the mud and moving animals, working on our own vehicles and cleaning out stalls. You really haven't lived until you have to get a 75 pound hog out of the back of a cage in a pickup when it doesn't want to go. *That* can be an experience in getting filthy.

For those who don't choose to become vegetarians, sooner or later will come the choice of either continuing to buy meats and poultry or purchasing feeder calves, pigs and chickens for later slaughter and butchering. Many farmers in this area have no idea of the cost of beef in retail stores these days. Their cost is the calf, plus whatever grain it takes to fatten it. They then kill the animal and butcher it themselves. For most of us, going beyond the slaughter stage may be impractical since we lack the butchering skills and the equipment needed to flash freeze the meat once the animal is cooled out and cut up. In fact, slaughtering may not be a good idea. That is something to take up locally as you may have no trouble hoisting a 1,000 pound steer onto the back of your pickup, but the local slaughterer may not wish to handle an animal killed by others.

In country living, the practicalities dominate. The closer you wish to come to the simple life, the more those practicalities are going to win out over anything else. Modern technology can cut farm work by a huge percentage, but there is no way to eliminate it. The less modern power used, the greater the amount of physical labor you'll have to put out and the longer each job will take. We hear a lot today about conserving energy by using various methods of producing other types of energy (methane gas, alcohol, etc.) for use with farm equipment. In almost every case, though, a small farmer will waste time and money trying to move to alternate energy sources. As an example, it now costs about $1650 to fuel the equipment to till a 40-acre farm, assuming 1250 gallons of fuel used at present prices. Producing enough 180 proof alcohol to replace the gasoline used would cost a minimum of $2100, and probably more, while taking five acres of land out of production to grow the grain crop for the alcohol to be distilled. That five acres can be considered a part of the cost, too.

So country living is not all getting away from rampaging

subways and snotty taxi drivers. But there is that part, too, along with the taste of fresh vegetables in season. There is the joy of knowing you have stocked enough food to get through the winter with no problems, and will have few food expenses beyond the stuff you choose not to grow yourself. You won't be jostled by crowds nor snarled at while shopping. My lawyer told me the other day the best part, or one of the best parts, of country life for him is not having to stand in line. Even when he goes to town to pay taxes or do some other chore, he is almost always the first, second or third person in line.

Taxes will be another item not quite as bothersome as in and around cities. Because of the lower level of services provided, property taxes in rural areas tend to be lower than around major urban areas. I can cite one example. In Westchester County, NY, a few years ago, a brick ranch house on one acre had taxes of $2380 annually. Here in Virginia, a smaller and less costly house on two acres had taxes of $77 last year, and probably not much more this year. Both regions have completely volunteer fire departments; neither has local police protection. State police and sheriff's deputies do that work. This area has no trash pickup (dumpsters are placed every few miles), while the New York region requires a monthly payment. Road care is excellent here and not so great in New York.

The only real difference is the number of children per family and the cost of schools. I'll admit I don't believe the schools here live up to those in Westchester County, but I also don't believe the schools up there are as good as they are perceived to be. And I graduated from high school and college in New York State.

A house evaluated at about ⅓ the market price of the New York house has taxes of less than 5 percent of those in New York. Services show little if any difference, except for town sewage and water, both of which must be paid for separately. Schools here are adequate if not excellent.

There are other differences, of course. Sales taxes here are about half those in most of New York, but the various fees on a vehicle are higher by quite a lot. In New York State, you pay a specific amount per pound of vehicle. In Virginia you pay a flat rate, which generally works out to be less than the New York rate. But you also pay a $10 annual city or county fee, plus a one time $7 titling fee and an annual personal property tax at a rate set in your locality. Obviously, not every area will work the way these two do.

Other financial factors will need to be considered when thinking about country living. How do you make a living? Can you maintain a comfortable living standard out in the boondocks? Don't count on farming to do it for you, as most small farmers today must work another job to get by. Have you some marketable skill such as welding that might provide at least a portion of your support in the country? While most farmers are able to weld at least a little, not all, or even many, are really proficient at the more complex types. Could you start cutting timber or pulpwood for a living? Can you do, carpentry, plumbing and electrical work? Skills like these are of great value in the country.

You will note that I have not listed such occupations as advertising copywriter or public relations counsel. While such work is available, it is much rougher to break into, no matter how much experience you have. It is hard to get ahead of any local people doing the work already, no matter how bad. If no one is doing such work, it is just as tough to convince local merchants and others that they need that work, even though the ads run are often abominable. In most cases, head and hands must be used to make a living in the country.

As far as trying to make it working with crafts—whether pottery, leather, macrame or other—you will do well to have some city outlets lined up. Again, practicality dominates. Country living can be a great joy, but two words take precedence over all else—*preparation* and *practicality*. We will try to prepare you for the pitfalls as well as the joys through the rest of this book.

Charles R. Self

Country Land

Buying country land doesn't seem like something requiring a great deal of thought and preparation. But it is. First, such land is becoming less readily available. What is often available is not at all suitable for many types of use, whether recreational or farming. Second, all land is rapidly becoming more expensive, thus worthy of more thought before purchase. Third, interest rates are now starting to drop from record highs, but there is little reason to expect the drop to be a great one, or even of long duration, so the land cost is even higher.

LAND USES

Your first job, before even considering an area of the country in which you might like to live, is to think of just what you want the land for. Horse farming is one thing, while raising corn or hay crops is entirely different. A horse farm can be located with most of the pastures on pretty fair slopes, as long as a reasonable amount of level ground is available for rest. Grain and hay crops need to be located on nothing more than gently rolling land, unless you get a particular thrill from seeing a $45,000 combine tumbling down an incline. A dairy farm can be run in moderately steep country, as can a beef operation (if you have an area where the beef can be finished without walking off too much weight). Most livestock can be raised and thrive on land not really suited to other types of farming.

As a not so incidental point, there are a lot of people around who feel we waste a great deal of cropland in raising livestock. These people may generally be well-intentioned. However, even though it takes more space to raise beef cattle than it does grains for human consumption, not all that much land is wasted. Some is, of course, and more is wasted in raising grains for feeding the livestock. Generally, world food shortages seem more to come from lack of knowledge and supplies of basic farm equipment than from lack of land.

CHOOSING AN AREA

Once you've decided on the use for the land, it is time to consider areas of the country, if you're not already living in a rural area you enjoy. Again, sit down and figure out what you like in weather and land types. My best friend moved from the East Coast to Utah a few years ago. He will not return East permanently because the high and dry climate agrees with him totally. I moved from New York, in the foothills of the Catskill Mountains, to Virginia, in the foothills of the Blue Ridge Mountains, and wouldn't return North on a bet. Moving only this far south brought the average winter temperature up about 20 to 25 degrees, and lengthened the growing season almost 45 days, without appreciably changing the heat of summer. If New York City is sweltering, I am likely to be a bit warmer than I really like, but that seldom lasts long (Fig. 1-1).

Do you wish to live by or near a lake of any size? If so, consider the importance of waterfront land to you once again, for the prices tend to start at the ridiculously high and go up quickly. In this area, where little land is really worth over $1500 an acre and some sells for as little as $750, waterfront property at Smith Mountain Lake has risen to as much as $25,000 an acre, with none available for less than $10,000. Prices at the lake are rising on an average of 100 percent a year.

Fig. 1-1. Shade trees can help reduce heat in country areas. This Norway maple is a fast growing variety.

PROPERTY SIZE

The size of your country property will be determined by the use(s) to which you put it. A small horse farm can be started on less than a dozen acres, but probably twice that is a better idea, and more if possible. Much depends on whether or not you intend any farming activity as an income supplement or, eventually, as a total source of income. In the last case, you could be in trouble. I can't think of a single small farmer I know who is not doing something else to pick up the gaps left by inflation and the vagaries of farming in general. By small farmer, I'm not talking of the federal figures of 50 or fewer acres, but people with farms up to and occasionally more than 200 acres. In any case, it is impossible to really give you an indication of the size farm needed for a particular purpose in any area you might choose.

While you may easily be able to raise a dozen horses on a dozen acres, buying winter feed, in many spots in the East, drier land in the West will force you to either buy feed for the whole year or have five, six or more acres per animal. Unless you're raising top of the line Arabians or Thoroughbreds, a dozen horses, even all mares, will probably not produce a foal crop each year large enough to support you. Though the cheap horse has just about disappeared, selling six foals annually for $1000 each will, if you're very lucky, cover the upkeep of the foals and the mares, but probably not the stud fees. Six foals that go for $5000 each might bring a slight profit, but the stud fees will be much higher. The profit increase will be a lot less than the gross increase in dollars.

For farm size related to needs, I would suggest a careful talk with the county extension agent for the area you are considering. He or she will also be able to give you some idea whether or not the kind of operation you are considering would make economic sense in that area. If there are already 10,000 quarter horses being raised in a two or three county area, you might just be wiser to consider the virtues of Appaloosas, Arabians, beef cattle or dairy cattle.

RENTING A FARM

Once the area is determined and you have pretty well solidified your wants and needs, I would suggest, particularly if farming is the object and you have little or no experience, that you either rent a small farm, instead of buying, or hire out. Pulling up stakes totally may not be a great idea. It is always possible to find a dream turning into a nightmare.

It is a good idea to spend some time familiarizing yourself with the neighborhood, as well as the work necessary. If you rent a farm or hire out on one, you'll begin to pick up some of the skills needed for success in the country, even if the type of farm work you hire out to do is not exactly the same as you intend on doing later. Much of the skill needed for one job will easily transfer to another, though the science of raising chickens doesn't move all that well to working with dairy cattle, from the point of view of livestock care. Still, the various carpentry chores, cleanups, watering and so forth are similar, even if you don't learn how to milk, mix cattle feed, store milk and do other such chores.

MOUNTAINOUS AREAS

If isolation is your desire, and you have some method of making enough money to live on, you may wish to look for what has become the cheapest land now available—mountain land, well up the side of the hill. Obviously this is not true in the Los Angeles area. In most mountainous areas of the country, though, that top of the hill acreage is appreciably lower priced than downhill slopes. The reasons are rather simple. Access can be extremely limited even in good weather. I once started to rent a cabin on a mountain, and took one look at the road in dry weather to realize that only a four wheel drive vehicle could make the trip after even a light drizzle. I like a certain amount of isolation, but I don't believe in extremes, such as being snowed in for weeks at a time. Such cheap land, though, could be a lifesaver if you're unable to locate anything else. But do not forget to include the cost of four wheel drive operation if it is needed. That is not a negligible item these days, with most four wheel drive vehicles costing over $9000 and getting under 10 miles per gallon of very expensive gasoline. Right now, used four wheel drive vehicles are drugs on the market in many areas, so it could easily be possible to get a decent deal on one.

CHECKING THE LAND

Land checks require many things. First, a bit of thought for your own situation is essential. Do you have children? If so, what ages? Schools become important when children are involved in a move to the country. It pays to find out which school your child will be attending and what sort of reputation it has. Too, in rural areas, find out how far the child must travel and about how long it will take. It is easily possible in my area of Virginia for children to leave home in winter before full light and get home as dusk falls. Many gravel and dirt roads in a county covering just under 771 square miles means a lot of time on a school bus for those in outlying and border areas. It might, in some cases, pay to jump a county line in order to save some of that travel time.

MEDICAL, TELEPHONE, ELECTRICAL AND POLICE SERVICES
Now check out medical services. Isolation and country

living is great, but a burst appendix or major injury with no assistance available can cost a life. Readily available medical assistance can save a life. My area is served by two rescue squads of volunteer members who are well trained and do a good job. In most cases, they can be contacted either by telephone or CB radio, and response time is good. As always, such crews receive about one-tenth of the assistance they really need.

Check local telephone service. I don't care what anyone says about telephones in the city, but to me a phone is an essential of country living. It is, for one thing, a major form of social contact. For another, it is a solid way of summoning help in emergencies. If you are locating on top of a mountain, the cost to run in a phone line can be prohibitive, though. I just recently spent $192 extra for about 3000 feet of cable because the nearest terminal prior to mine was more than 40000 feet down the road. The telephone company where I live pays for the first 1000 feet, but you pay $6 per hundred feet after that. Obviously, that doesn't really cover the cost of the cable and installation. But it does assure the company you are not going to move out in a month and leave them holding the sack for a large run they no longer can use.

Electrical service should be no problem in most areas of the country. You may face the same sort of charges as with the telephone if your place is extremely isolated and has never had electrical service run in.

Local police service is another point to check. Here we are covered by the sherriff's department and the state police. Don't ever let anyone kid you into believing there is less crime in rural areas than in urban areas. A quick reading of any day's paper will prove different in a rush. Crime is simply spread out more because there are fewer people.

Tax Rate

Regarding land, first check the tax rate. See how long since the rate has been adjusted and land re-evaluated. If there has been a long lapse since the last reassessment of property, you can bet it won't be too long before one comes up. Constant revision and reassessment is just as bad. A check with the local newspaper files will give you a better idea of what is going on here than will the word of any real estate agent.

External Requirement

Land checks are relatively simple. You've already made up your mind what sort of land you need or want. See if the land meets external requirements: number of acres, number of streams, pasture fencing, possible timber, pulpwood or firewood growing. I have now seen at least a dozen plots of land that were sold and, before closing, were logged off thoroughly, leaving nothing over 4 inches diameter to stand. Land does not always include timber. If you want timber to be left, make sure you say so and get it in writing. Check on the mineral rights, too, while you're at it. Most people do not and it is not often important, but you could be considerably upset to find that below surface rights have already been sold when a survey and drilling crew shows up. There is not a thing in the world you can do to get them out of your pasture. Now the title must be searched, and for this an attorney or title search company is your best bet. Not all country land has been surveyed, even today, so boundaries may be a bit less precise than in city sales. Make sure the title itself is clear, even if the deed reads something like 64 acres, more or less.

Percolation Test

Once these things are taken care of, you will want to find out how the land "perks." A *percolation test* determines just how the soil accepts water flowing into it. It is important around residences since you do not want the septic field to back up on your lawn. Most state health departments won't allow residential construction unless percolation is within certain limits.

If the land you're buying has no house, talk to your neighbors to see how deep they had to drill before getting a good supply of water. There are areas where you may only need to go down 50 to 100 feet, and others where no water can be found in 1000 feet. There is no guarantee that because someone down the road hit nine gallons per minute at 150 feet, you will do the same. It at least indicates that the water table has not dropped out of reach. If the house you buy is more than 20 years old, it would be a good idea to make the same check.

Check for rock outcroppings where you plan to site the house, and look for wooded areas as windbreaks. You will need to find out from what direction your local prevailing winds come to make this check. Rock outcroppings of any size can add a great deal to building costs, so you may well wish to re-site your house if there is a large one in the way.

FINANCING COUNTRY PROPERTY

Financing country property is no rougher today than financing most other property. In other words, it can be pretty rough. Mortgage rates are beginning to back off the 17 ¾ percent mark they had hit, but the drop so far is small and not spreading to a lot of banks. It will probably be quite some time before the rates drop again to a reasonable rate. My idea of a reasonable rate may differ markedly from a banker's. I feel anything over 10 percent is really stretching things. Farmers are in a bad way now, since almost all have to borrow to carry them through until crops are in. The cost of credit is going to force a loss on even the most efficient and possibly wipe out some of the less efficient. *Veteran's Administration* (VA) loans often look pretty good in relation to the standard mortgage loan, but many banks won't touch VA loans. The paperwork is one reason, and the present shortage of loan money is another.

If banks continually turn you down and you have some farming experience, there is another money source to try— the *Farmer's Home Administration* (FmHA). This is not a quick source of money for rural homes and farms. It can be a last resort to those with enough experience to draw up a reasonable financial plan, with enough detail to convince the local board you have a good chance of making it, and at low interest rates. Farm ownership loans at present start at five percent, and operating loans start at seven percent. This is, of course, likely to change as money costs change, but it has held fairly steady even though mortgage money and the prime interest rate have have soared to what only can be called usurious levels.

The process begins with an application form, available at most county extension agents' offices, called an *Application for FmHA Services*. You must be an American citizen, unable to get credit anywhere else, and own, wish to own or operate a family farm. The details then go to a country committee, after checking by the county supervisor. Your next step will be the detailed plan needed. This will list current living expenses, any current farming expenses, income from farm and non-farm jobs. If you have and expect to continue to have considerable non-farm income, you may, if you get the loan, end up paying the top rate of (currently) 11 percent for your loan.

Adequate farming experience is the key to getting the loan in a lot of cases. While a committee in one area may consider several years of part time experience enough, another committee can refuse the loan on the basis of lack of experience. Their discretionary powers are wide. Too, having too much of your income from non-farm sources can kill the loan. There has been a fair amount of scandal attached to FmHA services in the past when hobby farms and giant corporate farms got most of the money actually intended for small farms.

Decisions that go against you can be appealed to state and national offices. Reversals are not all that uncommon. The amount of money, though, is limited. The amount going in so-called limited resources loans to farmers has increased, by Congressional order, to a minimum of 25 percent of FmHA funds for farm loans. Most recent figures show that about half the farm ownership loans went out under that program.

Financing can be difficult and time consuming—FmHA loans take from two to six months to come through *after* approval—but there is money there. Once you get your land, it is time to decide just how to do what you want to do.

2

Building a Country Home

Once country land has been purchased, you'll need to build a place to live, if the original building isn't in livable shape. Or you will need to renovate the older place. In many cases, the simplest choice is to build, for renovatable houses are becoming less easily found these days, especially on farms which have existed for quite some time. Around here it is possible to count several such non-rebuildable places on almost every back road. In many ways it seems a shame, for the old clapboard, brick or stone buildings often have a basic style and grace that we can no longer afford to duplicate. Economics deny us the chance. Building materials for a small home now cost much more than would an entire farm, with buildings intact, less than 40 years ago. There are no more 6 or 8 foot wide staircases and no more 12-foot ceilings. Many more stately Southern homes featured such ceilings for two reasons. First, they are attractive. Second, rooms with high ceilings stay cooler in the sultry Southern summers. Double hardwood front doors are passe in these days when even a single solid 32-inch front door can cost nearly $300.

Still, some old, large homes that might be renovated can still be found. You may need to make a decision as to the work to be done. There are options, of course, but energy efficiency is a prime consideration these days with fuel oil costing upwards of a dollar a gallon. If it is impossible to live in a house while reconstruction goes on, costs have a serious and sad tendency to escalate strongly. Many old farmhouses have been left standing, more or less abandoned, since days before electricity and indoor plumbing were introduced. The work to wire and plumb such houses can be complex and hard, especially for the beginner with little or no experience. The construction of a smaller new frame house is comparatively simple or, at least, rather straightforward.

Siting was also poor on many old farmhouses. Places sitting atop a hill may provide a fine view all around and look majestic, but the increase in heating costs is horrendous. Insulating those old walls is a job for experts with the correct equipment and knowledge, adding to renovation costs. House design has changed radically in the past few years, though the basics are the same. The siting is one portion of the drastic change, as is the increase in insulation needs and heating system design.

SITING

Should you consider adding a new home to your farmstead, choose the site carefully. Protection from prevailing winter wind with exposure to summer breezes can help hold down heating and cooling costs, while attention to the directions of sunrise and sunset can aid in passive solar heating. Wider eave overhangs are easily used to shut out the summer sun—which stands higher in the sky—and allow winter sun to enter. Keeping windows to a reasonable mininum holds down heat loss, for even double and triple glazed windows lose appreciably more heat than does a well insulated wall. Keeping the wall with the maximum number of windows faced south or southeast also helps. Summer sun can be kept out with shutters or heavily lined drapes, while winter sun can be allowed in to warm the house. This is probably the simplest form of passive solar heat and is available to everyone siting a new home.

A full basement will tend to stabilize house temperature a bit and adds, at moderate cost, a fair amount of space useful in many ways. But a basement is something of a personal choice, and site considerations can interfere with such construction. If a building site is perfect in other ways, but offers rock outcroppings so heavy that blasting would be required, it is probably more economical to go with either a slab or pier foundation for the house. Where drainage might seem to be a problem, there are several solutions to help keep the basement dry. Most of these must be done before the backfilling is completed around the foundation. Retroactive measures, other than completely digging out around the basement wall and taking the measures needed in the first place, are seldom totally effective. Recently I have heard of a method that allows sealant to be injected into the ground around a foundation, with great claims for success. Somehow I am unable to figure just how this works, though I have yet to see it done or meet anyone who has. The process sounds to me a bit dubious.

Ground water can also be a problem with a full basement. In some areas, the water table is so near the surface that the excavation for the basement fills almost immediately. In such cases, it is probably best to simply fill in the excavation and move to a slab or pier foundation. The sump pumps needed to remove such dramatic amounts of water will cost a fortune to run. You will still have a wet basement much of the time.

Deciduous Trees

Deciduous trees are always a nice touch around a home. They can be useful as well, so careful planning is needed when trees must be removed. It is common around here for the builder to bring in a bulldozer and simply knock the trees back into a huge pile, stripping the land of just about all vegetation in the process. Then the contractor will build and plant a half dozen or dozen maple or oak whips 6 or 8 feet tall.

Select the site for possible shade trees, whenever possible. Remove only those that might be in the way or pose a danger to the house, or a later problem with the septic field. Deciduous trees provide shade for the house during hot summer months, and drop their leaves to allow winter sun through. If a windbreak is needed, the best method is probably an interplanting of conifers with deciduous trees so that the windbreak remains effective throughout the winter months. Some flat areas almost demand windbreaks. In other areas of the country, you will simply be able to site your home over the brow of a hill to force the prevailing winter winds to flow above the house.

Prevailing Winds

Prevailing winds will vary in most areas of the country, and they often vary quite a lot within just a few miles. In my present locale, winter winds arrive mostly from the North and Northeast quadrant, with summer breezes seeming to come in from the Northwest most of the time but actually varying quite a lot. In truth, either winter or summer winds can vary all around the lot. About a dozen miles from my location, almost all winter wind comes from the Northeast. But I am located in a valley, very close in on the Blue Ridge Mountains, and the shape of the valley often helps to determine just how winds can flow.

Doors and Windows

My house is sited in a rather unfortunate manner, but not quite as bad as it might be. The gable end walls, the short walls of the house, are almost due north and south. The longer walls, with the greatest number of windows, face east and west. I have removed one window entirely from the north wall and added a large sliding door to the east wall, while retaining the original number of windows. The door replaces one, but it provides about eight or nine times the glass area. The door is aluminum, but it is constructed in such a way as to provide what is known as a *thermal break*. This means that the cold exterior of the metal doesn't directly touch the warmer interior parts of the door. It also has a ⅞-inch vacuum between double glazed panes. Check the Montgomery Ward catalogs for such doors, if you can't easily find what you want locally, as that is where I got this one.

The wood casement windows in the house are all double glazed. These were an expense and a half, but heat loss over the original aluminum framed single glazed windows is really cut drastically. Light colored siding of insulated aluminum from Hunter-Douglas also aids things.

MATERIALS

The preceding paragraph illustrates the importance of materials selection for energy conservation, as well as for durability and attractiveness. In certain areas where expense is likely to be fairly high and you are renovating, it pays to buy the best materials. Make sure the selection is from a company apt to stay in business and with the same line for quite some time. Such a decision allows you to buy two or three windows at a time. Save up a few dollars and buy a couple more later in the year, or even years later. Materials such as the new *Luxaclad* siding from Hunter-Douglas are a gread aid to the less experienced home builder. They have a specially designed locking system that allows greater ease in installation. Installing aluminum siding still takes great care, even on a new home, and is not a single weekend job. The addition of foam backing to the Luxaclad siding provides an R-3 insulation value, and backer board over the sheathing can add another R-1 or R-2 depending on the type.

If 2 by 6s are used for all wall stud framing (check local codes first), they are usually placed on 2-foot centers and allow a full 5½ inches of insulation in the walls. This is usually about R-19, and cuts heat loss dramatically over the more normal 3½ inches used with 2 by 4 walls. With 3½ inches of insulation, the standard frame wall will lose about 4,700 Btus per thousand square feet per hour. Raising the insulation to 5½ inches thick cuts the loss to 3,300 Btus. Adding another R-3 to R-4 with insulated siding will cut heat loss by about 15 percent more. The most dramatic results are found in ceiling insulation, of course, since heat rises. Increasing roof insulation from 6 to 10 inches cuts heat loss per thousand square feet from 2,900 to 1,700 Btus per hour. Consider the fact that an uninsulated ceiling will pass about 22,000 Btus per hour. An uninsulated wall will let 19,000 Btus of your cash flow to the outdoors.

All windows should be double glazed, and really cold areas almost require triple glazing. Both add more than a little to the cost for windows, but the payback is getting shorter each year as the cost of fuel rises. The use of 2 by 6 framing instead of 2 by 4s will require you to buy windows and doors with slightly wider casings, adding slightly to the cost. Again, the payback is more rapid than ever before. As you design, though, consider that even double glazed windows pass about seven times the amount of heat as an insulated wall. Exterior doors can now be had with foam filled cores, and all should be supplied with good quality storm doors. Any metal exterior doors should be of thermal break construction, as should metal framed windows. Wood is generally a preferable material for door and window frames. Some companies now produce vinal cased wood frame windows. The final case covering of vinyl cuts down on the need for interior and exterior painting as well as helping to further retard heat loss.

HOME DESIGN

Designing a home is a highly individual matter or should be. Many of us can't afford architects. Nor will many people want exactly the floor plan, exterior design or interior decorating scheme available in many advertised home plans. Many of these plans can be easily changed. Some plan services will actually make suggested changes for a small fee. Floor plans are easily swapped around by the homeowner if a few points are kept in mind. Any non-load bearing partition wall can be moved. The simplest way to determine whether or not a wall is load bearing is to check and see if the house plans show a girder running along the center of the basement ceiling. If there is one, any wall situated along the length of that girder will be load bearing while others will not. Door openings in load bearing walls can be changed. If the structural design is marginal, though, it is best to make sure that the total opening width doesn't exceed that of the original plan.

Kitchen and Dining Room

Farm home, or rural home, design will usually differ in several ways from suburban and city homes, In general, the greatest difference will be in the kitchen. Farm kitchens are larger than city kitchens and need to be, if you have any intention of canning and freezing your own food. You will need space to spread out cooling jars, one or two canners, canning racks or, for freezing, *scalders*. I have seen several kitchens with more than one stove. One practical innovation I saw not too long ago provided a wood stove in a summer kitchen setup to supplement the regular kitchen.

There are at least three good reasons for using a summer kitchen (such a kitchen is usually a shed or other type of structure close to, or even attached to, the main kitchen). First, the steam from canning can soon ruin the best wall and ceiling surfaces. Second, a lot of room is needed for extensive canning, and a shed type structure can cheaply provide this space. Third, if a wood stove is used, you want open walls to allow the heat to escape. In most areas of the country food preservation takes place during the hottest months of the year. There is no need for a fancy setup for the summer kitchen. A shed of adequate size for the preservation activities you envision (I would suggest that the room size be no less than 12 feet square) can be made of pole construction using pressure treated lumber produced from Kopper Company's chemicals (*outdoor* and *Wolmanized* brand names), with a water supply and a properly installed wood cooking range. Electricity can be provided if desired, but it is not essential. Night canning can easily be done by kerosene lamps.

Farm living rooms need not be very large, but dining rooms tend to be larger than those in city residences. The reasons are rather simple. A great deal of farm social life moves around food, so that the kitchen and dining room (for the more formal, or non-family, occasions) are often by far the largest rooms in the house.

Front Porch and Deck

I would recommend both a front porch and a deck placed somewhere on the house, depending on your desires. The deck is a great spot to relax and a fine one, if large enough, to throw parties. We all have the image of the old farmer in the rocking chair on his front porch. It isn't just an image. A drive past any farm area after the sun begins to set will find people on porches, screened and unscreened, letting the heat of the day, and the day's work, fade from their bones as they gently rock.

Bedroom, Bathroom and Full Basement

Bedrooms and baths are pretty much as in other homes. Sewage disposal and water run-in require septic fields and wells, which adds to construction expense.

A large pantry off the kitchen would be desirable, but a full basement is nearly essential. I would recommend going at least one block higher than standard when constructing a basement. This greatly aids later basement finishing by providing a full height ceiling. The full basement provides storage for canned goods and tools needed close to or in the house, while also helping stabilize house temperature. A finished basement isn't essential, but it can provide extra living space at minimal cost. Soon, I'll be finishing the basement in my mother's home. Even with a 10 by 12 foot laundry room framed out, she will gain almost 700 square feet of living space, in this case a small apartment styled bedroom with den and a shower bath. Heat will be provided by electric baseboard units, supplemented by a small wood stove. Actually, the baseboard units will supplement the wood stove, as they will probably only come into use when the house is left vacant overnight. The wood stove will be small because the actual cubic footage to be heated is small and well insulated—only 4900 cubic feet with 3½ inches of fiberglass insulation to a depth of 2 feet below ground level. I do not approve of foam insulation for indoor use, as a few types if burned give off toxic gases. If the exterior wall is above grade, fine, but for below grade use there is nowhere for the smoke to go.

Window and door area is small, though larger than the original builder intended with the addition of one double hung wood window on a wall extending only 1 foot below grade. This is primarily to lighten the overall room, as basements can become gloomy. The stove will be placed at the opposite end of the house from that used to heat the first floor, and I may cut floor vents to the bedrooms above it. That would help keep the upstairs electric heat off on cold nights, without forcing us to leave bedroom doors open.

One entire 12-foot wall of the laundry room will be shelves for canned goods. An inset has been built to hold an upright freezer.

WATER SUPPLY

Rural water supply is a totally different matter than urban water supply. Drilled wells are the main source. Water may be, and often is, needed far from the main well head. Almost all drilled wells today are of the type called *double tubed*. Iron or other material is used for the outside casing of the well, down to the level of solid rock or extremely compacted soil. Inside this casing is a drop pipe extending down to the lowest water level. Such wells must be sited so that there is adequate surface drainage, in areas not generally subject to flooding. They should be uphill from and well away from any septic fields, abandoned wells and sinkholes so that there is no waste transfer to cause water pollution. In no case should any well be located within 50 feet of a privy, septic field, septic tank, barn, hogpen or other such pollution source, including feedlots.

Actual well drilling procedures and casing construction do not need to be covered here, since it is fairly safe to assume you will be hiring a professional to do the job. Make sure, though, you have some ideas of water needs. Discuss this matter with your driller and with your county extension agent in light of any farming plans you have. It is cheaper to drill a single, deep well with one setup of equipment than to come back later and drill a second well or redrill the original one more deeply to get a greater quantity of water. Do not kick the drilling off at the bottom of an old dug well, for the surface water in the old dug well will almost certainly contaminate the water drawn from the depths of the new drilling.

Pumps of many types and brands are available so as to be confusing. Surface pumps often have plenty of capacity with a relatively shallow well. Submersibles are in more general use today, though, and are less susceptible to problems of freezing. But they may be overrated for your needs if the well is shallow. Again, your well driller and county extension agent will be able to provide assistance in making a sensible choice. It is generally estimated that you will need 50 gallons of water per person each day. If water is needed for live-stock, allow for 10 gallons per day for each horse or cow, and about 2 gallons a day for every hog or sheep. The livestock figures would be reduced, naturally, if the animals were pastured with water readily available to them.

Water from all new wells should be tested before use, and water from wells in use should be checked periodically to insure freedom from pollution. It isn't always possible to smell or see pollution that can damage health, so at least an annual test is a good idea. New well pollution may be the result of tool handling and may disappear gradually if the well is pumped daily. Hypochlorite powders can be used to provide available chlorine to sterilize this type of pollution. Chronically polluted water may require the installation of commercial *chlorinators*, a sad thing to think of when one has moved from an urban area to, in part, get away from the nasty taste of treated water. Still, it beats illness such as typhoid fever or chronic dysentery. You can check with your local health department to determine area requirements for both testing and treatment of well water.

PLUMBING

Plumbing for a new building is rather simple to install, but some planning for future needs can cut later costs. Planning for later installations does not include the need to buy fixtures immediately. Simply decide what you wish to go where in the future and provide pipe runs, both supply and waste, to that area, capping the pipes until they are needed. This gives a very moderate increase in present costs and saves a great deal of money in the future.

Today, water supply pipe will be either copper or plastic. At one time galvanized pipe was popular, but it is harder to work with than either plastic or copper and requires more tools. Too, the inside surfaces of both plastic and copper pipe are smoother than that of galvanized, so there is less restriction to water flow. A smaller size pipe can be used. Waste pipe and vent pipe will be cast iron, plastic or copper. Copper is the most expensive and cast iron the hardest to work on. For anyone doing it alone, the best bet for DWV (drain-waste-vent) pipe is certainly plastic.

Plumbing planning should provide for the shortest possible pipe runs, as copper tubing is quite expensive. Long runs of hot water pipe lose a great deal of heat to the air, adding greatly to the cost of heating water, which can be a major factor in home expenses today. Locate plumbing, wherever you can, back to back on walls or, in multi-story homes, in stacks. Place the hot water heater as close as you can to the fixtures being served.

Roughing-In

Roughing-in for plumbing is best done before walls are closed up, of course, but in older homes plaster or wallboard will usually have to be ripped out. The rough-in consists of the pipe runs, which are tested for leaks before the walls are enclosed. Generally, rough-in work is done so that the stub outs for sinks allow a height of 36 inches, with lavatories set from 33 to 35 inches. These figures can be easily modified if members of a family are shorter or taller than average.

To test for leakage, follow your local code directions. Where there is no code for leakage testing procedures, which is often common in rural areas, plug all drainage openings except for the highest one. Then fill the system with water. After the water has stood for about 15 minutes, check all fittings for leaks. If your plumbing system is extensive, it can be checked in sections. Make sure you have a head (height) of water at least 10 feet when doing so. The supply system is tested in the same manner. You must be sure to use portable water and to bring the system up to its working pressure or, if that is not known, a pressure of at least 60 pounds per square inch.

Drainage Systems

Drainage systems consist of fixture drains, each of which must have a trap. Lavatories and sinks have traps you add, but toilets have built-in traps. They also consist of *fixture branches*, which connect several fixture drains; and *soil stack*, which is the vertical soil pipe to which the toilet is connected and which is vented to the roof. This vent is always open ended. In addition, there will be a building drain, the main horizontal drain to carry waste from the house to the disposal facility (usually a septic field and septic tank).

Minimum drain sizes are usually specified by local codes, but in some rural areas there are no codes to guide you. In such cases, bathtub, dishwasher, kitchen sink and laundry tub drains should be at least 1 ½ inches in diameter, while the lavatory can use 1¼-inch pipe. Floor drains, and shower stall drains, should be no less than 2 inches, while the toilet needs at least a 3-inch drain. Fixture branches should be at least a 3-inch drain. Fixture branches should be at least 1 ½ inches in diameter, and the soil stack must be a minimum of 3 inches. The building drain should be no less than 3 inches. Check for local codes, first. Also, check your fixtures, for they will often determine the size pipe you must use. Horizontal drainpipes should slope ¼-inch per foot if they are 3 inches or smaller, while larger drains slope at least ⅛-inch per foot.

Traps are simply devices to prevent sewer gases from backing up into the house. The water held in the trap forms a plug to keep these noxious fumes out. Some sewer gases are poisonous, while *methane* is explosive. They all smell bad, so each fixture must have a trap. Traps should be of the same diameter pipe as the drainpipe, and should be placed as close to the fixture drain as is possible. That pretty much covers the generalities of residential plumbing, and we will go into installation details later.

WIRING

A few people moving to the country may wish to return to the so-called simpler life of yesterday and not use electricity. Especially when the cost of electricity today is considered, using kerosene lanterns, gas refrigerators and other such appliances may seem attractive alternatives. Most of us, though, have become used to and dependent upon a reasonable supply of electricity and have no real desire to drop its use. Generating one's own electricity may someday be more practical than it is now. Windmills can be used in most areas, but the original cost is great, the need for storage batteries acute and expensive, and upkeep can be a problem. A fast check of the cost of kerosene—no longer coal oil, but a petroleum product—tends to negate any feeling of savings one might get from using kerosene for light. Kerosene lamps turn out a great deal of heat, making them a bit unpleasant on warm summer nights. It would be best in rural living to have several kerosene lamps or lanterns about for power failures, but I do not feel that, today, they are really practical as a primary light source.

All wiring done today must conform to the *National Electrical Code* (NEC). This is recommended even in areas where there are no local codes or laws requiring such conformity to the NEC. The reason is a simple one. Properly installed wiring is safe and will handle the job without causing problems. Improperly done wiring can quite easily burn down a house and everything in it.

Copper Versus Aluminum

Copper is the material of choice for wiring in all buildings. For a time, a great deal of aluminum was used. Aluminum has two qualities which make me exceptionally nervous when thinking of using it. First, if aluminum is not anodized to prevent corrosion, it rapidly turns black and can therefore create a high resistance point at a terminal. Second, aluminum has a much greater tendency to *creep* than does copper. Creeping is caused by the material expanding in response to heat and cold. Terminals can loosen, thereby causing high resistance and the chance of a fire inside a wall.

Circuits

Wiring should be planned to suit your needs which, today, almost certainly means the installation of a 150 ampere service box. Circuits are designed for several purposes. One circuit is usually split between two rooms, so that each room has two circuits or more feeding it. This provides a safety factor should one circuit breaker blow, as you will still have light from the second circuit. Circuitry will depend in large part on the appliances you use. For example, an electric stove requires 240 volts, as does an electric clothes dryer and hot water heater. Lighting circuits are normally 15 ampere services, using number 14/2 cable with ground, while appliance circuits are 20 amperes and use 12/2 with ground cable. All modern wiring circuits are of the grounded type. General purpose circuits, which may include lights and wall receptacles, should be 20 ampere, using 12/2 with ground cable.

The kitchen must have at least one separate appliance circuit and will probably be better served with two, in addition to a lighting circuit, which may be shared with another room. Laundry appliances are served with a separate 20 ampere circuit.

Wall receptacles should be spaced no more than 12 feet apart. Kitchen countertop receptacles are handiest when they are no more than 4 feet apart, allowing you to easily plug in appliances without having to move them about.

While it is not required, the NEC recommends a separate 20 ampere general circuit for every 500 feet of floor space, or a 15 ampere service for every 375 square feet. For greatest utility, it is probably best to cut those space figures by 20 or 30 percent.

For farm use, where outbuildings must be lighted and some appliances run, a 200 ampere main service is probably your best bet. In such cases where there is some distance between the house and outbuildings, check with your utility company about the possibilities of installing a yardpole service. Such a central service allows equal length, or near equal length, distribution lines and provides a chance to run three wire feeder lines to every area where they are needed. From the yardpole, with 200 ampere service, you can then run a 100 ampere subpanel to the house, three wires to a 60 ampere subpanel at the barn, and another subpanel of 30 amperes for a workshop or shed. From these subpanels, you can run lighter service wires directly to other buildings to provide lights and very small appliances.

Any wires used must be heavy enough to withstand ice and wind loads. The NEC requires that none be any smaller than a number 10, if the run is up to 50 feet, and nothing under a number 8 if the run is over 50 feet. Later I will go into more detail on determining wire sizes for loads carried and actual wiring installing procedures.

FRAMING

Framing a house can be a complex job, or it can be relatively simple. Complexity depends on house design more than anything else. Any home with a *gambrel roof* and a series of dormers is going to be much more difficult to frame than a simple house in generally rectangular shape. Roof framing is probably the most difficult part of building a home. Today, even that need not be done, as you can easily buy trusses that are simply nailed in place. Trusses provide both ease in getting ready to roof and the chance at a full span house (within reasonable size limits) with no interior load bearing walls at all. This allows just about total freedom in designing interior wall placement and makes for later ease if you feel a need to change the floor plan of the house. Load bearing walls can be removed, but if not done properly and if the correct size support is not used, sooner or later sag or collapse will become a problem (Fig. 2-1).

The house designs included here are for rather small homes for several reasons. First, the framing is easier since there is less of it. Second, small homes, even in the country, are more practical today than the huge places our ancestors were accustomed to building. The cost of lumber, land, labor, nails, wire, insulation, heating systems and everything else that goes into making a home has increased at an incredible pace over the past decade. Not many of us can afford a large house. Even if we build it ourselves to cut costs, the running costs for a large home can be disastrous. Rural living can be marginal in many ways as far as income goes, but marginal purchasing power need not be a worse problem with huge heating bills. With fuel oil around a dollar a gallon, it is far better to have a home which requires only 300 gallons a year to keep warm than it is to have one that needs 1500 gallons (Fig. 2-2).

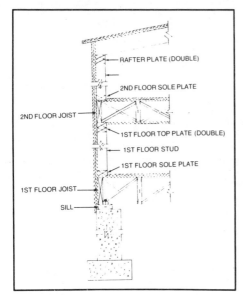

Fig. 2-1. Platform framed wall section.

Some people will still want larger homes. If you are one of them and can afford the construction or remodeling costs, that is fine. But I would strongly suggest the installation of one or more wood stoves to cut back on fuel oil use. Even one of my cousins, with her lovely 2600 square foot new home and a heat pump, keep wood on hand to feed through the *Heatilator* equipped fireplace. Pay special attention to extra insulation for larger homes, though even in small places correct insulation is of great value.

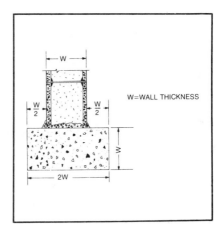

Fig. 2-2. Footing dimensions.

House framing consists of *joists* set on *sill plates*, over which goes subflooring and, for *platform style framing*, wall studs with double top plates (Fig. 2-3). The wall studs are also set on a sole plate that serves as a nailing anchor for wallboard or paneling on the interior of the home. Next come the ceiling joists and then the rafters. Collar beams may be used to join opposing rafters over longer spans, and some roof construction uses a *ridge board*.

Windows are framed with a header above. The size of the header depends on the size of the opening, with 2-inch nominal dimension lumber used, two pieces joined together to form the header, and shims used to bring it out to a full 3 ½-inch width to match the studs. The window is set on a piece called a *sill*, which may also be doubled if the opening is a large one. Doors use the same form of framing, but have no need for the cripple studs used in windows to support the sill.

Corner bracing is often used on frame homes and may be either nominal 1-inch stock inlet into the studs, or 2 by 4s, cut to fit at an angle between studs. Corner bracing is necessary with some forms of sheathing and not with others, but it is not particularly hard to do and serves to strengthen and tie the entire house together.

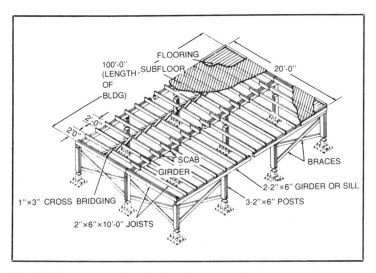

Fig. 2-3. Floor construction of a frame house on piers.

Actual stud size can vary. The smallest practical size is the more or less standard 2 by 4 (actually 1½ inches by 3 ½ inches). Today, more and more homes are being framed using 2 by 6s. There are two reasons for this sort of framing. First, it speeds the job as fewer studs need to be used since framing can be done, almost everywhere, on 2-foot centers instead of 16-inch centers as is required with 2 by 4 studs. Second, using 2 by 6s allows you to just about double the amount of insulation you can place in a wall, so that it is easily possible to have an R19 value wall now, as against about R11 with 2 by 4s. Because fewer studs are used, less heat is lost through them. Using 2 by 6s for studs requires a change in window and door depth, which must be kept in mind. It also allows for greater ease in setting plumbing runs and running wire as there is more room to work in (Table 2-1 and Figs. 2-4 through 2-26).

FOUNDATIONS

It may seem strange to discuss foundations this late in the chapter, but from this point on the instruction will be a bit more on the practical side. After looking at the various types of foundations, we will move on to excavation and the actual procedures of construction.

Houses have been built on the ground with no base at all other than bare earth, but in few areas is that practical. You might have some sort of base that goes below frost line. This is one item you will have to check locally, as it varies widely around the country. Ask your local building inspector. Materials such as poured concrete, concrete block, or rock can be used for the foundation, and it is also possible to use pressure treated wood. This last type is one I have heard of but never seen. I understand it has been approved for use in Federal Housing Administration houses, so it should prove durable. Poured concrete is a job for professionals, and rock can vary so greatly in density and strength that it is hard to recommend. In most cases, if you wish to build your own home, concrete block would be the material of choice. Quality control is easier. After about a day's work or two at the most, most people can pick up enough speed to make the job go

Table 2-1. Materials List for the Three-Room Frame Cabin.

CONCRETE-1:2:4

7 bags cement, ½ cu. yd. sand. 1 cu. yd. gravel, = 1.15 cu. yds. concrete

CHIMNEY

750 brick, 12 lin. ft. 8″×8″ flue lining, Mortar = 2 bags lime, 2½ bags cement, ½ ou. yd. sand.

LUMBER

9 - 2″×8″16′-0″-girders	4-6″×6″×7′-0″ porch posts
7 - 2″×6″×16′-0″-girders & plate's	2-4″×6″×7″0″ porch pilasters
21 - 2″×6″×18′-0″-joists	36 lin. ft. 1″×8″-porch trim
8-2″×6″×12′-0″-rafters	54 lin. ft. 1″ × 6″-porch trim
1-2″×10″×8′-0″-step carriage	350 lin. ft. 1″×4″-trim
7-1″×6″×14′-0″-collar ties	36 lin ft. 2″ drip cap moulding
140 lin. ft. 1″×3″-bridging	1 double-hung windows, 12lt. 2′-8″ × 3′-10″
875 ft. BM. 1″×6″-roof sheathing	7 double-hung windows, 12lt. 2′-8″×4′-6″
1050 ft. B.M. 1″×6″ - siding	8 window frames with outside trim and shutters
675 ft. B.M. 1″×4″ - flooring	1 - 2′-8″×6′-8″×1¾″ glazed door
760 sq. ft. roof area.	1 - door frame with outside trim
	2-2′-6″×6′-8″×1⅜″ inside doors

300 sq. ft. wallboard or beaded ceiling (interior partitions)

MISCELLANEOUS

16 - ¼″×1¼″ × 18″ strap anchors & ¼″ lag screws
1 - terra-cotta stovepipe thimble
1 - piece sheet metal, 24″×60″-flashing
Hardware, nails, paint, and equipment as selected

fairly quickly. In any case, if you plan to have a concrete floor in your basement, I would recommend having it poured by a professional. The odds on getting a really smooth and properly contoured surface are about 110 percent better.

Full basements, with footings below frost depth, are a great help in rural homes. They do add somewhat to cost, but I think they more than pay back any extra investment needed.

Foundataions can be of the *slab* type, using a perimeter footing with a concrete block wall to reach it, as the footing must be below frost line. Such a foundation tends to be expensive over and above its worth.

Pier style foundations, whether poured on-site or formed at a factory, are among the cheapest available but require good insulation of the space between the floor joists. They should also be supplied with skirting of the type used with mobile homes.

Crawl space styles are simply foreshortened basements. In most cases, excavating few more feet and adding to the wall height will provide a full basement at less than a 50 percent increase in cost. The equipment is already on site for the digging, so that all you really need add are the required cement block, mortar and labor, plus a poured basement floor if that is desired.

EXCAVATION

If you are excavating for a full basement, put away the pick and shovel. Digging an 8-foot deep hole possibly as large as 24 by 36 or even more feet is not what is classified as work

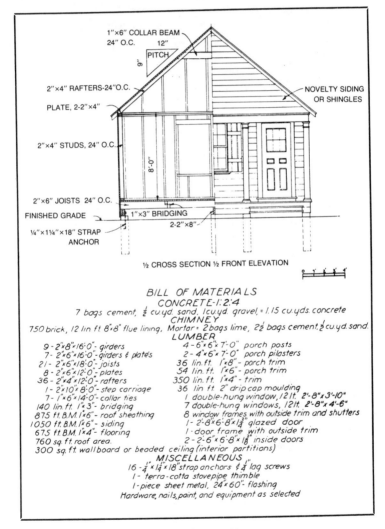

Fig. 2-4. Diagram of the three-room frame cabin.

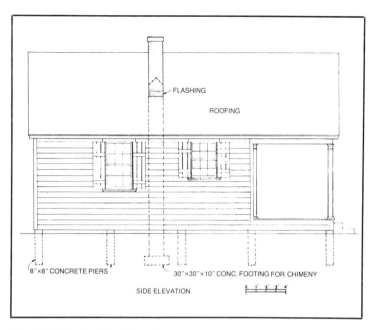

FLASHING

ROOFING

8"×8" CONCRETE PIERS

30"×30"×10" CONC. FOOTING FOR CHIMENY

SIDE ELEVATION

0 1' 2' 3' 4'

Fig. 2-5. Side elevation of the three-room frame cabin.

for the handyman. It would take days, perhaps weeks, and would leave you so worn out that the rest of the house would have to await a year's vacation. For excavation and later backfilling, your best bet is to use either a backhoe or bulldozer. The bulldozer will probably be faster, but it will have to dig a ramp as it excavates, which is another spot to be backfilled. Actually, if the basement must extend a full 8 feet into the ground, even a backhoe will probably have to work its way down into the pit. Most basements do not go that deep, though you must apply some consideration to the fact that the approximate year round temperature of the ground, below frost line, is on the order of 55 degrees F. Thus, the deeper you go, the less you need to insulate of the basement wall to maintain a stable temperature, no matter the weather.

Start your basement by laying out *batter boards* at each corner of the building. These are actually placed 3 to 4 feet out from the building line to allow space for excavation. Use three 2 by 4 corner stakes to support each pair of batter

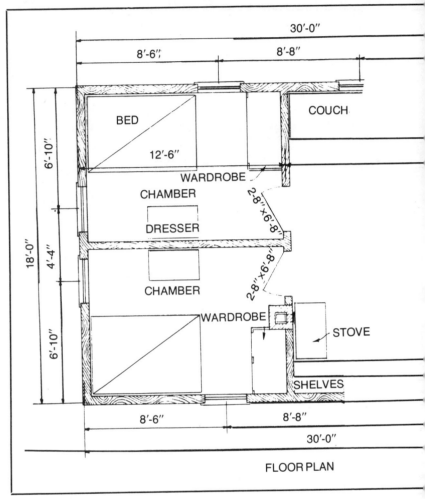

Fig. 2-6. Floor plan for the three-room frame cabin.

boards, and string *mason's cord* from nails in the batter boards, using a *line level* to keep the cord level, after either cutting slits in the boards or driving in small nails. If the corners are square, measuring 3 feet up one side of the cord, four up the other and five across the diagonal will prove it. Once all four corners are located, squared and strung, measure the diagonals from plumb bobs dropped at the point where the mason's cord crosses at each corner. If the diagonals are equal, then the building will be square.

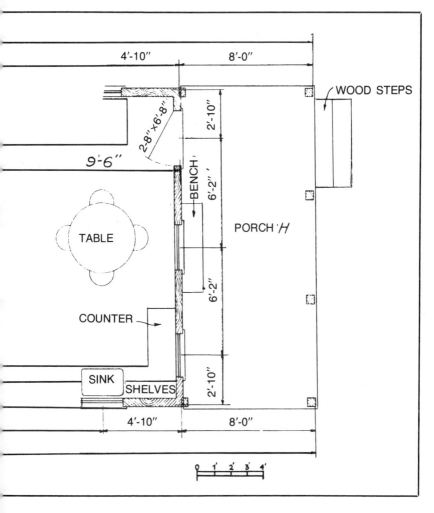

Excavations are usually made at least 2 feet wider—to the exterior—than the actual basement size to allow working space for laying block or pouring cement. Once the masonry work has set, this space must be backfilled. Allow for 9 extra inches in depth, too, as you will want a 6-inch gravel subbase for your 3-inch thick poured concrete floor.

I am not going to cover poured concrete basement walls since I feel the building of such forms, and the judgments of strength needed, are better left to professionals. Concrete will still need to be poured for footings.

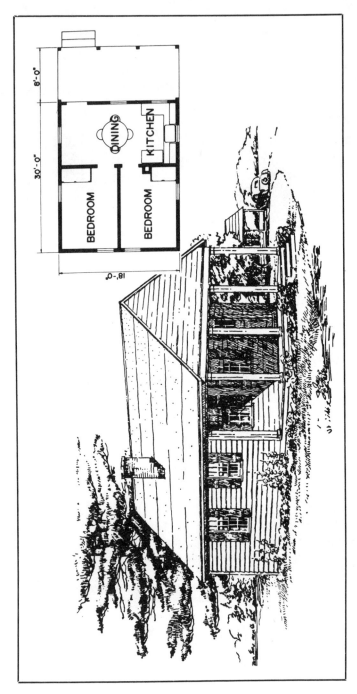

Fig. 2-7. Room layout for the three-room frame cabin.

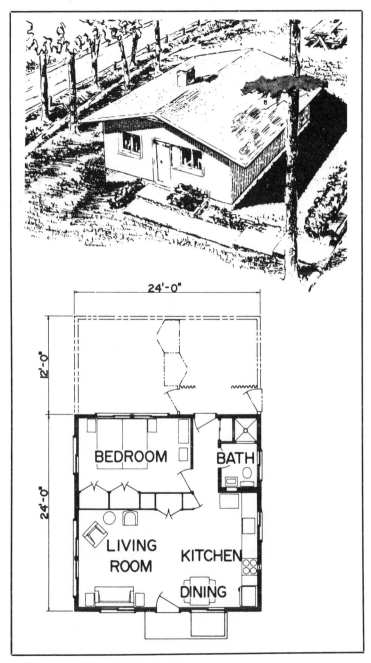

24'-0"

12'-0"

24'-0"

BEDROOM

BATH

LIVING
ROOM

KITCHEN

DINING

Fig. 2-8. The interior arrangement for the 24-foot square frame cabin is flexible.

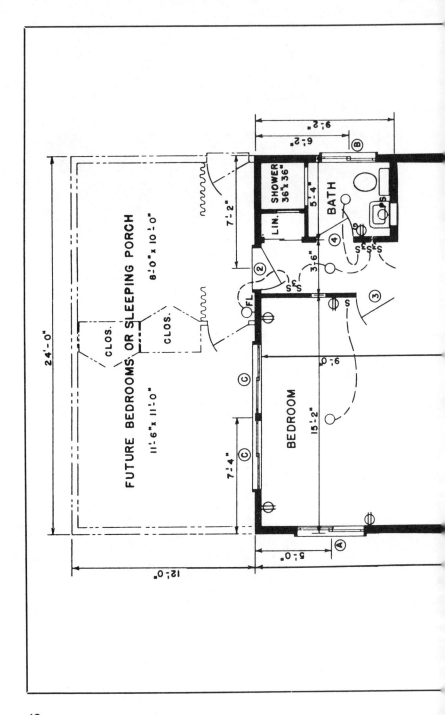

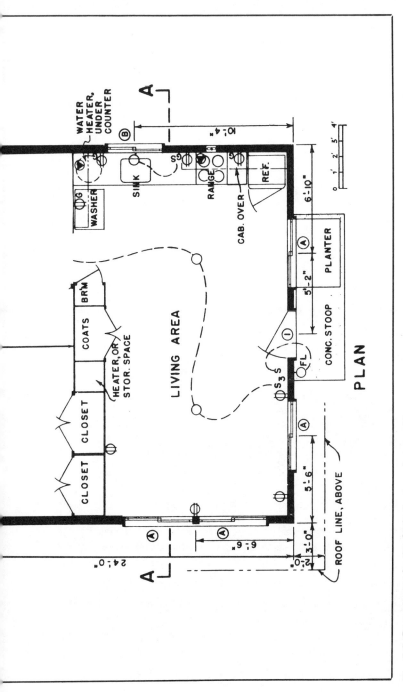

Fig. 2-9. Room layout for the 24-foot square frame cabin.

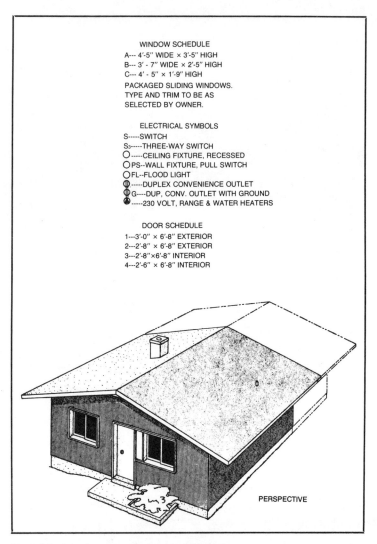

WINDOW SCHEDULE
A--- 4'-5" WIDE × 3'-5" HIGH
B--- 3' - 7" WIDE × 2'-5" HIGH
C--- 4' - 5" × 1'-9" HIGH
PACKAGED SLIDING WINDOWS.
TYPE AND TRIM TO BE AS
SELECTED BY OWNER.

ELECTRICAL SYMBOLS
S-----SWITCH
S₃-----THREE-WAY SWITCH
O-----CEILING FIXTURE, RECESSED
OPS--WALL FIXTURE, PULL SWITCH
OFL--FLOOD LIGHT
⊕-----DUPLEX CONVENIENCE OUTLET
⊕G----DUP, CONV. OUTLET WITH GROUND
●-----230 VOLT, RANGE & WATER HEATERS

DOOR SCHEDULE
1---3'-0" × 6'-8" EXTERIOR
2---2'-8" × 6'-8" EXTERIOR
3---2'-8"×6'-8" INTERIOR
4---2'-6" × 6'-8" INTERIOR

PERSPECTIVE

Fig. 2-10. Perspective view of the 24-foot square frame cabin.

Generally accepted construction practice has residential footings poured twice as wide as the block used for the wall. Since most basement walls today are constructed of 8-inch concrete block that would give you a footing 16 inches wide, but in sandy ground you would be wise to go at least 4 inches wider. Footing depth would equal block height—8 inches. If you are lucky, the excavation is clean enough at footing depth so that no forms will be needed to hold the poured concrete. Don't bet on it, though.

Footing forms can easily be made of the proper size rough cut lumber. Oil it for ease of removal, and brace to the sides of the trench as shown in Figs. 2-27 and 2-28. Poured footings should set for at least three days, during which they must be kept wet. A seven day set is preferable before any block is laid, as the increase in overall strength is great. Consolidate the concrete in the forms by using a spading tool to make sure the form is evenly filled as the concrete is poured. Then use a board to strike the concrete off level with the tops of the form. A week later, you are ready to begin construction of the block walls.

BLOCK MASONRY

As Fig. 2-29 shows, there are many forms of concrete block to be found today. Figures 2-30 through 2-33 show the tools needed to work with concrete block (or brick). The mortar used for masonry of this type differs from concrete in that lime is used, and no large aggregate (gravel) is needed. Portland cement/lime mortar is mixed with just enough water to produce a workable paste that doesn't run down the face of your block. The strongest mortar consists of a sack of cement, 3 cubic feet of damp sand and 13 pounds of hydrated lime.

Laying Out the Blocks

Before mixing any mortar, use a chalk line to snap a mark along the footing and lay out the first course of block without mortar. This provides a check on the need for half blocks. Remove the blocks from one corner and spread a full bed of mortar (about 1 inch thick) running a furrow up its center with the trowel. Lay the corner block first, and be very careful as to its position. Block shells are often tapered. The thicker edge is then laid up, as it provides more surface for the mortar bed for the next course of block. Lay the second corner block and then run the course out on each side of the corner for several block—five or six will be enough.

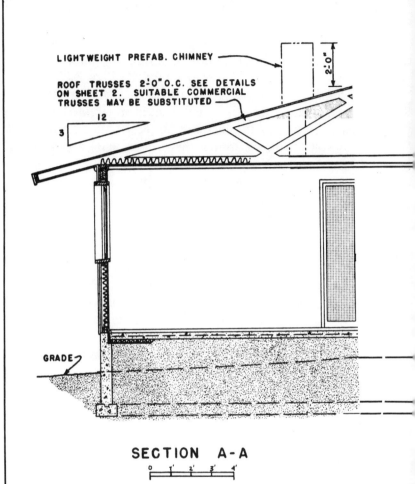

LIGHTWEIGHT PREFAB. CHIMNEY

ROOF TRUSSES 2'-0" O.C. SEE DETAILS ON SHEET 2. SUITABLE COMMERCIAL TRUSSES MAY BE SUBSTITUTED

12

3

2'-0"

GRADE

SECTION A-A

0   1'   2'   3'   4'

FOR ECONOMY AND EASE OF CONSTRUCTION, APPLY THE INTERIOR WALL, CEILING AND FLOOR FINISH BEFORE ERECTING ANY PARTITIONS. THIS WILL ALSO PERMIT FUTURE REMOVAL OR MOVING OF ANY PARTITIONS EXCEPT THOSE WHICH CONTAIN PLUMBING.

Fig. 2-11. Construction details for the 24-foot square frame cabin.

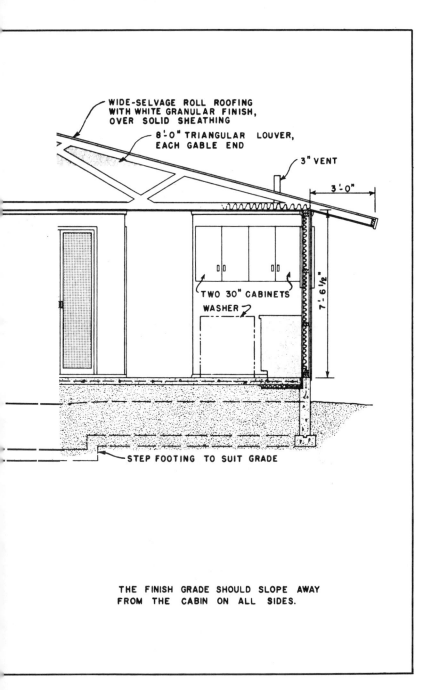

WIDE-SELVAGE ROLL ROOFING
WITH WHITE GRANULAR FINISH,
OVER SOLID SHEATHING

8'-0" TRIANGULAR LOUVER,
EACH GABLE END

3" VENT

3'-0"

7'-6½"

TWO 30" CABINETS

WASHER

STEP FOOTING TO SUIT GRADE

THE FINISH GRADE SHOULD SLOPE AWAY
FROM THE CABIN ON ALL SIDES.

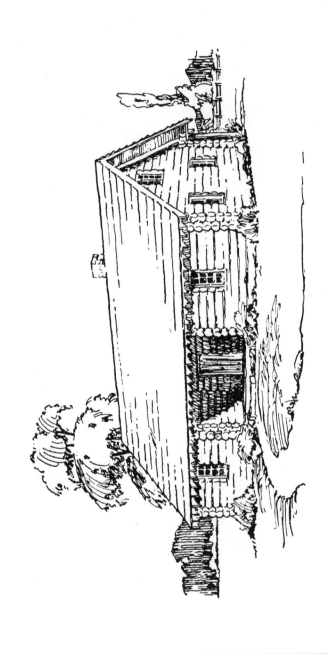

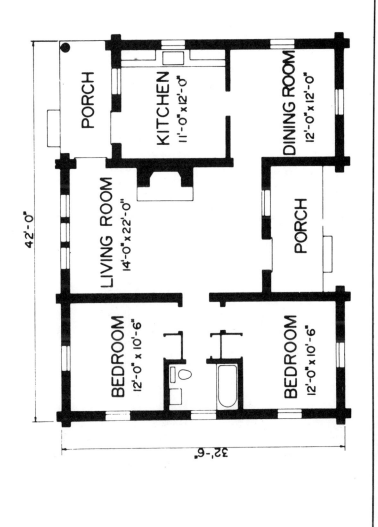

PORCH

KITCHEN
11'-0" x 12'-0"

DINING ROOM
12'-0" x 12'-0"

LIVING ROOM
14'-0" x 22'-0"

PORCH

BEDROOM
12'-0" x 10'-6"

BEDROOM
12'-0" x 10'-6"

42'-0"

32'-6"

Fig. 2-12. This log cabin would make a nice house for a small family.

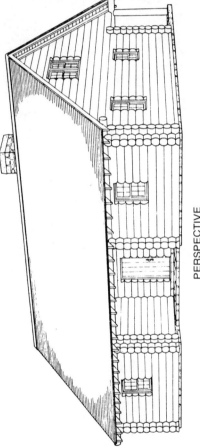

PERSPECTIVE

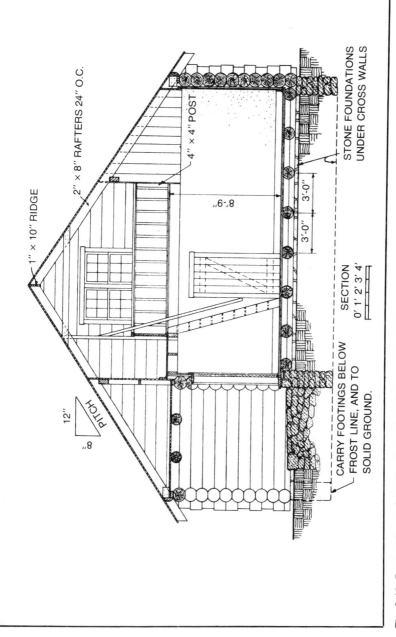

Fig. 2-13. Perspective and section views of the five-room log cabin.

57

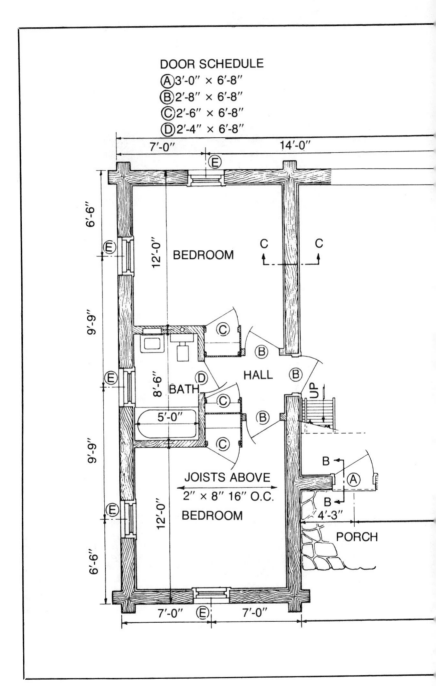

DOOR SCHEDULE
- Ⓐ 3'-0" × 6'-8"
- Ⓑ 2'-8" × 6'-8"
- Ⓒ 2'-6" × 6'-8"
- Ⓓ 2'-4" × 6'-8"

Fig. 2-14. Floor plan for the five-room log cabin.

58

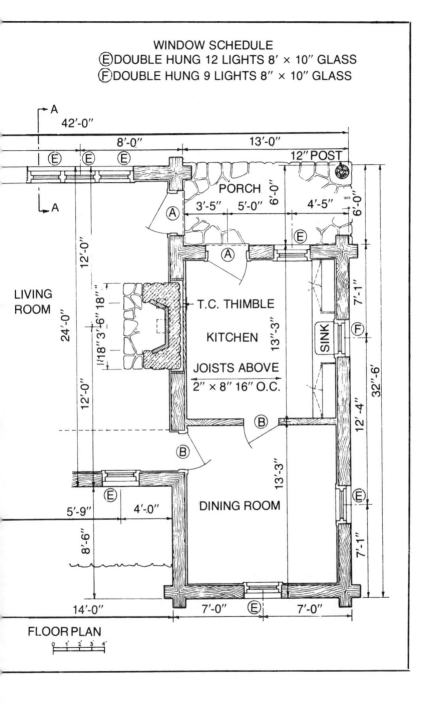

WINDOW SCHEDULE
Ⓔ DOUBLE HUNG 12 LIGHTS 8' × 10" GLASS
Ⓕ DOUBLE HUNG 9 LIGHTS 8" × 10" GLASS

A

42'-0"

8'-0"   13'-0"

Ⓔ   Ⓔ   Ⓔ   12" POST

A

PORCH   6'-0"

Ⓐ   3'-5"   5'-0"   4'-5"   6'-0"

Ⓔ

Ⓐ   7'-1"

LIVING
ROOM   12'-0"

T.C. THIMBLE

18" 3'-6" 18"   KITCHEN   13'-3"   SINK   Ⓕ

24'-0"

JOISTS ABOVE
2" × 8" 16" O.C.   32"-6'

12'-0"   Ⓑ   12'-4"

Ⓑ

13'-3"

Ⓔ   Ⓔ

5'-9"   4'-0"   DINING ROOM

8'-6"   7'-1"

14'-0"   7'-0"   Ⓔ   7'-0"

FLOOR PLAN

0 1 2 3 4'

59

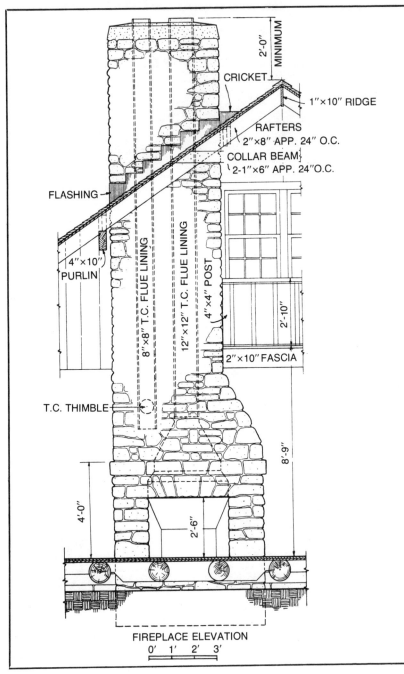

Fig. 2-15. Fireplace elevation details for the five-room log cabin.

60

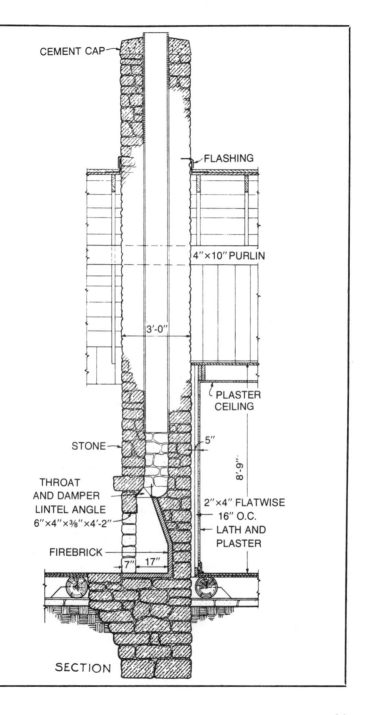

CEMENT CAP

FLASHING

4"×10" PURLIN

3'-0"

PLASTER
CEILING

STONE

5"

THROAT
AND DAMPER
LINTEL ANGLE
6"×4"×⅜"×4'-2"

8'-9"

FIREBRICK

2"×4" FLATWISE
16" O.C.
LATH AND
PLASTER

7"   17"

SECTION

61

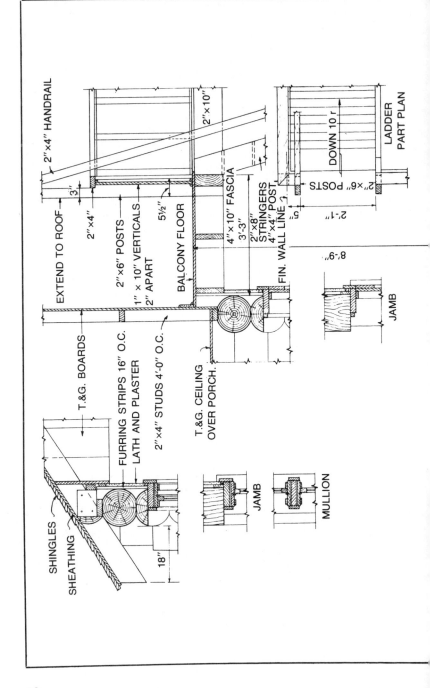

EXTEND TO ROOF

2″×4″

2″×6″ POSTS

1″ × 10″ VERTICALS
2″ APART

BALCONY FLOOR

T.&G. BOARDS

FURRING STRIPS 16″ O.C.

LATH AND PLASTER

2″×4″ STUDS 4′-0″ O.C.

T.&G. CEILING
OVER PORCH.

SHINGLES

SHEATHING

18″

2″×4″ HANDRAIL

3″

2″×10″

5½

4″×10″ FASCIA

3′-3″

2″×8″
STRINGERS

4″×4″ POST

FIN. WALL LINE

JAMB

MULLION

JAMB

LADDER
PART PLAN

DOWN 10 r

2″×6″ POSTS

6″

2′-1″

8′-9″

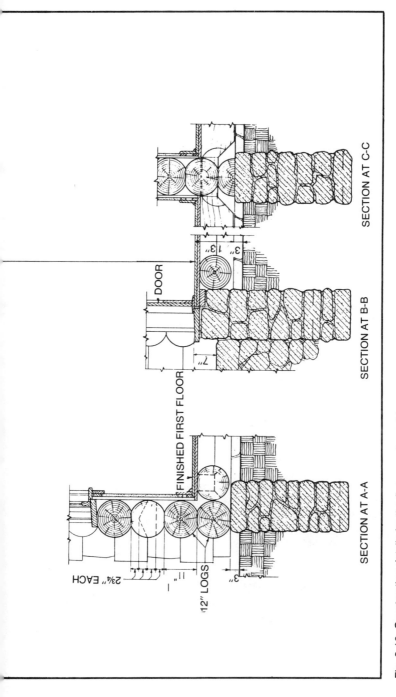

Fig. 2-16. Construction details for the five-room log cabin.

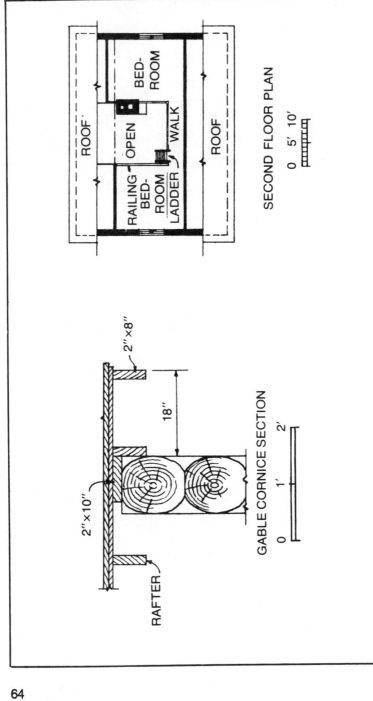

SECOND FLOOR PLAN

ROOF

BED-ROOM

OPEN

WALK

RAILING

BED-ROOM

LADDER

ROOF

0 5' 10'

GABLE CORNICE SECTION

2"×8"

18"

2"×10"

RAFTER

0   1'   2'

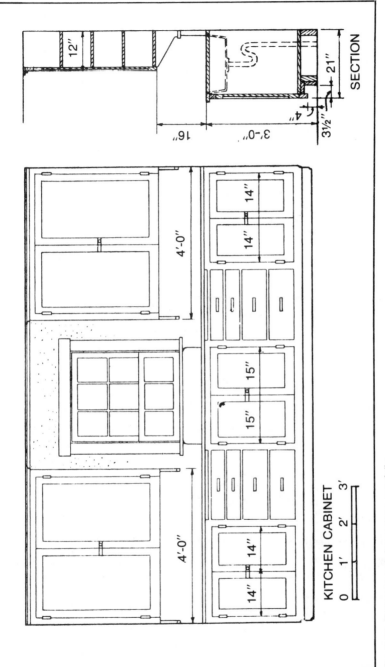

SECTION

12"

21"

16"

3'-0"

4"

3½"

14"

14"

15"

15"

14"

14"

4'-0"

4'-0"

KITCHEN CABINET

0   1'   2'   3'

Fig. 2-17. Follow these dimensions carefully.

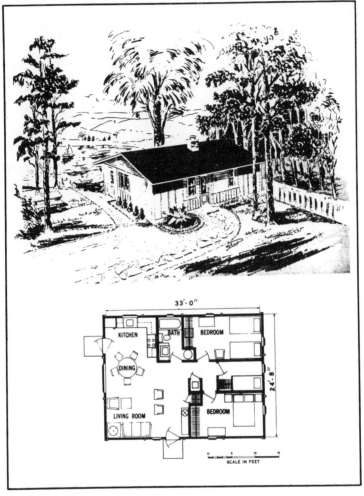

Fig. 2-18. This two-bedroom frame vacation home features a post-and-girt construction and a free-floating floor.

From this point, you begin the second course, again on a full bed of mortar. Only the ends of the shell—the protrusions at the end of the block—are "buttered" with mortar before they are placed against already laid block.

Once you have three to four blocks laid in any course, use a mason's level to assure the course is level and to check for straightness along the top of the course. After the first course is laid, place mortar only along the shell edges for the mortar bed, as it is not necessary to fill the cores. Keep the corners four or five courses higher than the rest of the wall (until they reach full wall height). The wall should be continually checked in several places to make sure it is both level and plumb.

If you use a mason's line from each course, attached at the already laid corner courses, it is much easier to keep the wall plumb. You can use a straight board, a 1 by 2 is fine, marked for the block sizes plus mortar joints (joints should be ⅜ of an inch thick) to assure correct block height as you go along.

Mortar is laid only three to five blocks ahead of the actual laying of block to assure a good bond. Excess mortar is cut from the joints with a trowel. Once the mortar sets to the point where it will just take a thumbprint, it must be tooled. The mortar is compressed in the joint using either the tip of the trowel or a jointing tool.

Once the wall is within 18 inches of its top, you will want to install anchor bolts to hold the sill boards in place. Anchor bolts are ½ inch by 18 inch metal bolts, and should be spaced no more than 4 feet apart in the wall. The blocks are placed in the cores of the top two courses of block. Those cores are then filled with mortar. If you place pieces of metal mesh just under the tops of the anchor bolts, mortar will stop there and will not go on down to unnecessarily fill other cores. Of course, the threaded end of the bolt should extend above the top of the wall.

Door and Window Openings

Plan for door and window openings carefully so you have the correct number of half or other size block on hand, and thus will not need to cut block (Fig. 2-34). Lintels for door and window openings can be built up, as you can see in Fig. 2-35, or they can be brought precast. Being lazy, I prefer the precast style. These openings do not require any time to make and are generally easier to install. The cost is not that great.

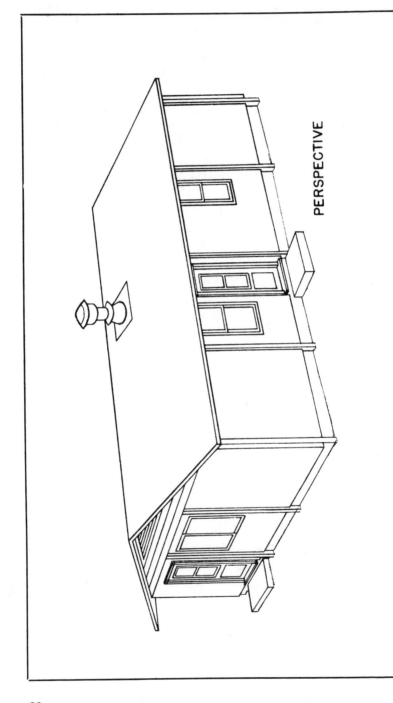

PERSPECTIVE

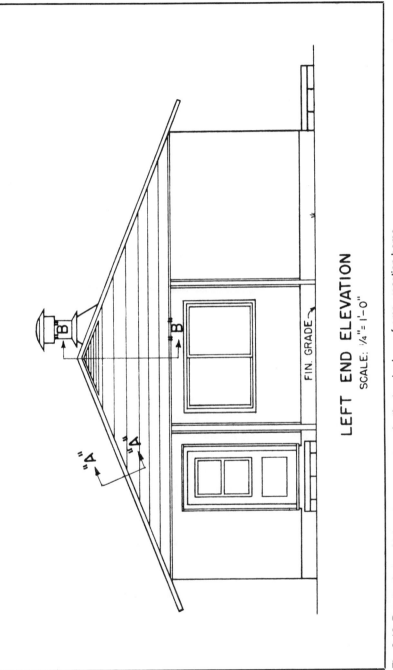

LEFT END ELEVATION
SCALE: 1/4" = 1'-0"

FIN. GRADE

Fig. 2-19. Perspective and left end elevation views for the two-bedroom frame vacation home.

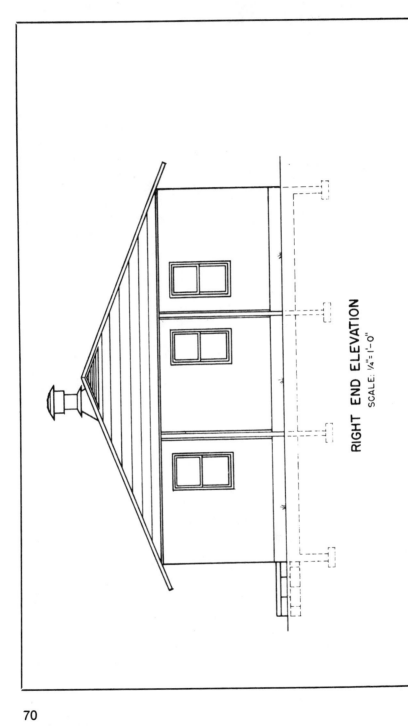

RIGHT END ELEVATION
SCALE: 1/4"=1'-0"

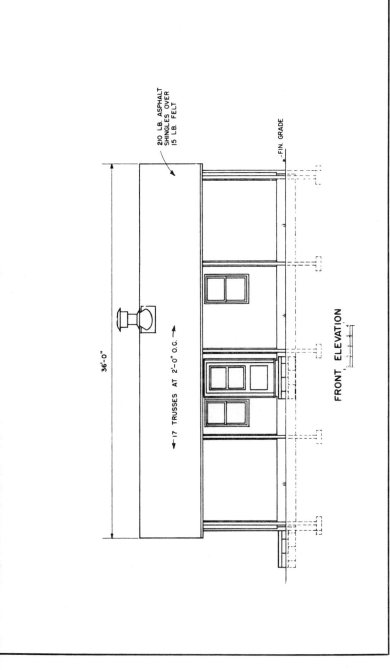

36'-0"

210 LB. ASPHALT
SHINGLES OVER
15 LB. FELT

17 TRUSSES AT 2'-0" O.C.

FIN. GRADE

FRONT ELEVATION

Fig. 2-20. Right end elevation and front elevation for the two-bedroom frame vacation home.

71

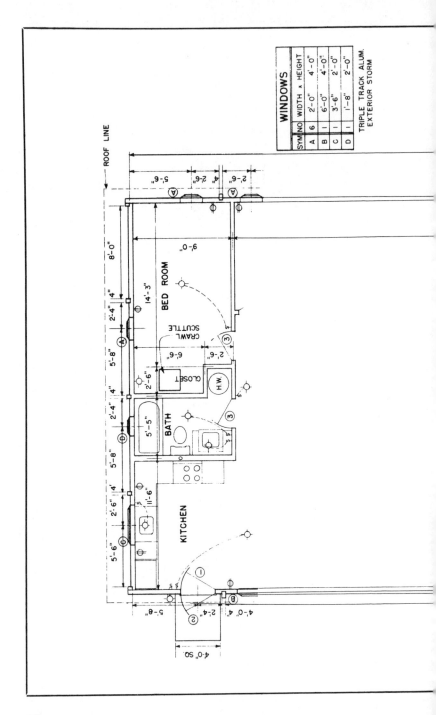

WINDOWS		
SYM	NO	WIDTH x HEIGHT
A	6	2'-0" 4'-0"
B	I	6'-0" 4'-0"
C	I	3'-6" 2'-0"
D	I	1'-8" 2'-0"

TRIPLE TRACK ALUM.
EXTERIOR STORM

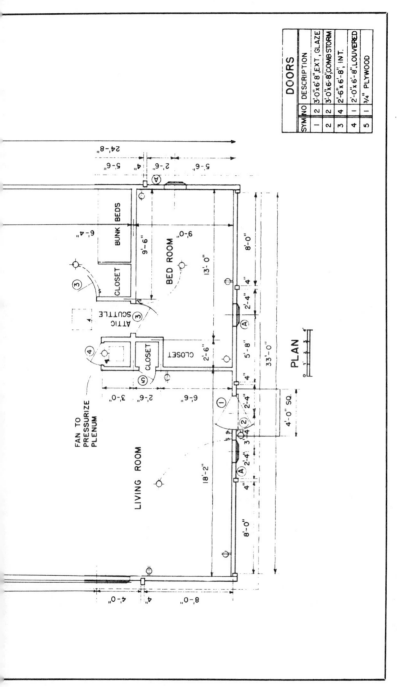

Fig. 2-21. Room layout for the two-bedroom frame vacation cabin.

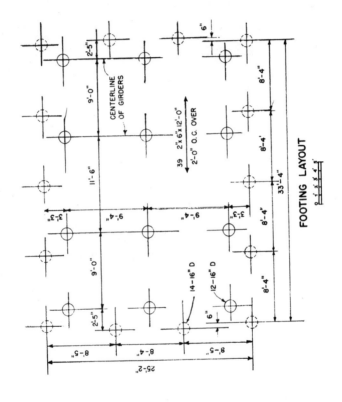

FOOTING LAYOUT

0 1 2 3 4 5

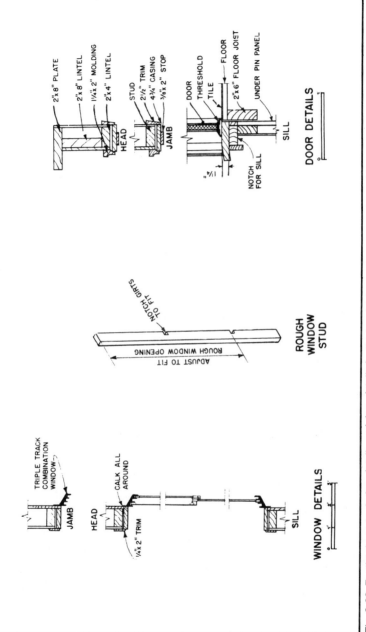

Fig. 2-22. Footing layout, window details and door details for the two-bedroom frame vacation cabin.

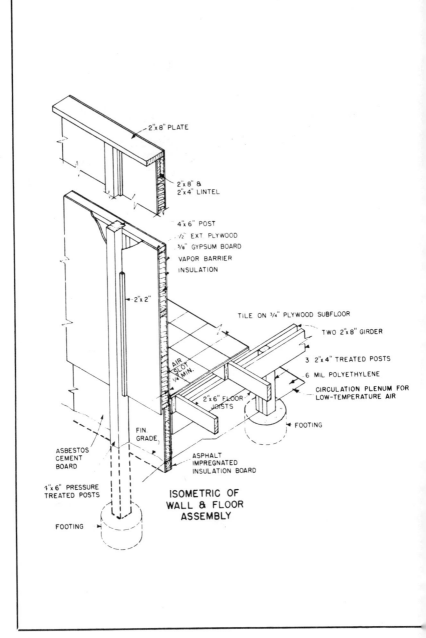

2"x 8" PLATE

2"x 8" &
2"x 4" LINTEL

4"x 6" POST
1/2" EXT PLYWOOD
3/8" GYPSUM BOARD
VAPOR BARRIER
INSULATION

2"x 2"

TILE ON 3/4" PLYWOOD SUBFLOOR

TWO 2"x 8" GIRDER

3 2"x 4" TREATED POSTS

6 MIL POLYETHYLENE

CIRCULATION PLENUM FOR
LOW-TEMPERATURE AIR

AIR
SLOT
1/4" MIN.

2"x 6" FLOOR
JOISTS

FOOTING

FIN.
GRADE

ASBESTOS
CEMENT
BOARD

ASPHALT
IMPREGNATED
INSULATION BOARD

4"x 6" PRESSURE
TREATED POSTS

ISOMETRIC OF
WALL & FLOOR
ASSEMBLY

FOOTING

Fig. 2-23. Construction details for the two-bedroom frame vacation cabin.

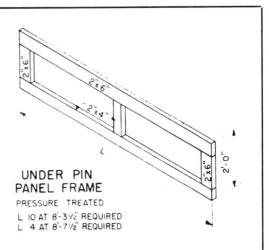

UNDER PIN
PANEL FRAME

PRESSURE TREATED

L 10 AT 8'-3½" REQUIRED
L 4 AT 8'-7½" REQUIRED

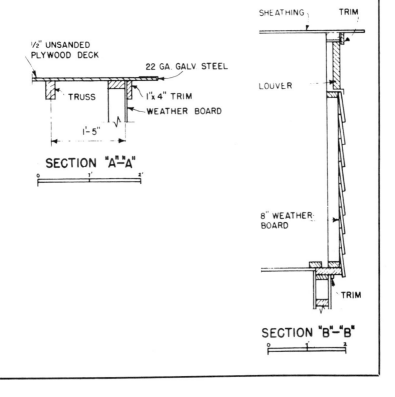

SECTION "A"–"A"

SECTION "B"–"B"

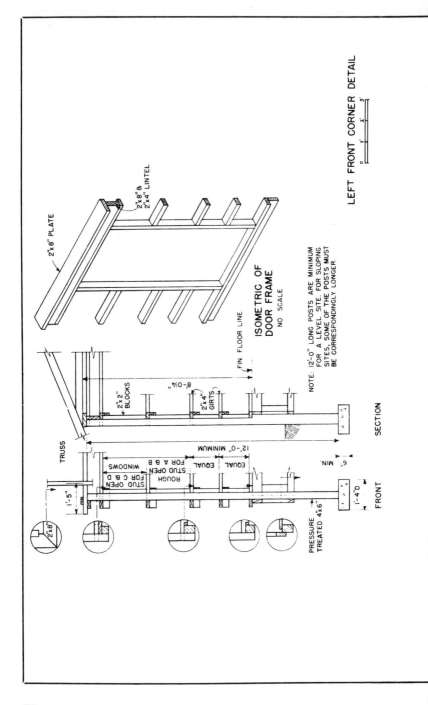

LEFT FRONT CORNER DETAIL

ISOMETRIC OF
DOOR FRAME
NO SCALE

2"x8" PLATE

2"x8" B
2"x4" LINTEL

NOTE: 12'-0" LONG POSTS ARE MINIMUM
FOR A LEVEL SITE. FOR SLOPING
SITES, SOME OF THE POSTS MUST
BE CORRESPONDINGLY LONGER.

FIN. FLOOR LINE

2"x2" BLOCKS

8'-0½"

2"x4" GIRTS

SECTION

TRUSS

1'-5"

WINDOWS

ROUGH
STUD OPEN
FOR C & D

STUD OPEN
FOR A & B

EQUAL   EQUAL   EQUAL

12'-0" MINIMUM

6" MIN.

2"x8"

PRESSURE
TREATED 4"x6"

1'-4"D

FRONT

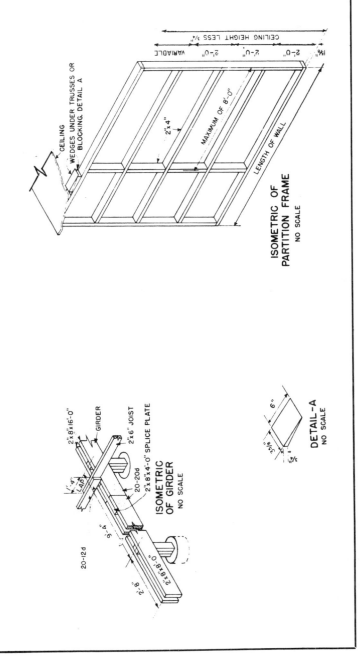

Fig. 2-24. More construction details for the two-bedroom home.

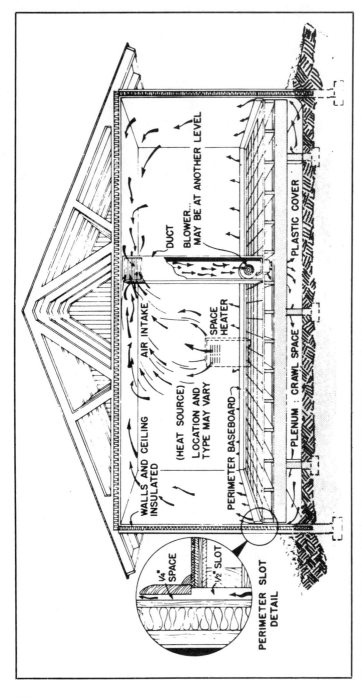

Fig. 2-25. An air diffusion system using subfloor plenum with perimeter slot.

80

Below Grade Walls and Basement Floor

Below grade walls must be sealed before the backfilling is done. Start by mixing mortar using a bit more lime and apply, over a dampened wall, ¼-inch coat. Bring the first coat from 6 inches above the grade line right down to the footing. Once that is partially set up, about the same thumbprint hard as for tooling mortar joints, rough it up with a wire brush. After 24 hours, apply a second ¼-inch coat. Keep the wall damp for at least two days.

Once the plastering is dry, apply a good quality asphalt coating from the grade line down to the footing in two coats. If the area is poorly drained, place about a foot of gravel around the outside of the footing and set drainage tile in the gravel. Make sure the drainage tile is covered with a foot of unwashed gravel before backfilling.

The basement floor can be left dirt, as was done in many old homes, or it can be covered with tamped gravel. In most cases a nice, smooth concrete floor serves best. Again, a professional is your best bet here. He or she will make sure the floor slopes properly to the drain and will have the skill to get the smoothest of surfaces. Pouring a concrete floor is not difficult; getting it smooth is tough.

Once you've got that fancy hole in the ground, you will want to cover it as quickly as possible. First, though, I will look at another type of foundation which may save you money and time, especially if you are locating in an area with many rocky outcroppings and can't afford blasting.

Column Foundation

Column, or pier, foundations go in more quickly than do wall foundations, and are much cheaper than slab styles. Columns are spaced to carry the load needed, and in most residential construction that will mean 8 feet on center, with the columns being 16 inches square on 32 inch footings. In most areas, a pick and shovel will knock out the needed holes in little or no time. The forms can be put together quite easily if masonry units or poured concrete are to be used. If the footing rests on rock, you will need to pick up a special bonding agent. If you are working in dirt, you can make the

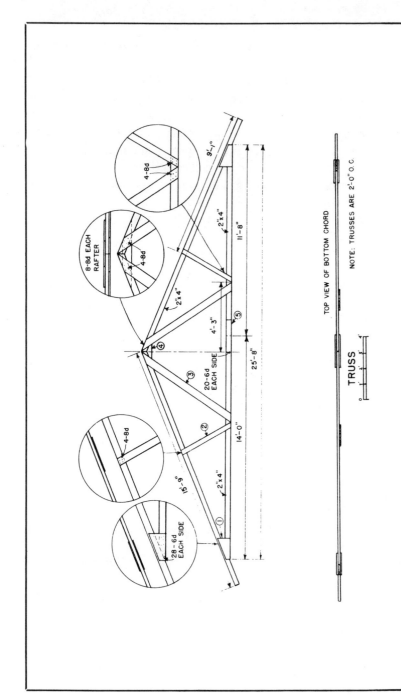

4-8d

8-8d EACH RAFTER

4-8d

4-8d

2"x 4"

9'-1"

2"x 4"

11'-8"

4'-3"

20-6d EACH SIDE

25'-8"

14'-0"

2"x 4"

15'-9"

4-8d

28 - 6d EACH SIDE

TOP VIEW OF BOTTOM CHORD

NOTE: TRUSSES ARE 2'-0" O.C.

TRUSS

0   1   2   3   4

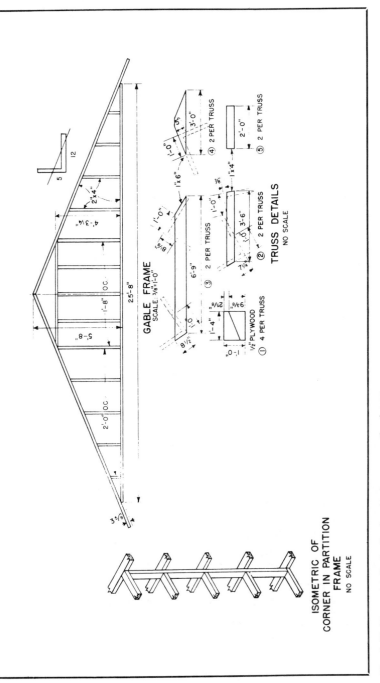

GABLE FRAME
SCALE: 3/16"=1'-0"

TRUSS DETAILS
NO SCALE

① 1/2 PLYWOOD
4 PER TRUSS

② 2 PER TRUSS

③ 2 PER TRUSS

④ 2 PER TRUSS

⑤ 2 PER TRUSS

ISOMETRIC OF
CORNER IN PARTITION
FRAME
NO SCALE

Fig. 2-26. Truss details for the two-bedroom vacation home.

83

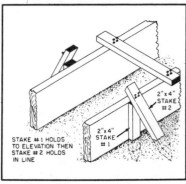

Fig. 2-27. Typical wall footing form.

STAKE #1 HOLDS
TO ELEVATION THEN
STAKE #2 HOLDS
IN LINE

2" x 4"
STAKE
#1

2" x 4"
STAKE
#2

columns from pressure treated wood. Make certain the wood is of the type retaining enough preservative to be classified for in-ground use. Bracing is generally needed for wood piers, and it should be placed on 4-foot centers. I would still use a poured concrete footing, with an anchor bolt of galvanized steel onto which the wood pier would be screwed.

With this type of foundation, it is an absolute that the underfloor area be well insulated (at least 6 inches of fiber glass and probably 10 in colder areas). Polyethylene sheeting should be used as a ground cover to prevent the rise of dampness. Skirting around the base of the house is also a help. Still, this foundation does cut costs, labor and building time, though you lose the convenience of a full basement.

WOODWORK

Once the foundation is in, the woodwork begins. The sill is the point where you begin to learn to be a better than average country carpenter, for it is the base for the entire wood portion of the house. If the sill is messed up, the house is sure to be in poor shape. Your anchor bolts are in. You will be using *platform framing*—the most practical and simplest style. So a box sill will be used, with the first sill plate or board bolted to the anchor bolts. First, you lay a bed of fiberglass insulation along the top of the foundation and, if your area is one of heavy termite activity, an aluminum shield which overlaps the block 1 inch on the outside edge and is then bent down. This shield goes over one layer of fiber glass and under another, but it should not extend all the

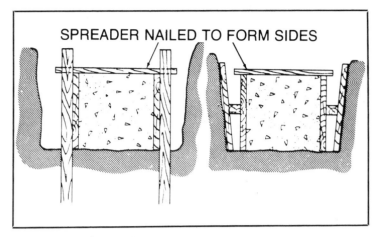

Fig. 2-28. Braced footing forms.

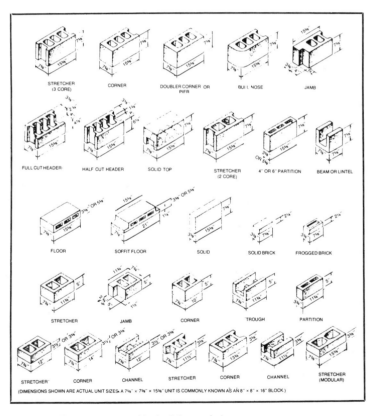

Fig. 2-29. Typical concrete block styles and sizes.

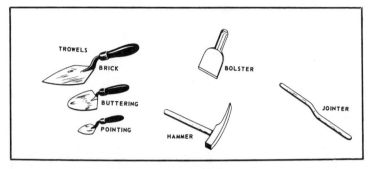

Fig. 2-30. Trowels, bolster, hammer and jointer.

way to the interior of the house—to the anchor bolts is far enough. Once the sill plate is in place, the sill is laid on edge along the outside edge of that plate. The sill plate will be a 2 by 8, but the sill will be determined by the size of your floor joists which, for long spans, may be as large as 2 by 12.

The floor joists butt into the sill and lie on the sill plate. The sill is toe nailed to the sill plate, and the joists are nailed to the sill from the outside. As with all framing construction carpentry, also called *rough framing,* nails used must be at least three times the length of the piece being nailed. In this case, you would need to use at least 20 penny nails, which are 4 inches long, though the 4½-inch long 30 penny nails seem a better choice. Do the toe nailing with the longer nails, as the 20 penny nails will provide sufficient strength to hold the place together, when used at the joists (Fig. 2-36 and Table 2-2).

Joist Work

If a girder is used, and if your house is much wider than 14 feet it will have one, it will usually be of lumber the same

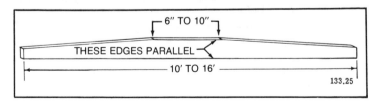

Fig. 2-31. A mason's straightedge.

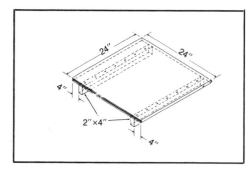

Fig. 2-32. Mortar board.

size as the joists, tripled and, if needed, supported every 8 to 10 feet with posts. When the joists butt the girder, a 2 by 2 or 1 by 2 ledger should be nailed along the bottom of the girder—use 20 penny nails on 16-inch centers—and the ends of the joists notched to tightly fit over the ledger. The joists are then toenailed to the girder, using two 20 penny nails per side. You can also use Teco joist hangers instead of a ledger board. I have to admit that they cut down on cutting, speed nailing and just generally are helpful. The added cost will only be a few dollars, and overall strength is probably greater. There is also less chance of cocking a joist while toenailing, a feat most non-professional carpenters find quite easy.

If you are going to have an opening in your floor, it is necessary to use a few special framing techniques. With no opening to a basement, you really limit it to outside access and cut its possibilities drastically. The parts of the joists which would extend across the opening are cut away and cripple or tail joists are butted against doubled headers, while double trimmer joists are used on each long side of the opening. If your headers are less than 6 feet long, use 20 penny nails. The length of such floor openings is usually limited to about 10 feet, unless some support is provided in addition to the trimmer joists.

Fig. 2-33. Mortar box.

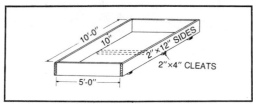

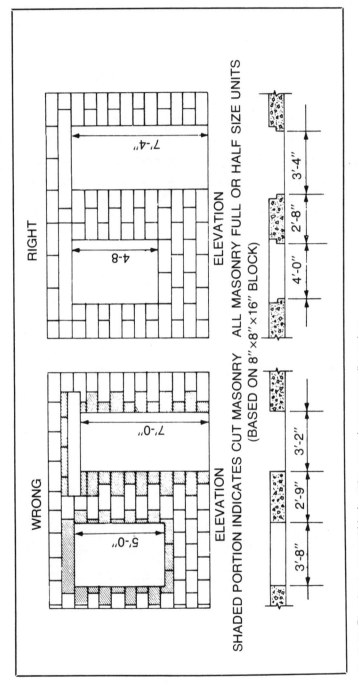

Fig. 2-34. Planning to prevent block cutting around masonry wall openings.

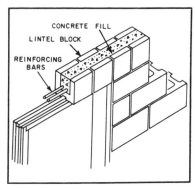

Fig. 2-35. Lintel made from blocks.

If a partition wall is to run along the length of a joist, the floor will need added strength to support the weight of the wall. This is especially true in kitchen walls, as you can never be sure but what sometime in the future you may decide to put a 500 pound freezer, refrigerator or wood cook stove along that wall. Simply run a bridge well between them. Actual distance between the joists should be determined by the thickness of the partition wall, and all bridging used is solid.

Various types of bridging between joists is used today. All are good, though some are a lot simpler to install than others. Least often used is wood diagonal bridging because of the cutting at angles needed. Solid bridging using material the same size as the sill plate is easier to install. Easiest of all is metal bridging of the type made by Teco. You do not need nails, as the ends are designed to be driven into the wood. Bridging serves to help tie the joist system together (Fig. 2-37).

Bathrooms require some special joist work, too. The section of the floor under the bathtub requires at least one extra joist and preferably two. After all, a fully loaded bathtub may weigh over 600 pounds before anyone steps into it.

Subflooring

Once the joists are in and bridged as needed, the time has arrived to cover the holes with *subflooring*. Subflooring serves to hold the joists plumb and adds reasonable amounts

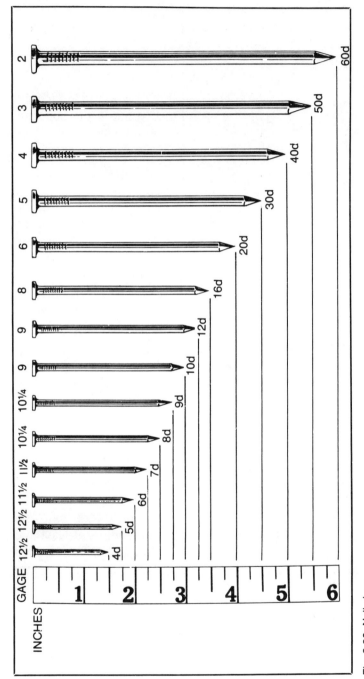

Fig. 2-36. Nail sizes.

of rigidity to the floor system as a whole. You may wish to use number 2 6-inch wide *tongue and groove sheathing*—this is nominal 1-inch lumber. If so, it should be laid at a 45 degree angle to the joists so that any finish flooring can be laid either directly perpendicular to, or at 90 degree angles to, the joists. Laying board subflooring at 90 degree angles to the joists forces you to lay finish flooring in the opposite direction, which may not be suitable in some rooms. Nail board subflooring with 8 penny nails, using two every time the board crosses a joist (using screw shank nails will help cut down on any future floor squeaking).

Plywood subflooring comes with specifications printed right on the board as to its suitability for a particular joist spacing. Plywood marked 16/32 is suitable for use on joists set on 16-inch centers. This makes selection quite easy, as you don't have to spend a lot of time and energy figuring what thickness and how many plies are needed for the job at hand. *American Plywood Association* grading standards have already done the work.

Plywood is also nailed with *screw shank* 8 penny nails, placed every 6 inches along the outside edges of the sheet and every 10 inches along the joists in the center. Grain direction of the face of the plywood should always run at right angles to the joists. Joints are staggered so that two butting boards or sheets end on the same joist. A bit of planning— simply outline the floor and its dimensions and then make a rough-in drawing of the plywood needed as it would lie over the joists—can save some cutting and probably quite a bit of plywood.

Because the subflooring is almost certain to get wet during the rest of the construction of your country home, it is best to select a grade made with exterior glue. Cover the subfloor on nights rain is expected. Again, plastic sheeting will serve admirably.

Wall Framing

Once the subflooring is down, the process of *wall framing* can begin. The simplest way to erect walls in any platform framed house is to build the walls in sections, on the

Table 2-2. Schedule for Nailing the Framing and Sheathing of a Wood-Frame House.

JOINING	NAILING METHOD	NUM-BER	SIZE	PLACEMENT
Header to joist	End-nail	3	16d	
Joist to sill or girder	Toenail	2	10d or	
		3	8d	
Header and stringer joist to sill	Toenail		10d	16 in. on center
Bridging to joist	Toenail each end	2	8d	
Ledger strip to beam, 2 in. thick		3	16d	At each joist
Subfloor, boards:				
1 by 6 in. and smaller		2	8d	To each joist
1 by 8 in.		3	8d	To each joist
Subfloor, plywood:				
At edges			8d	6 in. on center
At intermediate joists			8d	8 in. on center
Subfloor (2 by 6 in., T&G) to joist or girder	Blind-nail (casing) and face-nail	2	16d	
Soleplate to stud, horizontal assembly	End-nail	2	16d	At each stud
Top plate to stud	End-nail	2	16d	
Stud to soleplate	Toenail	4	8d	
Soleplate to joist or blocking	Face-nail		16d	16 in. on center
Doubled studs	Face-nail, stagger		10d	16 in. on center
End stud of intersection wall to exterior wall stud	Face-nail		16d	16 in. on center
Upper top plate to lower top plate	Face-nail		16d	16 in. on center
Upper top plate, laps and intersections	Face-nail	2	16d	
Continuous header, two pieces, each edge			12d	12 in. on center
Ceiling joist to top wall plates	Toenail	3	8d	
Ceiling joist laps at partition	Face-nail	4	16d	
Rafter to top plate	Toenail	2	8d	

Nailing method	Number	Size	Placement
Rafter to ceiling joist	Face-nail	5	10d	
Rafter to valley or hip rafter	Toenail	3	10d	
Ridge board to rafter	End-nail	3	10d	
Rafter to rafter through ridge board	Toenail	4	8d	
	Edge-nail	1	10d	
Collar beam to rafter:				
2 in. member	Face-nail	2	12d	
1 in. member	Face-nail	3	8d	
1-in. diagonal let-in brace to each stud and plate (4 nails at top)	Face-nail	2	8d	
Built-up corner studs:				
Studs to blocking	Face-nail	2	10d	Each side
Intersecting stud to corner studs	Face-nail		16d	12 in. on center
Built-up girders and beams, three or more members	Face-nail		20d	32 in. on center, each side
Wall sheathing:				
1 by 8 in. or less, horizontal	Face-nail	2	8d	At each stud
1 by 6 in. or greater, diagonal	Face-nail	3	8d	At each stud
Wall sheathing, vertically applied plywood:				
⅜ in. and less thick	Face-nail		6d	6 in. edge
½ in. and over thick	Face-nail		8d	12 in. intermediate
Wall sheathing, vertically applied fiberboard:				
½ in. thick	Face-nail.		1½ in. roofing nail	3 in. edge and 6 in. intermediate
25/32 in. thick	Face-nail		1¾ in. roofing nail	
Roof sheathing, boards, 4-, 6-, 8-in. width	Face-nail	2	8d	At each rafter
Roof sheathing, plywood:				
⅜ in. and less thick	Face-nail		6d	6 in. edge and 12 in. intermediate
½ in. and over thick	Face-nail		8d	

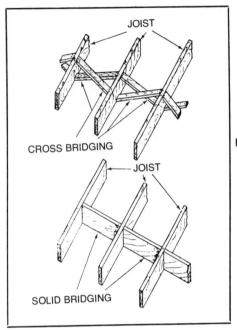

JOIST

CROSS BRIDGING

JOIST

SOLID BRIDGING

Fig. 2-37. Bridging types.

subflooring, and then tilt them into place where they are braced, plumbed and nailed. Obviously, the job is most easily done, for large wall sections, with a few friends in to help, at least with the tilting in place and bracing. Even one person can tilt up a pretty fair sized chunk of wall framing if necessary. Lay out the on center distances on the sole plate and the bottom top plate. Turn the sole plate on edge and place the first stud, cut to size and squared at both ends in place. Place both feet tight around the stud, and butt it against the sole plate. Drive in two 20 penny nails. Do the same with the top plate. Now move on to the opposite end and repeat the process. After that, it is a simple matter to place all the studs and nail them in place, using cripple studs where window openings are to go, and top cripple studs of correct length where needed. Nail in headers and sills as needed.

Now all that is required is to tilt the wall in place and place 1 by 4 braces at several points along the wall. Adjust the bracing until the wall is plumb and nail the sole plate into the sill. Do the same for the rest of the wall sections, making sure that all corner posts consist of at least three studs. The third is added after the wall is up. If you are using inlet bracing, the cuts are made and the bracing nailed, with 10 penny nails, before the wall is tilted up. You must make sure the corners of the wall section are exactly square before doing the inlet cutting and again before nailing the bracing board (Fig. 2-38).

Once the walls are tilted into place, the second top plate is placed, and overlapped at the corners, tying the structure together even more. Again, 20 penny nails are used to tie the two top plates together.

Interior partition walls can be built in the same manner and tilted right on up. The top plate on interior partition walls, where they join exterior walls, should overlap the lower portion of the exterior wall top plate whenever possible. Interior wall top plates should intersect in the same manner.

Roof Framing

If trusses are to be used for the roof, they can now be set in place and nailed, after making sure they are plumb. If trusses are not used, you will want to install ceiling joists before installing the rafters. Otherwise, the pressure from

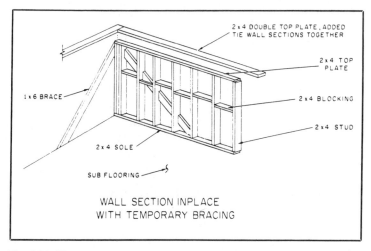

Fig. 2-38. Wall section in place and temporarily braced.

the rafters may force the walls out of plumb. Like floor joists, ceiling joist size depends on the span required. For houses over 12 feet wide, a load bearing partition wall directly over the basement girder will usually allow you to use 2 by 8 material with a span of about 12 feet. For more than that, go to 2 by 10.

Once the ceiling joists are in, you can consider the rafters. Only a single rafter need be measured to make an equal *pitch* roof which, other than a *shed* roof, is the simplest design. Unfortunately, a few technical terms are needed to understand how to make the pattern rafter. If after the full explanation you still feel unsure of things, I would select some nominal 1-inch lumber and make up two pattern rafters as a check. The material loss is less if you make mistakes in measuring or cutting.

The roof we will work on here is an equal pitch *gable* style. Two roof slopes meet at the center, or ridge, and form a gable. In actuality, I believe it is simpler to design and build than even a *shed* roof.

Rafter Layout

Rafters are the main pieces of the roof framework and do the same job for the roof that the floor joists do for the floor. They are inclined, and on-center spacing can vary from 16 to 48 inches, though the most common residential spacings are 16 inches and 2 feet. Bottoms of the rafters rest on the top plate of the exterior walls. They may be cut to fit over the top plate—a *bird's mouth*—or simply toe nailed to the top plate. You can also use a Teco framing anchor.

The pitch of a roof is the angle it makes from a horizontal line. It is expressed in numbers, so that a 5 in 12 roof will rise from the horizontal 5 inches in every foot (Fig. 2-39).

The span of the house is the distance between the outside edges of the top plates that run in the same direction as the roof ridge. The total rise is the distance from the plate to the top of the ridge, vertically. The total run is the level distance over which any rafter passes. For our purposes, the total run is always half the span (Fig. 2-40).

Your first need is to determine the length of the lumber needed for the rafters. If you are working from a detailed

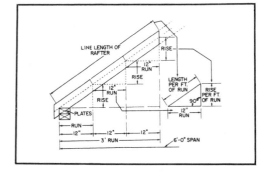

Fig. 2-39. Roof pitch.

plan, this may already be included. There is no more work to do until you start stepping off actual rafter length in readiness for cutting. If not, measure the distance across the top of the house—the span. Take half this distance—the total run. Assume a run of 10 feet, with a rise of 5 inches. Take your *rafter square*—this tool is essential to laying out both rafters and stairs—and measure the distance between 5 and 12.

My handy *Stanley Powerlock II* gives me 13 inches as an answer, so the length needed is 130 inches. Assume no

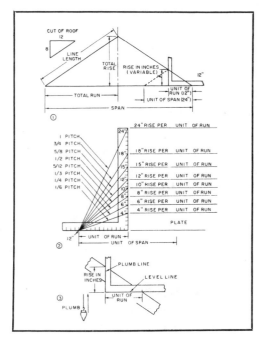

Fig. 2-40. Roof terms.

overhang is wanted. You want an overhang of at least a foot on each side of your building. On houses where there is a desire to keep the high summer sun to aid cooling, and overhang of 18 inches is better. That is a total piece length of 148 inches, or 12 feet 4 inches, and one odd size to buy. But few runs are actually 10 feet long, and this is only an example. Still, remember when measuring and designing that until metrics slaps us under lock and key, lumber is sold in pretty much standard 2-foot full lengths, with few variations.

Once you've gotten the length of the lumber and picked it up, lay one piece on a couple of sawhorses. If there is any crown to the piece of wood being used, keep it towards you as you lay out the rafter. Keep the rafter square tongue in your right hand and the heel away from your body, and place the square as close to the top end of the rafter as you can. Place the figure 5 and the figure 12, as shown in Fig. 2-41, and mark along the tongue edge of the square. This will be your top, or ridge cut. If you decide to use a ridge board, you will later need to mark off half the thickness of the ridge board for removal. Keeping to the 5 and 12 marks, along the rafter, step off the same number of marks as there are feet in the run. If there is an odd number to be cut, which is almost a certainty, make a mark at that odd number (along the blade).

Now move the square until the tongue rests at the odd number mark. Mark along the tongue. Any overhang is marked in the same manner. At the last mark involving the actual rafter length—before the overhang starts—make a plumb, or square mark, across the rafter. You may need to cut the rest of the rafter first and then place it correctly to get the cut needed for the bird's mouth, should you choose to go this way, but it can be marked as shown in Fig. 2-42, once the measurement is known. Rather than bothering with a bird's mouth, I would use Teco framing—anchors—in preference to simple toe nailing of the rafter to the top plate.

Cut a second rafter to the same pattern and have someone help you get it in place and temporarily nailed to check fit—don't nail permanently yet. If the fit is okay, take it down and cut the remaining rafters from the pattern rafter. Remember, you need one more set of rafters than you have

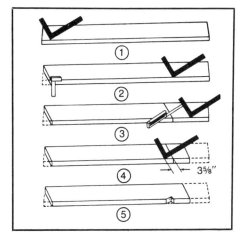

Fig. 2-41. Scale method of laying out a rafter.

on-center distances. As an example, a 48-foot long house using rafters on 2-foot centers would require 25 pairs, not 24.

Collar beams can be used on rafters to help stiffen the structure and are especially handy over long spans. They provide nailing surfaces for any time you might decide to finish the attic space. Use at least 2 by 6 material and 20 penny nails.

Roof sheathing differs little from subflooring and, in fact, often the same materials are used. Sheathing can be of boards, or of plywood, with plywood going on more quickly. Again, plan things so there is little waste and so no two butting pieces end on the same rafter.

Fig. 2-42. Step-off method of laying out a rafter.

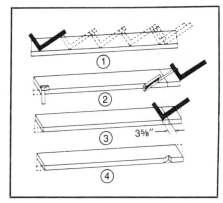

Wall Sheathing

Today you will find a great many ways to sheath building walls from the old board sheathing to many types of plywood, some of which serve both as sheathing and siding. My personal preference is for plywood because of its greater rigidity and ease of application. Do not goof cuts around door openings, for like all building materials today, plywood is not cheap. The plywood will specifically state what type of on-center distance it is to be used for, but under no circumstances should you use anything less than 5/16-inch thickness, and that only if you have closed things up to 16 inches on center (Fig. 2-43 and 2-44).

Wood sheathing is usually of 1 by 6 boards and may be square edged, tongue and grooved or shiplapped. Wood sheathing must be covered with at least 15 pound builder's felt, but plywood sheathing need not be in most areas (check local codes first, of course). Wood sheathing can be applied at a diagonal or horizontally, while plywood is almost always installed vertically. Diagonal nailing of wood sheathing is stronger than horizontal, but requires a great many mitered cuts (most all, though, will be a simple 45 degree angle).

SIDING

These are so many types of siding to be found, and more coming all the time, that it is hard to keep up to date. As I have already said, some forms of plywood sheathing also serve as siding. In other cases, the plywood is bought as siding to go over sheathing; other materials are of great utility. Clapboards look just great and tempered hardboard goes up quickly and is not that costly. Vertical boards of rough cut lumber can be used and may, if there are local sawmills in your area, be the cheapest way to go. These can be applied as board and batten, board and board or reverse board and batten, but should be air dried for at least four months before use to prevent cupping and warping (Fig. 2-45).

One rather new product comes to mind, Luxaclad, put out by Hunter Douglass, Inc. This is an aluminum siding system designed to be put on by the homeowner instead of

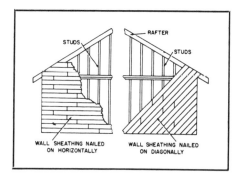

Fig. 2-43. Wood sheathing.

the professional. Special snaps hold the siding pieces together (they're also nailed to the sheathing or already installed siding). Luxaclad can easily be bought with already installed poly foam backing to provide an extra R3 insulation rating in your walls. It comes in a number of colors—about six or eight right now—and can be had in both vertical and horizontal styles. While siding with this material is not any weekend project, it is far simpler than the work I've seen my brother do as a professional in aluminum siding. Cutting can be done with normal power or hand tools (make sure you use the finest toothed blades you can get for smooth cuts), and the snap on system allows ease of installation. But handle it with care, for aluminum dents easily and bends easily.

When aluminum siding is installed, nails are driven with light taps, not slammed home as with wood. If you can find one, a sliding nail set is a good idea for tight places.

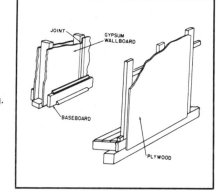

Fig. 2-44. Plywood sheathing.

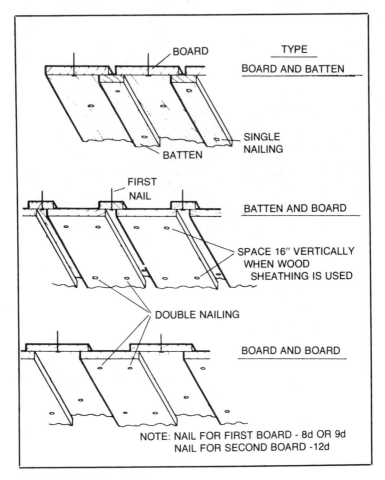

Fig. 2-45. Vertical board siding.

Start by nailing furring strips to create a level surface. If you're working on new construction, this probably won't be needed. A starter strip is leveled and nailed in place, and the corner posts are nailed on. These things are exceptionally fragile, so use extreme care. The first row snaps onto the starter strip and is nailed at the top.

Soffit is sold in 12-foot strips, and you can cut it to width. I had never done it before a couple of weeks ago, but careful measurement and a tight hold allowed me to cut three panels at one time.

WINDOWS AND DOORS

One of the greatest benefits of modern carpentry is getting out of having to mortise doors for hinges, mortise the jambs, cut holes for locksets and install all the hardware after building up the door frame. Maybe it's laziness on my part, but I much prefer to work with a prehung door than with any other kind. Unfortunately, sooner or later I have to completely build doors and door frames for two really odd shaped areas, one on the house and one on an outbuilding. Both areas are of concrete block, and I don't feel like knocking that down just to fit in a more standard prehung door. But, in general, prehung doors are much simpler to work with, though the prices today take my breath away. What I paid $17 for back in 1962 or 1963 now goes for at least $48. And the door isn't as well made, unfortunately, with too much finger gluing in the jambs and on the molding, and too many staples replacing nails. Still, properly hung, even the hollow core interior doors will last for years.

Exterior doors are another matter entirely. They are, or should be, made of solid wood, with excellent locksets and small lights (windows) to make it difficult for anyone to reach the inside handle of the lockset by breaking glass. Exterior doors are now often made of metal, with foam filled cores to provide insulating value. These tend to be a bit cheaper than the top quality wood doors, and until recently I didn't think I would care for the appearance. Once painted, it is nearly impossible to tell the difference, though. The metal is of fairly good gauge (thickness), but it is a long way from impervious to damage.

Framing for doors and windows should be as level and plumb as possible. Dead on is best. The rough opening dimensions should be ½ inch larger than the dimensions of the unit being installed to, allowing for shimming the door or window to plumb and level.

Sit the unit in place, with the factory bracing still on, if possible, and shim until it is plumb. Then drive 10 or 12 penny finishing nails part way in and re-check the plumb and level. If all is still well, finish driving the nails, set them and fill the holes with wood putty (Fig. 2-46).

Your house is now enclosed under a sheathed roof. All that remains is to shingle it.

ROOFING

While *roll roofing* can be used, asphalt shingles are the most popular choice for roofs today. Your first job is to install flashing around the chimney so that the shingles can cover it and make the seal watertight. Most asphalt shingles today come in a 12 by 36 inch size with 5 inches of the material exposed to the weather. A top grade of shingle is recommended and some companies, such as Certainteed, make shingles of different compounds that are longer lasting (generally based on fiber glass). These are more expensive than asphalt shingles, but may outlast them (Fig. 2-47).

Cedar shakes also make a good looking and long lasting roof, though they are a bit more complex to install and cost quite a lot. I've seen cedar shake roofs, though, that have lasted over 75 years in the worst conditions possible.

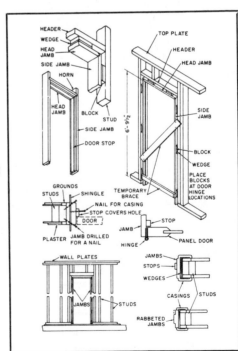

Fig. 2-46. Door jamb and door plates.

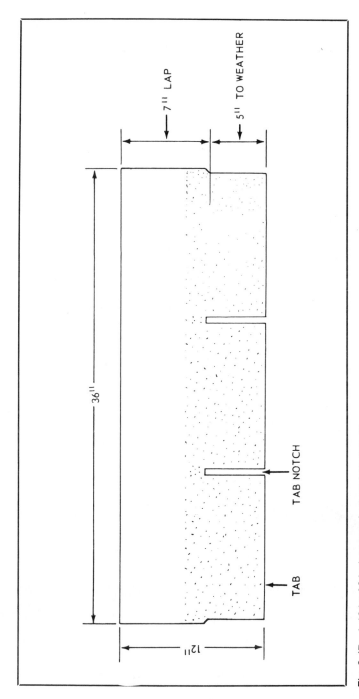

Fig. 2-47. A 12 by 36-inch square butt asphalt shingle.

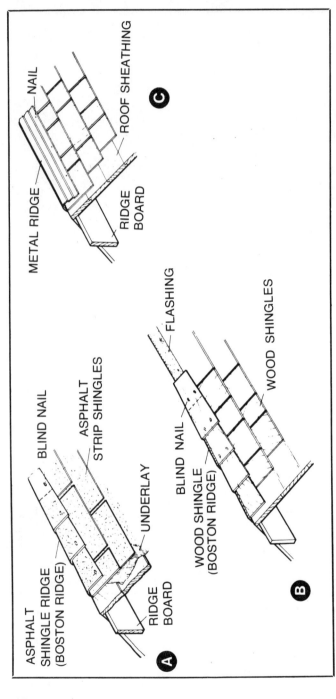

Fig. 2-48. Methods of capping the ridge when shingling. (A) Boston ridge with asphalt shingles. (B) Boston ridge with wood shingles. (C) Metal ridge.

Shingling starts with a roofing felt underlay over the sheathing, making sure there is at least a 4-inch overlap on each successive sheet. Now, snap a chalk line one shingle depth up the roof. This is the nailing line for your starter strip. The starter strip is always reversed. The part of the shingle that is not to be exposed to the weather is placed along the eave line. Use two 1-inch hot dipped galvanized nails to each butt (six per shingle). Directly over the starter course, you lay the first weather course, nailing in the same manner. From this point, it is a simple matter to snap a chalk line along the 5-inch mark for each row of shingles and go on up the roof until you reach the ridge.

The ridge is capped with single butts cut from full shingles and laid, as Fig. 2-48 shows, so that they are blind nailed (the nails are covered by the next butt). Of course, the final cap piece will have two exposed nails. These should be well coated with roofing tar. For areas where there are many high winds associated with heavy rain or driving snow, aluminum flashing can be placed under the cap ends, but in most areas it really isn't needed. It is also possible to buy metal ridge caps.

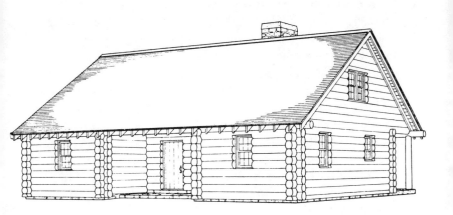

3

Inspecting Old Homes

In many cases appearances of old homes can be deceiving. Some of the most deteriorated looking older homes can be easily saved and remodeled. Others, not nearly so old, may collapse as you try to shore up the original builder's shoddy work.

According to Agriculture Handbook number 481, limited tests were conducted on some timbers from Japanese temples ranging in age from three centuries to 1300 years. The apparent major finding is that shock resistance of the wood (no specification as to type) is seriously cut by aging, but that other properties are relatively unaffected. This is good news, since most of the available old homes in this country are of wood frame construction. The benefits of renovation over new construction can be many, including more space for the money, a.possibility of luxurious features beyond the reach of the average millionaire today, and some financial savings over new construction.

KNOWING YOUR LIMITATIONS

A couple of years ago I looked at a place that almost literally made me drool. It was an 11-room house, on a stone foundation, located on a hillside and well out in the country. The house was on about 40 acres of land and had two creeks running almost through the front yard. As a matter of fact, it was necessary to ford one of the creeks—naturally, the larger and deeper, another argument in favor of owning a pickup truck—on the dirt road to the house. I did not know the exact age of the house. Neither did the real estate agent or the people who owned the place, but it was certainly pre-Civil War. The front doors were 10 feet tall, 4 feet wide and were doubled. The foyer was about the size of most modern living rooms. The stairs to the second floor were 8 feet wide.

This place had been abandoned for years. All the wiring and plumbing was gone, every window broken out, and the floors were covered with trash. Tramps had used the place for rest. All the outbuildings were in an advanced state of collapse and the house, as it stood, was unlivable. The price asked was about double the worth of the land alone. I made a counter offer which was laughed off. I could have cried, but I also could not and would not pay any more. As far as I know, that old house with its stately, but shabby, elegance, remains, two years later, unsold and still abandoned.

The moral of this story is to know your limitations, financial and otherwise. I have a fair amount of wiring and carpentry experience and have installed sinks, toilets and similar items more than once. I have done roofing and fencing (not a foot of fence was still standing on this place). Just about everything needed could be done, but at that time I figured the cost, not counting my labor, at about $20,000 for materials at a minimum, and not including the cost of fencing the place to run horses or other livestock. So I passed. Besides, I don't care for the idea of living in a pup tent for most of a year. Yet, even today, I regret my decision, though I know it was the right one considering my limited resources, both in time and money.

CHECKING THE FOUNDATION

Once you've got your limitations firmly in mind, start looking. When you find the place of your dreams, you can see if the dream has any foundation. And that's where you begin your check to see if a house is worth fooling with. Your first check should be a careful one for uneven settling of the foundation. Some settling is likely in old homes, but too much uneven settling will distort the frame of the house and can in extreme cases rip it apart. Distortion will pull window and door frames out of square, loosen the interior finished walls and ceilings, and create cracks of varying size throughout the house (Fig. 3-1).

Some settling around one corner of the house, though, doesn't mean you should take a walk. First, find out what is causing the settling. One corner of the masonry may be going or gone. A joist or beam may be out of level, or even rotted, and still leave the place able to be renovated.

If the settling isn't generalized, then there is some possibility the house is worth fooling with. However, if several sections of foundation have settled or large portions of sill are rotted, then the house may be in no shape for any kind of rebuilding (Fig. 3-2).

Cracks and crumbling mortar in old houses can usually be repaired if the extent of the damage is not too great and is not accompanied by generalized settling. In older houses you will seldom find poured concrete foundations, but usually those made of rock. Often the sills are so large that an entire corner of the house can be sagging on its deteriorated foundation without causing great structural damage to the overall building.

Fig. 3-1. Uneven foundation settlement.

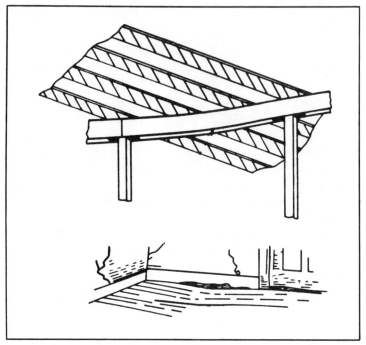

Fig. 3-2. Sagging beam and uneven floor.

SURVEYING BASEMENT WALLS AND CHIMNEYS

Once the foundation is checked for soundness, take a look at the basement walls. This is best done in wet weather, for you're now searching for conditions which might cause a damp basement for the entire year or for several months of the year. Most often, damp basements are caused by water run-off from the surface, either from improperly set, or cared for, down spouts or from improper backfilling. Cracks in the basement walls will often let in water. Any of these can be rather easily corrected, but a high water table that continually floods the basement cannot. This will require sump pumps set in shallow wells cut in the floor. Having lived for five years in a house with such a pump, I can assure you that you will still have a damp basement, though it may not be totally waterlogged.

Old houses will usually have *chimneys*. Looking around this area, I see many made of unlined stone. These are often poorly maintained, even in occupied dwellings, and are a danger in any case. It is impossible to properly clean the creosote out of an unlined chimney. Assuming the chimney footing is in good condition and not pulling away from the house, the best resort in such cases is to line the chimney. Fortunately, the variety of multiple walled metal chimneys available today make this, if not an easy job, at least a more practical one than in the past. Too, old fireplaces often had no dampers. An internal damper can be impossible to install. This creates an almost unbelievable heat loss. Again, with the new popularity of wood heat in the 1980s, this is a problem rather easily solved. Chimney top dampers are readily available now, though they were nearly impossible to find five years ago.

Check fireplace draw by first shining a flashlight up the chimney to make sure it is clear of obstructions. Then open the damper and light a few crumpled sheets of newspaper on the hearth. If the fireplace takes more than a minute to draw the smoke, then you will find yourself with problems getting the fireplace to work. I will cover some of the difficulties possible later in the book, which could range from partial obstruction to trees to close to the chimney's top to a chimney that is too short.

As a rule, chimneys must rise 2 feet above any obstruction, within 10 feet (for peaked roofs) and three feet above for flat roofs. As another rule, fireplaces are poor heat sources. They usually contribute to an actual heat loss from the dwelling, though this can be modified with modern appliances so that a good fireplace will present nearly as much heat as a poor wood stove. The basic importance of a clear drawing chimney in a house to be renovated, though, lies in the possibility of inserting a wood stove smoke pipe into the flue and placing the stove itself on the hearth. Some models now are installed directly in the fireplace.

WOOD FRAME CHECK

The basic tools for a check of *wood framing* in older houses are a good, powerful flashlight and either an *ice pick* or an *awl*. Most old homes have the basement floor joists exposed. It is usually fairly simple to see the sills between the floor joists. *Dry rot* becomes a real problem as wood ages, especially if the building is not properly ventilated (one area in which most modern homes are better than older ones) so that humidity can escape. Dry rot only occurs in the presence of excess moisture over a long period of time. Insect damage, primarily from termites, is another problem to check for.

Start the check by looking at the floor support system. The interior support is usually a beam, or girder, of wood, set on wood posts (newer houses will use steel posts and may also use a steel girder). If the basement has a concrete floor, wood posts should *not* be embedded, but instead set on small piers of concrete. If the floor is of dirt, as in most really old homes, the posts should be set on flat rocks. These girders should be checked for sagging and, looking at the sill ends, for dry rot. Take the flashlight and shine it up close to the sill. See if the ice pick or awl will penetrate the wood. If it does, the girder will have to be replaced. Posts are less of a problem to replace, as usually a new post can simply be set beside the old one, and the older member knocked out. It is more or less up to you as to what decision to make if the girder shows end rot. If it does, the girder will have to be replaced. The job is a major one, but quite possible. It requires a great deal of bracing and care but can be done, though I would not recommend such a course for someone with no heavy carpentry experience at all (Figs. 3-3 through 3-5).

The joists extend from the girder end at the sill, or sill plate. It is important that they also be checked for sag, and that the sill and the joists be checked for decay and insect damage. Because the sill in older homes was laid directly on the foundation wall, insect damage is more likely than in modern construction where a fiberglass insulation blanket—to cut down drafts—and a metal termite shield are usually used (not always, so check even on relatively modern houses). Check the sill end of the joists and the sills themselves with the ice pick. Either joists or sills can be replaced, with the sills being much harder job, if you have the skills and wish to spend the time. If more than a few joists are affected, in addition to the sills, and one or both ends of the girders are

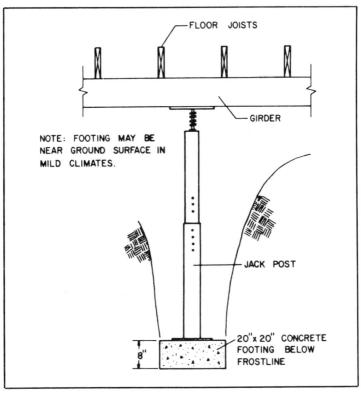

Fig. 3-3. Jack post supporting a sagging girder in a crawl-space house.

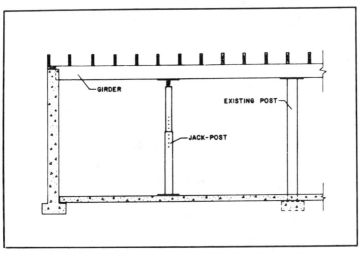

Fig. 3-4. Jack post used to level a sagging girder in a basement house.

115

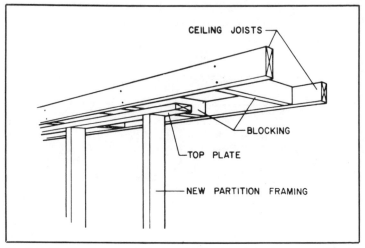

Fig. 3-5. Blocking between joists to which the top plate of a new partition is nailed.

decayed or infested. I would forget it. There is simply too much to be done to make such a house habitable again.

Check carefully around stairwells for sag, as this is a point where many old-time builders tended to fall down on the job. In most such cases, a careful leveling with jacks and then added reinforcement will cure the sag if any has developed.

If you haven't brought a framing square with you, check wall trueness by opening and closing as many windows and doors as possible. One of the not so joyful things about old houses is the number of coats of paint applied to improper places on old windows, making them nearly impossible to open.

If the house has any really wide window openings, check those for sag, just as you did the floor joists. From the exterior, try your ice pick or awl on the sections of wood around the tops and upper sides of windows and doors. Rot can easily occur in such places through water seepage.

SIDING AND TRIM INSPECTION

Paint bubbles and peeling should have little effect in deciding the condition of a house. Any place not cared for or lived in will deteriorate, some places more quickly than others. Even rotted siding is not totally a reason for turning down a house, though it's a good idea to check and make sure you can still buy matching siding for older homes. If not, the entire house may have to be resided to present a uniform appearance. While doing that job isn't the worst thing in the world, not the most expensive, it does run costs up more than a simple patch job and a few coats of paint do.

Siding should be checked for gaps—peer along the edges of horizontal siding—and for rot at points where boards butt. A few gaps mean little, as they can usually be caulked, but many gaps may well mean re-siding the house, as may a large number of warped siding boards.

CHECKING WINDOWS AND DOORS

Old windows can present many problems. You can almost be certain that if replacement isn't needed, storm windows and a good caulking will be. Old, single glazed windows often become loose in their frames over the years. Single glazing passes a huge amount of heat anyway. Replacement windows can be considered, but tend to really jump expenses. In a house I am now completing the remodeling on, the single largest expense has been the replacement of old, single hung (only the bottom half opens) aluminum single glazed windows with more modern double glazed casement windows. Even the insulated aluminum siding costs less and is easier to install, using Hunter Douglas's new Luxaclad material which is specifically designed for homeowner installation. If you do plan to install new windows, get them as close in size to the old as is possible.

Exterior doors should fit tightly without sticking when opened. Weather stripping will almost surely be lacking in older houses, but for once this is a cheap and easy item to add on. Check door size, too, as the installation of a storm door is less costly if you don't have to order a custom size. Check along the threshold and the lower part of the door for rot. If the threshold is too worn, it must be replaced—not an easy job but not overly difficult.

Interior doors should open and close easily. If the home is old enough to have paneled doors, make sure they are all in place and in good shape or easily repaired. Replacing such a door today can be monumentally expensive, unless you care to have mismatching doors throughout the house. About all that is readily available today is the hollow core door, and even those cost more than they should.

ROOFING CONSIDERATIONS

First, consider the type of roofing on the house. Some really old houses may have slate or tile roofing. If it is in bad condition, you may be in for a lot of trouble. I haven't even met anyone who knows how to work with these materials in the past 15 years. Material cost is on the prohibitive side. In most cases, a damaged slate or tile roof is best ripped off and replaced with other roofing materials, whether asphalt or cedar shingles or shakes. Check flashing at points where the roof intersects and forms valleys, as well as around chimneys and plumbing vents through the roof. Check gutters and downspouts for loose straps, or other holders, as well as for corrosion. In some houses, wooden gutters were used. These are extremely susceptible to decay. It would, in most instances, be best to plan on replacing them with aluminum gutters in the near future, even if they appear solid at present.

EXAMINING FLOORING

Interior wood floors are delightful features and, in homes built before 1900, can add a real aura to a country home. Wide boards, secured with square headed nails, really do look fine. Such old flooring will be of different materials in different areas of the country and, though we now seem to prefer maple and oak for flooring, many of our ancestors used hard pines for flooring. I have seen such flooring laid down with boards no less than 2 feet across, something nearly impossible today. Of course, the wider the floor boards, the more likely they are to be cupped, warped or to have shrunk and left fairly large gaps between boards. Make sure any old flooring is thick enough to allow sanding for refinishing, unless you plan to refloor the place. Laying new flooring is not really difficult, but it can be costly if many rooms have to be done.

WALL WORK

Interior walls in old homes will often be covered with plaster over wood *lath*. In some, wood wainscoting or paneling may have been used. Often the wainscoting or panelling will be covered by several coats of paint.

Often, plaster will be in poor shape, especially if a house has been abandoned for some time. In such cases where the plaster bulges or has many large holes and cracks, the only real solution is to rip it out and put in new walls. Usually, it's best to go right to the studs. These is a sound advantage to doing this in that it allows you to insulate any exterior walls without having to hire a contractor to blow in insulation. Half-inch gypsum wallboard is your best bet for economy of reconstruction here, though you may wish to use wood paneling in dens, libraries and such rooms.

You will often find it necessary, when using wallboard or paneling to refinish old interior walls on the studs, to use some form of shim stock to plumb the surface. Often old studs were not very accurately cut. They did not need to be as the lath used for the plaster could be used to plumb the surface (Fig. 3-6).

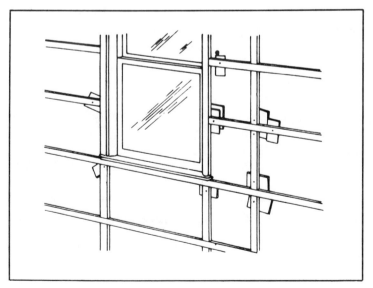

Fig. 3-6. Shim stock used to produce a smooth surface for refinishing.

LOOKING FOR INSECT DAMAGE

Decay is often easily recognized by color change. The wood may be either darker or lighter in color than the rest of the area, with fine black lines running through it. In really advanced stages, wood may check or become pulpy and powdery. For a further check, and to inspect the extent of damage, use your awl to pry out slivers. Decayed wood will break off in square, or near square, ended chunks. Healthy wood pulls out in long splinters.

Checking for insect damage is important in almost any old house. There are three types of insect you are likely to find causing trouble: *termites, carpenter ants* and *powder-post beetles.*

Termites are divided into two types. The *subterranean* termite needs access to the ground or some other water source, while *nonsubterranean* termites do not. Subterranean termites are often indicated by dirt tubes running over the surface of the foundation walls, giving a passage from soil to the wood above. Too, swarming occurs early in the spring and fall, and you can tell termites from flying ants by simply checking the waistline of the insect. Flying ants have slender waists while termites do not (Fig. 3-7). Use your awl to probe any wood in areas where tunnels or swarms are found, as the termites will often tunnel along the grain, leaving a shell of sound wood.

Nonsubterranean termites are not an inland problem, and need be checked only in Hawaii and on the coastal strip from central California to Virginia. These termites will often first indicate their presence by leaving sandlike excretory pellets outside the wood. Again, these insects swarm. If the wood is cut across the grain, then you have nonsubterranean termites.

In most cases, if termites are present and the damage is not too extensive, it is best to call in a professional to get rid of them. The poisons used are not pleasant to work with. Professional exterminators have, or should have, the equipment and knowledge to deal with any termite problem effectively.

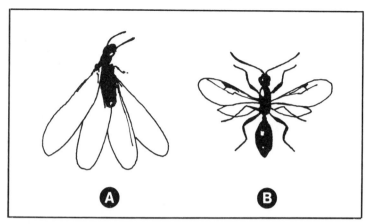

Fig. 3-7. Note the differences between a termite and a winged ant. (A) Termite. (B) Winged ant.

Carpenter ants leave piles of coarse sawdust-like wood piled outside the wood. Carpenter ants don't eat the wood, but use it for nesting. They work in high moisture areas. Using a good insecticide to get rid of them as a start is fine, but eliminating the high moisture condition will prevent their return.

Powder-post beetles leave borings about the same consistency as flour. When adult, they leave the wood through holes about the diameter of a pencil lead. If the infestation is heavy, the wood can look as if someone used birdshot on the wood's face.

Again, humid locations promote the beetles. Removing the humidity, if possible, after killing the beetles helps to prevent reinfestation. Severe infestations will require a professional exterminator.

In all cases of insect damage to homes, high humidity is a sure drawing card for the little destroyers. Controlling humidity is one way to prevent the occurrence, or any reoccurrence, of insect damage. Fix leaks, install flashing, etc (Fig. 3-8).

HUMIDITY AND INSULATION CONSIDERATIONS

We've already looked at one reason to control excess humidity in walls, the control of decay and rot, plus the

Fig. 3-8. (A) The northern limit of damage in the United States by subterranean termites. (B) Damage limits by drywood or nonsubterranean termites.

control of insect damage problems. Still, some humidity is essential will occur naturally during home living. Cooking, bathing and laundering all give off appreciable amounts of water.

Older homes almost never have vapor barriers in the exterior walls. In those mostly uninsulated homes, the humidity passes easily through the air space to the exterior and the excess is gone. Add insulation, though, and it will usually trap enough humidity inside the walls to cause some problems. A vapor barrier must be added to most homes built since about 1935 on.

Almost all older homes will be under-insulated for to-day, if not totally uninsulated. After all, it has not been that long since fuel oil was under 8 cents per gallon, instead of the present and rising $1.20. Attics should be checked first, as they're usually the easiest to get to. You may find some poured in insulation. Check underneath for a vapor barrier. Plan on installing no less than 6 inches of insulation, with a foot needed in northern climates. To check wall insulation, you'll probably have to remove some siding or a portion of interior wall.

Vapor barriers are important. They always go on the warm side of the insulation—that is, to the interior of the house. Vapor barriers prevent or retard the passage of interior moisture into the walls, where it will condense and form water droplets that may eventually cause water damage or attract insects. Check crawl spaces as well as walls and ceilings for vapor barriers. In almost all cases, if the crawl space has no vapor barrier, sheet *polyethylene* is easily added to provide one. If the home is built on a slab, and the slab is continually damp, you will have to add a vapor barrier on top of the slab and then lay a new finish floor. This is quite a job and not necessarily that effective, so I would use it as a reason to reject a slab house.

Ventilation was something more or less ignored by old-time house builders. Attic vents at gable ends are essential, as these allow the passage out of moist air as it migrates up from the house. Crawl spaces must also be vented, if enclosed (Fig. 3-9).

Fig. 3-9. Recommended average moisture content for interior finish woodwork in different parts of the United States.

LOOKING AT MECHANICAL SYSTEMS

The mechanical systems in a house are the *plumbing, wiring* and *heating* systems. Almost all homes built before 1950 will have inadequacies in one or more systems. The extent of the inadequacies can determine the reasonability of your buying the house. Wiring has to be the easiest and cheapest to change over. Still, it can be expensive to completely rewire an older house. Plumbing is probably the worst, both as to expense and effort, though heating can approach plumbing changes in cost and complexity.

Always keep an eye on local codes when checking out the mechanical systems. Any updating must meet the codes or you will not get a certificate of occupancy—or the present certificate may be pulled. The next three chapters go into some detail on plumbing, heating and wiring installations.

Plumbing

Your first check with plumbing is the water pressure. Turn on several faucets at the same time to determine if pressure is adequate. If the pressure is low, look first at the pipes. Older homes may have galvanized pipe. If a pipe has been updated at any time, the pipe will be copper; if the updating was recent, it may be plastic. If the pipe is of lead, as it may be on very old houses, plan immediately on a complete replacement of the system. For galvanized pipe, the feed line from the main or well should be at least 1 inch in inside diameter, while copper can be ¾-inch. All main distribution pipes should be of the same size as the main feed line, while interior branches to individual appliances such as kitchen sinks can be ½-inch copper.

If the pipes are galvanized, there is a possibility of mineral buildup cutting down the flow of water, since this type of pipe has a rough interior. Copper and plastic have smoother interiors, which is one reason a smaller size can be used, and they are less likely to be obstructed by mineral buildup. Still, with copper mineral buildup is possible.

If the pipes are copper or plastic, check the supply pressure. For rural homes, this will almost be a well. A look at the gauge on the pressure tank will quickly tell you if things are okay there. If the pressure is under 20 pounds, the pump is not operating properly, or the pressure is set to low on the cutoff. For really adequate pressure, you will need a reading of from 40 to 50 pounds (Fig. 3-10).

Look for leaks along the lines of the entire system. Leaks are not always indicated by moisture, as this is often simply condensation forming on the pipes. Check for white or green shades crusting the pipes around fittings. This does

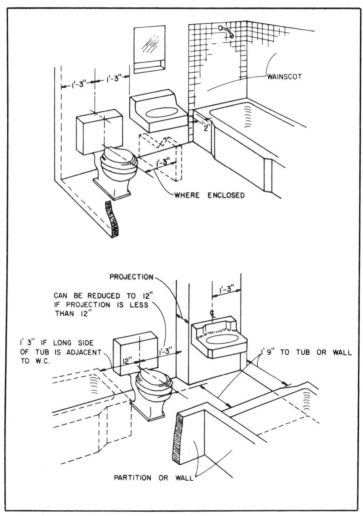

Fig. 3-10. Fixture placement for bathrooms.

not always indicate a leak (condensation may build up in such places and form encrustations).

Have the well water checked. County agents can tell you where the check can be made. Usually the health department will do the job. Even a well in constant use should be checked. A well in an abandoned home must be inspected, as even drilled wells can be infiltrated by bacteria. Treatment usually consists of adding a chloride powder to sterilize the water.

Not only is the incoming water supply important, but the sewage system must be adequate and safely installed. Flush toilets to see if they work sluggishly, and repeat the process by filling the bathtub, lavatory and kitchen sink and pulling the plugs. Drainage systems can be clogged in many areas, right from the traps under the sinks out to the septic tank and field. Check local codes for vent pipe sizes required. See that the ones installed meet the codes and are not plugged. Look for trees growing close to septic fields, as the roots may clog the lines. Roots can be mechanically cut out of septic fields, but often that becomes a job that needs repeating every few years, unless the tree doing the plugging can be cut down.

Inspect the water heater. If it operates on gas, you will need a minimum 30 gallon capacity. If it is electric, look for at least a 50 gallon model.

As far as plumbing fixtures go, the selection today is extremely varied. Replacement of old fixtures is really no problem, but it can get expensive. If rust stains are the major problem, I'd let these sit until really major work is done.

Heating

Heating becomes the major expense in any area with cool or cold winters. I once rented a small house—six rooms, none overly large—with a gravity hot air furnace that had been converted from coal. In a more or less cold area of the country—about 70 miles north-northeast of Manhattan—that thing would gulp as many as 11 gallons of fuel oil a day. By 1973, I had a wood stove in the house. We were using something like 1100 gallons of fuel oil each year and were still chilly. At 20 cents per gallon, the cost wasn't bad. Add a dollar a gallon to that, and your wallet really feels the pinch.

Modern furnaces are designed to operate more efficiently. Any gravity warm air system should almost certainly be replaced with a forced air system, with a new furnace. With proper insulation and good sealing around doors and windows, this will pay itself off in savings quite rapidly. I doubt the payback period would be more than three years, even if someone else contracts the work for you.

Gravity steam systems can be found in many old homes. Such systems look very much like hot water systems and may provide plenty of heat, but they take a long time to warm things up and give little control. I would suggest replacement of such systems. The most economical replacement is usually a forced air system, even though radiators and steam lines are already in place.

Electric panel heat, or *baseboard* heat, is not really economical in many areas of the country. In Virginia it's still not outrageous yet, especially if supplemented with a wood stove or two, but even here electricity is getting up near 5 cents per kilowatt. Baseboard heat could be overly expensive if totally relied upon in a large home. I am about to install electric baseboard heat in my mother's home, but it will be divided into four zones and supplemented by two wood stoves. Actually, the wood stoves will provide the main source of heat, with the electrical units turned as low as they will go.

Wood heat is one more form. Today, it need not be used only as a supplement. Many companies make multi-fuel furnaces now. These will often take a load of wood that will burn for 24 hours or more, after which the oil or other fuel comes on line if the furnace isn't tended. Too, wood stoves have gotten a great deal more efficient in the past five or six years and can be easily used to heat an entire house, My cousin and her husband have a large farmhouse not far from my place, and it has now been two winters since their furnace even came on. That's with one wood stove installed in the huge kitchen and vents left open. Some upstairs rooms get chilly at night, but no pipes freeze and most of the house is quite comfortable. The stove has been in use for three winters. Original cost was not much over $400, with an additional $70 going for a stovepipe blower that takes waste heat, or what would be waste heat, and distributes it with a fan. Total savings are hard to really estimate, but a good guess at the gross savings would be close to $2500 and possibly more. Last winter the price of fuel oil rose to almost a dollar, and the furnace came on only during a test.

Wood stoves require good chimneys, but we've already covered the checks for chimneys. Installation is now being put under code restrictions in some areas. You should also check with your fire insurance company to see what they consider to be a safe installation.

Wiring

Electrical wiring is first checked at the entrance panel. Check to see how many amperes the entrance service is. Modern appliances demand 100 ampere service. A range or electric hot water heater will bring requirements up to 200 amperes, as will the need to run lines to outbuildings.

Whenever and wherever you can, check any exposed wiring for deteroration. If the insulation on cable appears to be crumbly, plan on replacing it. If any BX (metal armored) cable is used, make sure it hasn't rusted anywhere. Make the same check on any conduit used. Modern NEC requirements may not have to be met in older houses, but it's a good idea to make sure the wiring is safe and that there are sufficient outlets for your purposes. Any additional wiring you put in must meet the NEC requirements and those of any local codes.

ROOM LAYOUT

Many older houses are laid out on a catch-as-catch-can basis, with rooms having been added as needed. Children being born would often result in the raising of a new room, but there was often no telling just where that room might be. Check traffic patterns for convenience throughout the house. In general, traffic through a room should be kept to one side of the room. Rooms should be arranged so that the house has three areas: sleeping, kitchen and utility rooms and recreation.

The sleeping area should be separated from the living and work area, both visually and acoustically if possible. The bedroom area would include the bathroom. Each bedroom should have access to a bathroom without a need to go through another bedroom. It also should not be necessary to go through one bedroom to reach another. Bedroom size depends on the type of beds to be used. A double bed should be placed in a room no less than 125 square feet in area, while twin beds require about 25 square feet more. Smaller bedrooms are usable, but can severely limit the type of furnishing. A minimum size for any bathroom is about 64 square feet. In many old farmhouses, this isn't a problem, as the bathroom will be converted from another room, often a pantry or other room much larger than the average modern bath. One of my mother's sisters lives in a house about 100 miles north of here that has a bathroom so large you almost feel a need to pack one lunch to walk to the tub.

The work, or kitchen and utility, area should have direct access to the dining area. It should be easily reached from the drive or garage so that packages of groceries can be easily carried in. Traffic in the kitchen should be routed around the work area (the kitchen sink/refrigerator/stove area). Kitchen size is a function of use. If you plan to do much food preserving, a fairly large kitchen is a good thing to look for in an old house.

The relaxation area includes the dining room parlor, living room, den and family room. It usually also is near the main entrance to the house, and you should have a coat closet near the main entrance.

I'm not going to make any remarks about the style of the house. Houses that appeal to me may well not appeal to you, and there is no real reason they should. A diversity of style is a good thing, no matter where we live. One consideration should be given to appearance. If a house is too out of the ordinary in extreme ways, its resale value is going to be lower than a simple, functional and attractive house of about the same size in the same area. Confusing roof lines and many kinds of siding give a house a rather busy look that many people don't care for. It is probably best to make sure

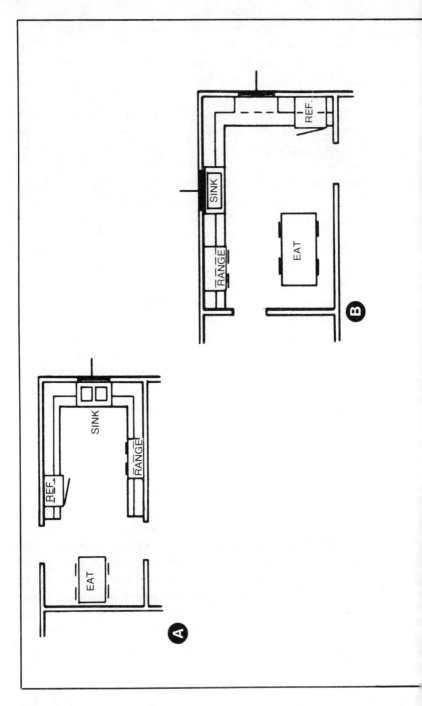

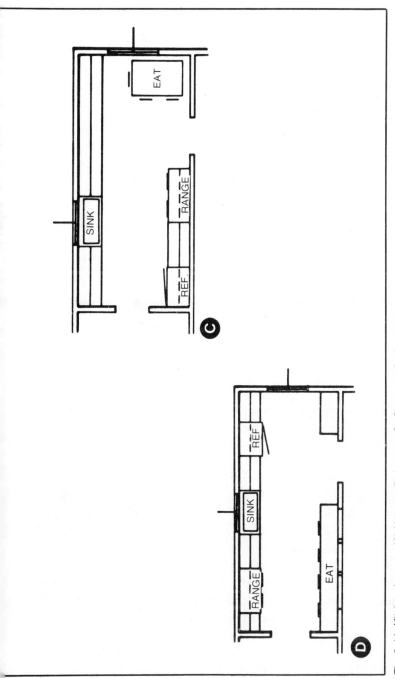

Fig. 3-11. Kitchen layouts. (A) U-type. (B) L-type. (C) Corridor. (D) Sidewall.

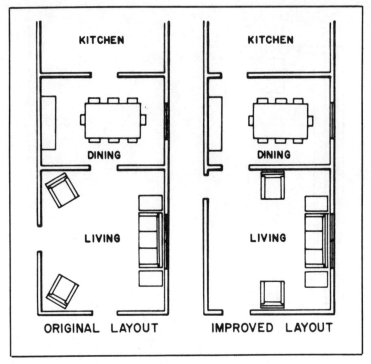

Fig. 3-12. A way to improve traffic patterns.

no more than two or three siding types are used. Any additions to the house should have roof lines that match, or complement, the original roof line.

REASONS FOR REJECTING A HOUSE

There are three major reasons to reject a house when you are evaluating with the purpose of restoring any home. First, if the foundation is not repairable, forget it. In a very few cases, you might find it worthwhile to move the house to a new foundation. Most of the time, though, it just isn't worth the expense, particularly if other work must be done. Second, the frame of the entire house may be out of square to an extent that would make much work difficult. It may be infested and badly damaged by insects or decay. Finally, if the repair list is too long, forget it. It's one thing to need to do some interior refinishing, add a new roof and put in heat. If you also need to put in new plumbing, new wiring and new floors, the job is out of hand.

Consider the cost of the land and the house first, after checking things over to see what needs to be done. While reconstruction contractors generally figure the cost of rebuilding an older house shouldn't exceed two-thirds of the cost of a similar house built new, if you're doing the work yourself, the costs are cut considerably, though the work takes a great deal longer. A lot depends on your desires. Some of us can easily live in the shambles of remodeling for many months, even years, with little real distress. Others need a shorter term mess and quicker, clean and amenable living quarters. Higher costs can be overridden in the first case, as the costs can be spread over a longer period of time.

Consider also your own handiness with tools. An awful lot of people think they are better, or can be better, than is true. I've seen porches put on houses by people who should never pick up a hammer, and the result is not pleasing to anyone. So consider your own skills carefully in your final evaluation.

Plumbing

Plumbing for rural areas requires some family planning. The family should do it, as there is no one else who is likely to know your needs as exactly as you do. Local and state codes must be checked, and all installations kept in line with them. But the state or county will have difficulty in telling you where to place frost-free faucets for outdoor use, where to place waterers for livestock, what to put in your bathroom and how many bathrooms you're liable to need.

PLANNING

It will pay to keep in mind the future as you draw up your plans. If you want a basement half or full bath in the future, it costs much less to set the pipe runs and stub outs in place now than it will later. Actually, if the money for the pipe runs and stub outs seems likely to run you over your budget, simply place a few *tees* in the proper spots in the system, cap them and go on. Such work saves a lot of later cutting and fitting. Such planning for the future can extend to outside plumbing, too, with tees capped off and later pipe runs made to outdoor faucets.

The planning must include the three main areas in a small home where water will be needed: the kitchen, bathroom and laundry. For rural living, life is much easier if

135

water is available at, or close to, buildings where any sort of livestock is kept. If you have dairy cows and a milkhouse, you need to provide facilities for water at the milkhouse as well as at the dairy barn. You may want water in a shop area, or you may not, depending on your habits, in part, and in part on how close to the main house the shop building is.

Proper waste disposal is imperative to a modern plumbing system. Improperly handled wastes can contaminate the entire water supply and cause illness, in addition to problems with clogged drains.

Locating fixtures back to back on a wall or in a stack will cut down on material costs whenever either is possible. The shorter you keep hot water runs, the less loss of heat there will be along those runs and the lower your water heating costs will be.

ROUGHING-IN

Roughing-in is the process of placing pipe that will be hidden in walls and under floors of the building as construction goes on. Fixtures are connected to the roughed-in pipe after other construction is completed. Building drains are laid in before the basement floor is poured and, often, before the footings are even poured. The process of roughing-in includes the testing of water supply and drain pipe, and the locating and installing of fixture supports (such as lavatory wall mounts). Height and location of sinks, lavatories and other fixtures must be precisely indicated before actual home construction begins.

The drainage system is tested by plugging all but the highest opening. The system is then filled with water and the works allowed to stand no less than 15 minutes. If no leaks occur in that time, closeup work can proceed.

The water supply system is tested in the same manner as the drainage system, but only drinkable water can be used. The system must be pressurized to at least 60 pounds per square inch.

TOOLS

To work with plumbing, you will need a few tools that may not be on hand. While most of us have a *hacksaw*, not everyone bothers with a *tubing cutter* (Figs. 4-1 and 4-2). For copper pipe installations, the tubing cutter is nearly essential (you can actually use a hacksaw and file, but the cutter is neater, faster and relatively inexpensive). Pipe wrenches are needed (Fig. 4-3). A *strap wrench* can prove very handy when installing fixtures, as it can be used to tighten faucets without worrying about the marring a pipe wrench would cause. A *basin wrench* is an odd looking and cheap, little device that allows you to reach up under fixtures, such as kitchen sinks or lavatories, and fasten the taps in place.

For work with copper, a propane torch (you do *not* need the extra heat provided by a Mapp gas torch) and some solder and flux are needed to make joints (Fig. 4-4). The process of sweat soldering used to make plumbing joints is a simple thing to learn. Mechanically clean the inside of the joint, and the exterior of the pipe or tubing after it is cut and reamed. Reaming helps remove sharp edges on the inside of pipe which could cut water flow and add to mineral buildup. Use steel wool in most cases, and take off just enough material to get a sheen. Next, flux the areas to be coated with solder. Assemble the joint and apply heat with the torch. Take your solder and apply it to the side of the tubing or pipe opposite that on which you are applying heat. Move the solder and the torch around the joint until you can see a bright line of the solder all the way around. Once that line of solder turns dull, the joint is complete. That's it. A few extra fittings and some short lengths of tubing will suffice for practice. The process is simple and depends on *capillary action* drawing the solder into the joint.

FIXTURES

You name it, today, and you can find it. Bathroom fixtures come in a bewildering array of styles, sizes and prices. You can select a lavatory that costs about $30 or one that costs nearly $330. You can choose a toilet that costs $50 or one that costs nearly $700. Fittings can be chrome, brass or gold plated as you choose (Figs. 4-5 and 4-6). In most cases, it is best to avoid the ends of the ranges in price. In the middle price ranges, you will find a good combination of

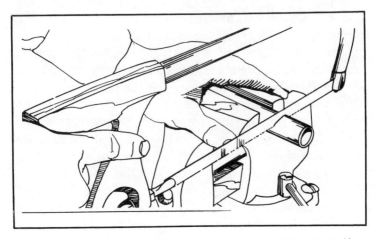

Fig. 4-1. Rigid plastic pipe can be cut easily with a hacksaw fitted with a fine-toothed blade.

quality and economy most of the time. Plumbing fixtures are one series of items that should be selected for quality, unless you enjoy replacing them. The bottom of the line models are usually, almost always, the least well made, while the top of the line models usually owe an awful lot of their cost to

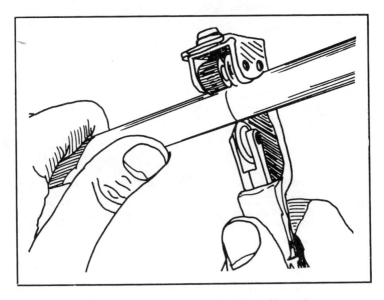

Fig. 4-2. Small diameter pipe is effectively cut with a tubing cutter.

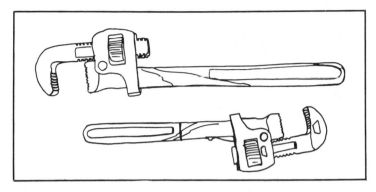

Fig. 4-3. Stillson or pipe wrencnes are indispensable for many plumbing chores.

fancier plating, designer colors and so forth. Fixtures in the middle price ranges will most often have a combination of good quality and good appearance, while not being any more ridiculously priced than is anything else today.

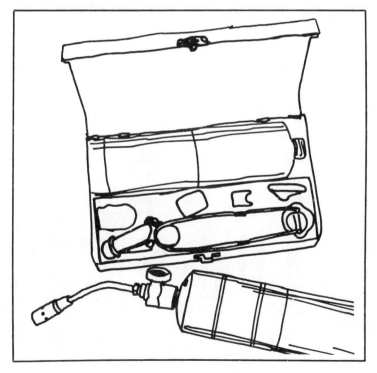

Fig. 4-4. A typical propane torch kit.

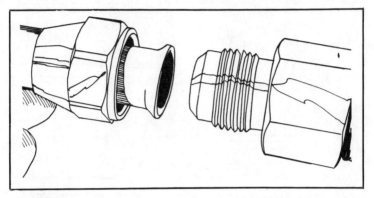

Fig. 4-5. Brass flare fittings can be used with flared CPVC or PB pipe or tubing.

WATER HEATERS

Water heaters are needed in most homes, though a few people with hot water heat try to get by without one (Fig. 4-7). There is a good variety now on the market, both in gas and electric models, with some now made as energy saving types with, reportedly , greater efficiency. You can now add some efficiency by buying a kit, for under $25, to add insula-

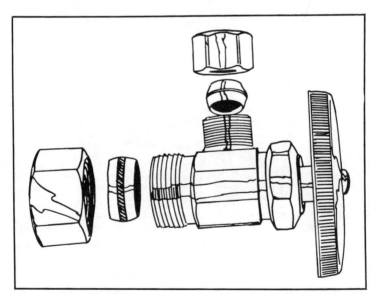

Fig. 4-6. Chrome-plated brass compression fitting angle stop valve.

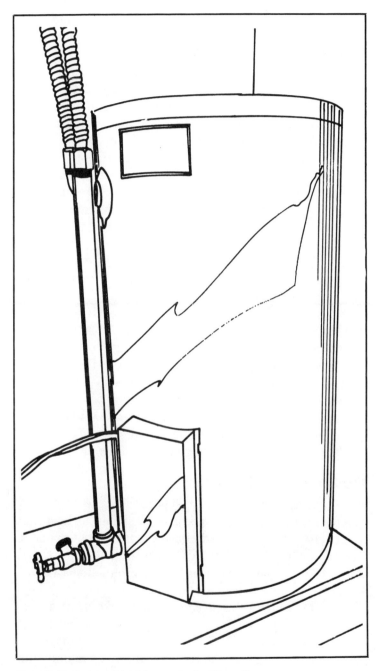

Fig. 4-7. Typical small tank-type water heating unit.

tion to older heaters. These kits, such as the *Thermo Saver*, are installed in minutes and can save, even at 5 cents per kilowatt, something like $30 a year.

In addition, several companies make solar energy water heaters, though the cost of the heater and installation tends to be rather high. Still, with rising energy costs, even these should provide a payback in a decade or so. While I'm not a great fan of solar heating systems, in the future, we may have no choice. It seems a bit odd that in my lifetime my grandmother went from a wood stove with a water heater to electric heating for water. Shortly we may almost all be doing the same, in reverse. My present objection to solar energy use for home heating is the need for a backup system, added to the heavy overall startup expense of the system itself. Passive systems cost less than active systems, but are also generally somewhat less efficient. Still, new designs crop up almost daily now. Sooner or later the government has to offer a tax break for people installing such systems. A meaningful tax break would mean a payoff in six or seven years, instead of around 15 years, as things now stand.

When buying a hot water heater, check its efficiency rating and its recovery rate. Size is less important than recovery rate, though the larger family still is best served by a larger hot water heater. A fast recovery rate, though, may help keep bills down. There is less water to be kept hot in fast heating small tanks during periods of non-use.

SERVICE BUILDING PLUMBING

Any areas where stock are kept should have water, and in most cases the biggest problem is simply to keep the water supply from freezing during the winter. At one point, I carried water several hundred yards to a horse. During winter I had to go out and break the ice several times a day. I ended up, because of the ice, carrying upwards of 30 gallons of water instead of the actual dozen the horse needed. Underground pipe is usually the best bet, with a freeze-free tap rising from it. You can than extend a hose from the tap to any point needed, with only the requirement that you drain the hose after each use in winter to prevent freezing. Watering bowls can be used, with the supply pipe rising directly to the bowl feed. Such pipes will need protection from freezing. You may, in colder climates, need to install an immersion heater in the bowl to prevent freezing. If you have a milkhouse, it will require both hot and cold water, so you will need a second water heater.

Freeze-proof hydrants or faucets are available just about everywhere in rural areas, as are the sort of immersion heaters needed to prevent watering bowl freezing. A frost-proof or freeze-proof hydrant is planted in the ground, so that its base is below frost line. It is designed so that any water left in the hydrant after use drains back into the line, below frost level. It is a good idea, around such hydrants, to place gravel to a depth of at least 6 inches so that water is absorbed back into the soil. Water sitting on the surface can often cause freezing even in frost-proof hydrants if the weather gets cold enough.

In cases where dairy farming is planned, it is best to get in touch with your local dairy inspector to see just what the codes are. Much will depend on the class of dairy you plan, and on the area of the country. In some places, only hot and cold running water are required, while in other places you may have to install a washroom with a toilet. Wastes from such systems must be kept separate from dairy wastes and barn wastes. If you plan to sell milk, you have to conform to the codes or you're out of luck.

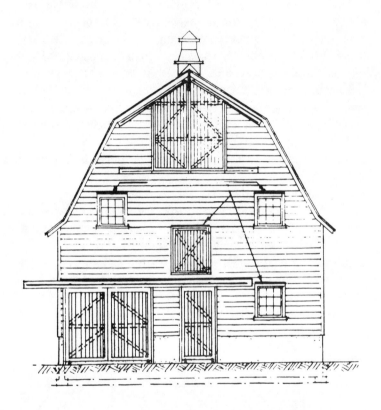

5

Heating

The reduction of heat requirements is, today, the first thing
to look over when planning to install heat in any home or
other building. Make a check to be sure all windows are
tightly caulked, and check the insulation is under 6 inches,
bring it to at least that level, and in northern areas add
another 6 inches. The few hundred dollars such a job costs
will be rapidly repaid in today's era of expensive fuel. Windows should be at least double glazed, or have storm windows installed. Triple glazing is now an option with many
companies, and when you can afford the cost is a good idea.
First, let us take a look at heating with wood.

PRACTICALITIES OF WOOD HEAT

One of the finer aspects of rural living is the use of wood
as a fuel during cold months. There are a lot of old sayings
about wood heat circulating because of the ever rising cost of
other forms of energy (wood, cut by someone else, is also
rising in cost, though not as rapidly as fuel oil and electricity). Wood warms you twice is one of the maxims. In most
cases, such old sayings are only partially true. Wood heat
tends to warm more than twice. Consider. First, wood must
be cut down and cut to length. Even with a chain saw in use,
effort is expended. Then it is loaded on a truck and brought

home to be unloaded and stacked. Then the wood is burned. At least three times the wood has warmed you, while providing beneficial exercise. If it must be split, then you can add another time.

The practicalities of wood heat might take a back seat to the pleasure. I know that the thought of not burning fuel oil is a great pleasure to me, as is the thought that my own efforts were what supplied the heat source. Too, wood is a renewable resource, if handled correctly. Estimates are that in the East, every acre of woodland would be improved if the owners would take from 1 to 1 ½ cords of wood in the form of firewood each year.

SECURING PERMISSION TO CUT WOOD

The first chore is to find out who owns the wood and get permission to cut. In some cases, the wood will be in a state or national forest. Permits can be bought for low cost. In other cases, the wood will be on private land. You may have to pay a stumpage fee to cut even blown down trees. With the increased use of wood as fuel, the old days of free wood are fast passing. As with most other things, everyone wants to make a buck and doesn't much care how, as long as there is no need to expend any effort.

Use care when selecting areas from which to cut wood if you don't own a woodlot. It isn't worth the involvement and anger that might otherwise be caused. I've reached the point where even seeing road crews downing trees to widen roads is no longer enough. I want to make sure I've gotten permission from someone to take the wood. Certainly I'd rather have neighbors like one of my mother's, who had a road run through and some timber taken out of a part of his property. He dropped by a week of two later to say we could go in and take out a few loads of firewood, if we wished. It helps him clear the slash and helps us get firewood. Not everyone is as generous.

WOOD STOVES

Fireplaces are notoriously inefficient as heat producers rather, as heat throwers. They produce plenty of heat, but about 90 percent or more goes up the chimney unless the fireplace is modified. Wood stoves are much more efficient. A few of the top of the line models may actually approach 50 or 60 percent efficiency. Don't believe too much of the advertising that claims a 70-80 percent efficiency rating. Testing is going on in a few places now, but I know of none that shows that kind of rating for any wood stove. Most oil-fired furnaces don't rate better than about 65 percent, and wood is cheaper than oil.

Today the number of wood stoves available is wider than ever before. You can still buy the old style *cast iron* stoves, in various models, and *sheet metal* stoves are still available in a variety of styles and sizes (Sheet metal stoves were, and still are, noted for buckling and for wearing out quickly. A few years ago, though, I picked up a used sheet metal wood stove to heat a small house I was renting. It worked extremely well, with a layer of sand in the bottom to prevent burn through, and cut my electric heat bill down to about $35 for the entire winter. Still, more modern designs such as the Fisher can provide more heat from less wood and hold a fire over much longer periods of time. Such stoves are called airtight, though they actually do leak some air in places other than around the draft controls. They are controlled draft models. A few will actually hold a fire for as long as 14 or 16 hours, and most will do the job for at least 10 hours.

The old style cast iron stoves, whether replicas or actually old, leak a great deal of air. The fire burns hotter and faster than you usually want, even when the stove is shut down as much as possible. My mother's parlor stove is such a model, and while much more attractive than her Warm Morning coal/wood stove, it holds a fire for a much shorter time. In fact, after about four hours, even totally shut down, the parlor stove has nothing but embers left.

Sheet Metal Stoves

Sheet metal stoves come in models other than the type I used a few years ago. Some models, such as those made by U.S. Stove Company, are made of heavy sheet metal, and have a firebox lined with firebrick so that warping and burn-through aren't likely. I used one of these to cut fuel oil use in a home from 1100 gallons to well under 200. Such stoves have thermostats and ash pans, and mine would have a slight blaze going after about 10 hours, if the draft was cut back and the stove completely filled before leaving it. The stove took 2-foot long logs, which is a saving grace. Until you have cut a great deal of firewood, you will not realize how difficult it is to have to cut everything to 16-inch or shorter lengths. The longer the wood a stove will take and the greater the diameter, the less actual work you will have in cutting things up for it, not to mention the work in splitting wood.

Loading Methods

Some consideration, when selecting the stove, should be given to those who will have to load it. Shoving several large 3-foot-long logs in a wood stove isn't really a job a weak or incapacitated person is going to enjoy or be able to do. If the person using a stove is elderly, then the stove size can be reduced so that wood weight isn't as big a problem; or the wood can still be cut smaller and more pieces added at one time.

Loading methods deserve some thought, too. Top loading is often convenient and side loading can be too, if the stove is properly constructed. Front loading is also handy. Many stove models come in styles that offer two or three of these loading methods. When considering the loading of the stove, think about how much bending you wish to do—top loading models require less, usually. But top loading models also tend to release more smoke into the house while loading is going on.

Installation

Once the stove is considered and bought, installation time comes. If you've already got a chimney in good shape, then the problems are fewer. If you haven't, repairs must be made. If no chimney is available, one must be constructed. Chimneys may be constructed of brick, with a *flue liner*, of concrete block with a flue liner (the block is available in square units that simply set in place over and around the flue liner, making the job somewhat easier), or you can use one of the metal chimneys available today, such as Majestic's thermo-siphoning model. This triple-walled chimney system requires only about 2 inches of clearance from combustible material, and has an inner liner of stainless steel for long life. As Fig. 5-1 and 5-2 show, the chimney must terminate no less than 2 feet above anything within 10 feet of its top. It should never be less than 3 feet from the roof top to the chimney top, while angled applications are possible when needed. You're advised to check your local codes to make sure that these minimums are required in your area.

Most stove manufacturers will provide information on setting up the stove you buy safely, but at the very least it should be set on a non-combustible base that extends out 18 inches on each side of the stove. This base can be brick laid in sand and held in place with a simple form of wood, or brick mortared in place. I've also used slate for this, but it is laid over a 24 gauge metal plate, since the base is only about 1 ½ inches thick and a 2 or 3-inch thickness is safer. The back of any stove should be no less than 18 inches from combustible material, and heat radiating types need twice that distance. If the wall is of drywall construction or is paneled, and you wish to move the stove in closer, construct a fireproof shield of metal or asbestos board 6 inches from the wall and fill the open space with glass wood insulation (Fig. 5-3). The stove can then be placed with its back about a foot from this fire shield.

For any further information on heating with wood, check with your fire insurance company. Some have different requirements. To keep insurance costs in line, you must follow their guidelines to the word. Any form of heat can be dangerous if improperly installed, but wood heat appears to give the most danger because of the size of the fire used and the propensity of the fuel to throw sparks at unexpected times. Too, wood stoves radiate a lot of heat and can set combustible materials aflame too easily. Any time you have a wood stove that makes a wall behind it or beside it too hot to touch, then it is time to modify the installation. Either move the stove out from the heated surface or protect the surface in

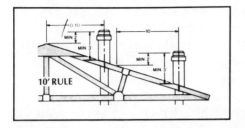

Fig. 5-1. Chimney clearance needs.

some way. This advice also applies to ceilings. Always make sure you have at least 2 feet, and preferably three, of clearance above a stove pipe.

Flues and Stovepipes

Flues should not be shared unless you are certain they are large enough. That would mean that with a 6-inch stove pipe and a foot square flue, you could actually install seven stoves. The flue area should never be smaller than the area of the pipes entering it. I wouldn't recommend it, though. As things stand, many flues now are 6 inches square. I would recommend no more than two stoves to them and four to the foot square models. This allows a bit of margin for safety.

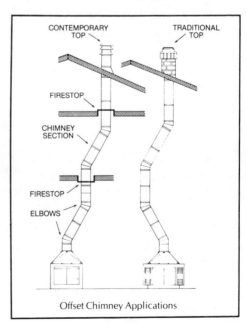

Fig. 5-2. Offset chimney applications.

150

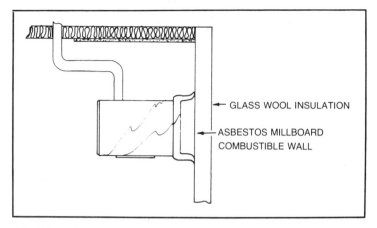

Fig. 5-3. Asbestos board under fiberglass insulation used to reduce space from a wall stove that must be placed. The stove can be placed with its back about a foot from this fire shield.

Stovepipe can be bought blued or galvanized, with the galvanized pipe usually being heavier and more expensive. All joints should face the stove. Each joint should be secured with three sheet metal screws. The laborious job of installing such screws can be cut by using the type of screw that will fit in a special wrench with a shaft that fits an electric drill. Long stovepipe runs are to be avoided wherever possible. If the run is well secured and has a good angle (dropping to the stove) to allow creosote to run back, you can use as much as 15 or 16 feet of run. I didn't like it, but the house had no chimney and I had to run the pipe through a fire stop I built into a window. One major disadvantage of such a long run—or my bad nerves—was the need for disassembly to remove creosote at regular intervals. These intervals jumped up to about a month as the weather got really cold, for the pipe clogged quickly when the stove was well fed.

Keep a good fire extinguisher of the chemical powder type on hand. It should be kept as near to the stove as possible, but far enough away that any fire won't block access. The reason for using the chemical power type, which is more expensive than soda-acid, is simple. A stream of water, or even worse carbon dioxide, shot at a hot stove can cause the metal to warp or, if the stove is cast iron, crack and fall

151

apart. While the chemical power is somewhat less effective in fighting this type of fire, it does the job without destroying the stove. With stoves costing more than $500 in many cases today, you sure don't want the thing ruined.

WOOD HEATING COSTS

The cost for using wood as heat will differ from area to area. Much depends on the cost of the stove at the outset, naturally, and how much work must be done to install it safely. Then, if you cut your own wood, you need to take into account tool costs, transport and so on. If you don't cut your own wood, direct costs are easier to figure in comparison to oil and electricity costs.

If we assume a cord of beech firewood weighs about 4000 pounds, we get a gross *British thermal unit* (Btu) output of 28 million. That matches 200 gallons of fuel oil and adds on six million Btus, making up for any efficiency difference. For electricity, you would need 4,200 kilowatt hours to produce 14 million Btus, which, at the 100 percent efficiency of electric heat, matches the other two. At today's prices, the oil would cost $240. At the present 5 cents per kilwatt hour, the electric heating cost would be $210. By those estimates, you would break even, buying wood, as something around $200 a cord. As far as I know, there are few places in the country where seasoned hardwood has reached that high. I know in many areas it goes for $100 or more a cord, and down here a pickup load can sell for $50 in a town or city, but I don't know of anywhere where $200 a cord is common. The pickup load will, if it is an 8-foot bed, be about three-fourths of a full cord. The last time I bought wood, I paid $50 for two heavy duty pickup loads, but they were close to a full cord each and all oak.

My figures can't be exact for your area, but then it is impossible to tell just what your installation cost, too. Still, if you assume a use of 1000 gallons of number 2 fuel oil per winter, that's a price of $1200. If the wood stove cuts that back to 200 gallons, at a cost of $240, you have $960 to spend on wood. Assuming you use five cords of wood to make the cutback, and pay $80 per cord, you have $560 left to pay for the stove and installation. It seems worth it to me, even with the extra work and dirt of wood heat. If you cut your own wood, even with having to buy a new chain saw in the $300 to $350 range, then the cost will remain about the same. Consider, though, with cutting your own wood the cost of the second year: stumpage fees, if any; transport; and fuel for the saw.

Stumpage fees vary widely even within a given area. I have a friend who cuts pulpwood for a living, and his fees on small pine will range from $5 to about $8 per cord. Hardwood fees shouldn't be any higher, but they may be now , as the price of firewood is higher than what is given for pulpwood. Landowners don't often take into consideration that part of the reason, for the higher price is the need to put in extra work cutting the wood to length and splitting it. Pulpwood is cut to 5 or 6-foot lengths and just stacked on the truck. Firewood is not.

If you already have a chain saw and have no place, or time, to cut your own wood, you might try locating someone who will deliver longer logs for you to cut to length and split. It should be cheaper by a third, and the exercise is generally a good idea. One of the unusual things about wood as heat is the fact that most of the time you come out of the winter in better shape physically than you went in. Even if all the wood is laid in during spring or fall, there always seems to be a need to cut and split some more. Carting the stuff into the house is good exercise. Actually, most old-timers seem to think it is best to lay in next winter's supply during the present winter. I do, too, though I never quite seem to get it all done.

TYPES OF FIREWOOD

For a more complete discussion of wood types useful as fuel in the United States, you might look at my *Wood Heating Handbook* (TAB Book No. 872). Generally, the heavier hardwoods such as oak, maple and beech are better heat producers than are the softwoods such as pine. *Shagbark hickory* is about the best firewood to be found, though I have seen only two or three trees since moving south. Still, around here there is a good quantity of *mockernut* and *pignut hickory* as well as white oak, black oak, red oak and a few maples. Hardwoods give about 200 BTUs *less* heat per pound than do the resinous softwoods but weigh a lot more per cubic foot, so that a log doesn't disappear into ash quite as quickly.

A cubic foot of dry white pine will weigh in at about 25 pounds, while a cubic foot dry beech will weigh about 45 pounds. The heaviest hickory, shagbark, weighs about 55 pounds.

Several woods should be avoided—*sycamore* is probably the first and foremost. About three years ago, I tried a sycamore tree as firewood. It is about the wettest wood, standing, that you will find. And it is close to impossible to split. I ended up doing a lot of the splitting with my chain saw and still left a good sized log lying around out of disgust with the excess work required. Too, the wood *stays* wet. After more than seven months, the stuff would almost put out a fire if just dropped on before the fire was well built up. Even considering the fact that completely air-dried wood will still hold some 20 to 25 percent of its moisture, sycamore is ridiculous. I have no facts on hand, but it seems to hold at least 50 and maybe 60 percent of its moisture. Gum is another wood to avoid, as it is very tough to split—nearly impossible, in fact.

There is some argument now, after a bit of research, about the creosote buildup qualities of various woods. It used to be assumed that the resinous softwoods such as white and yellow pine created more buildup than did hardwoods, and the use of green wood of any type added to it. Now, there is some indication this isn't so, but I plan to wait a time before using much pine. I like to air dry pine for at least two seasons before use, whenever possible. But then it is excellent for those early morning fires when you want heat and want it now. It catches easily and burns hot and fast.

Sawmills are another source of firewood, though much will depend on the area of the country in which you live as to availability. I like to get at least one load of mixed slabs each winter, for the smaller pieces make excellent kindling and the larger are almost as good as split logs. The place I deal with delivers the wood cut to about 14-inch lengths in a high bodied dump truck that holds about 2½ cords of mixed woods—pines, poplar, oak and hickory. The man will not deliver a non-mixed load. Right now, the cost is $40 a load, though I expect it will rise as fuel costs continue to rise. Three years ago, it was $25. Such wood may be cheaper in other areas of the country, though I tend to doubt it very much, if for no other reason than the large number of small sawmills, usually family-run, in this area of the South. Most of the wood sawmills cut goes for outbuildings, and most is now selling for less than a quarter a board foot (up from 15 cents just three years ago).

Wood cutting now comes up, and I will assume you've found a place to get wood, or own a woodlot. Tools are essential to woodcutting, and the proper tools can make the job a great deal easier and simpler. In this case, no matter your views on getting back to the land, the chain saw is just about essential to getting work done in a reasonable length of time.

CHAIN SAWS

My greatest amount of experience with chain saws has been with those made by *Homelite*, though recently I got a *McCulloch 610* and am quite pleased with it. I had planned to test it against my much older Homelite 360, but managed to smash the 360 to pieces as I started the test. I dropped a tree right on the 360. The saw had been through about everything else in the past few years, but that was too much for the tool.

Chain saw size is an important part of selection. The little suburban saws with 1-foot bars just won't do the job in rural areas. I've got one, but it is restricted to use in limbing and pruning operations, or when climbing is required to trim a tree and the bigger saws are too unwieldy. What you need is the pro model for farm work. You may want to go with the lowest line pro models, as I do, but the saw needs to be one that will carry a 16-inch bar and chain, and sometimes even a 20-inch bar, easily. You need a saw with enough power to keep from stalling out constantly when cutting heavy wood, as you will often be doing.

The expense is considerable, since the chain saws I am recommending will run from $300 up. But the life of the saw is greater and the need for constant sharpening of the chain-saw is greater and the need for constant sharpening of the chain is cut because of the number of teeth on the bar. Of course, when sharpening time comes, it takes a bit longer, but not that much. Actually, the lighter, less powerful saws will force you to work harder than the heavier saws because they require much more time to make a cut.

Roller tips are nice to have but not essential. I've worked with and without them, and find they do allow you to pull the chain up tighter, thus cutting down on chain adjusting time. They do cut friction a bit, allowing the saw to be more efficient. Whether they're worth the extra cost or not, I can't objectively say. I like them. Most professional loggers don't use them.

Avoid, whenever possible, automatic appurtenances such as automatic oiling. My Homelite 360 had this feature, but it was accompanied by an easy adjustment, which I kept at the wide open mark all the time. My McCulloch has both automatic and manual oiling, which is my preference. It allows you to pump out extra oil as needed when making a hard cut. As far as I can tell, saw-mounted chain sharpeners do little more than wear out the chain prematurely. I prefer to sharpen my own.

You'll also need a good gas can, some sort of plastic or metal jug in which to carry chain oil, six round files of the correct size to sharpen your chain, a depth gauge and a couple of flat files. An extra chain is also a good idea.

After you get the saw, read the instruction manual carefully. The chain saw is probably the most dangerous tool available to the average person, and it is the only power tool with which I have ever injured myself. Last year I knicked my knee with one, and was lucky not to take off the kneecap as well. It was purely and simply my fault, since I kept working when I knew I was too tired. All directions should be followed explicitly.

Several felling wedges can be handy in directing the fall of a tree, but proper cutting procedures will usually keep you from needing such items. Still, all of us bind a saw now and then. Being able to drive in two or three wedges to free up the cut at times may save you the need of leaving the woods to get a friend's saw to cut yours loose. It's embarrassing to admit, but it happens to all of us from time to time.

Chain Saw Use

Probably one of the handiest tools on any farm is the chain saw. It can be used to clear land for fence or pasture, cut timber for sale, cut firewood, cut fence posts and do many other chores. Proper use is essential, especially when cutting trees. While the cutting of trees up to 18 inches or 2 feet in diameter for firewood is not comparable in danger to the work of the professional lumberjack dropping trees 3 feet and larger, any tree over about 4 inches in diameter is capable of killing you when it's felled. Under the right conditions, even the smaller trees can cause major injury. Proper handling of the saw and the cuts can prevent injury or, at the least drop the likelihood to near nothing (Figs. 5-4 and 5-5).

Proper chain saw use starts at fueling time and carries on through until the saw is shut off and stored. Fueling should be done at least 25 feet from the area in which cutting will take place, and the same distance from the area in which the saw will be started. For the environment's sake, always fuel the chain saw on a stump or rock, as pouring gas over the forest floor isn't a good way to get plant life to grow.

Start the chain saw with one hand firmly on the top grip and a toe holding the handle down. You'll often see pros starting a saw by simply holding the top grip and yanking the

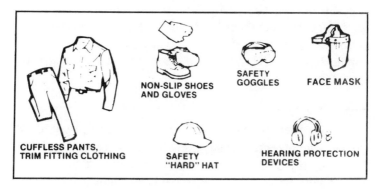

NON-SLIP SHOES AND GLOVES

SAFETY GOGGLES

FACE MASK

CUFFLESS PANTS, TRIM FITTING CLOTHING

SAFETY "HARD" HAT

HEARING PROTECTION DEVICES

Fig. 5-4. Proper clothing for chain saw use.

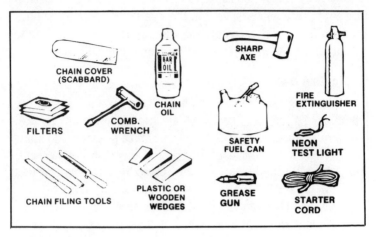

Fig. 5-5. Tools needed with the chain saw.

starter cord; unless you're exceptionally strong and very experienced, I would firmly advise against trying this procedure (Figs. 5-6 and 5-7).

Make sure everyone in the cutting area is at least two tree heights away from the felling. Take a proper grip on the saw, with the hand on the upper grip having its thumb wrapped around the grip. Make sure your footing is good, and keep cuts below chest height.

Kickback during cutting is a problem with chain saws. Kickback occurs when the saw recoils after the tip of the bar comes in contact with the wood or another object. The more powerful the saw, the harder and higher it will kick back on you. Sooner or later, any saw is going to kick on you. Therefore, you should make cuts so that the bar and chain are out of line with your body. Also, oddly enough, keeping the engine operating at full speed tends to cut the chance of kickback (Fig. 5-8).

Safety Procedures

Wear clothing that is fairly tight, but not so tight as to restrict movement. You should select two escape routes at 45 degree angles from the tree, and you may need them (Fig. 5-9). Tight clothing that keeps you from running if the tree goes the wrong way is a problem, as is something like a loose

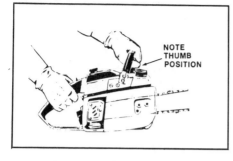

Fig. 5-6. Note the gripping position for the chain saw.

scarf that may catch in the chain. Wear shoes with sturdy non-slip soles. I like to wear an old pair of hiking boots with Vibram soles. Good work gloves are also an idea, since you will need to adjust and sharpen the chain during a day's cutting. That chain is sharp, even when too dull to do a good wood cutting job, so fingers need protection. A chainsaw vibrates quite a lot, even the newer models with vibration isolators, so the gloves help to prevent blisters.

I wear glasses with safety lenses. For others, I would recommend safety goggles. Hard hats are fine, too, though I can't seem to keep one on my head. Keep a good watch for loose limbs above you. Even a small one can cause a very bad headache should it fall on you.

Carry a small fire extinguisher with you. While it isn't sensible to be in the woods cutting when the trees are crackling dry, there is often a lot of dry material around that

Fig. 5-7. Start the chain saw correctly.

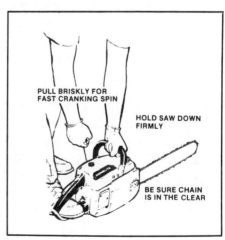

PULL BRISKLY FOR FAST CRANKING SPIN

HOLD SAW DOWN FIRMLY

BE SURE CHAIN IS IN THE CLEAR

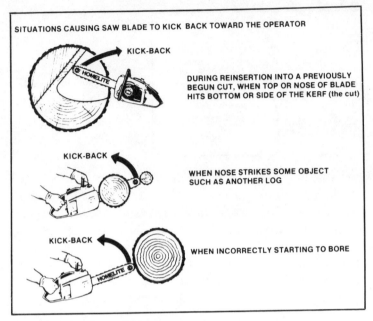

Fig. 5-8. Kickback possibilities.

might catch fire from a spark thrown through the muffler, even when the weather is not dry. Never cut in rain, snow or icy conditions.

FELLING A TREE

Felling starts with a check of the tree to see which way it leans, and to which side the heaviest branches grow. Those

Fig. 5-9. Escape path angle.

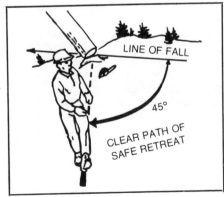

two factors help determine the direction of a fall, as they can overbalance even the most careful notching job. Once those items are checked and you've looked up for loose limbs, select your retreat paths. You want to be well out of the way, for the butt of a cut tree can kick back quite a ways if it totally breaks loose from the stump. If your job is done properly, when notching and then making the back cut, the tree will fall on a 2-inch hinge of wood. Kick back won't be a problem. You will be able to sit your saw down and walk away. If that hinge is cut too far through or the tree is rotted, it may decide to go in a rush, at which time you will want to leave in a rush. If that occurs, drop the saw and move. Saws can be easily replaced.

Check the wind direction and strength. Gusty, hard winds may convince you to lay off cutting for the day. It becomes difficult to tell just when a tree will go if a hard wind is blowing. If your area gets the same kind of many-directioned gusts we get, you may not be able to tell where the tree is going.

You start by making the bottom of the notch cut, and will go a third of the way through the tree. The slanted cut for the notch then is brought in to meet it. If you're unsure about being able to hold a steady line about the tree on any cut, use a crayon to draw a line for the cut. After a time, you won't need the guide, but at the outset you may. The back cut is brought in 90 degrees behind the notch, and should be no less than 2 inches above the bottom of the notch. For larger trees, estimate about 10 percent of the tree's diameter (Fig. 5-10). The back cut should be as level as possible to prevent the stump for barber-chairing (splitting the tree trunk and leaving a standing mess of splintered wood on the stump) (Fig. 5-11).

On very large trees, you may find the tree settling back onto the bar and pinching it. It is at such points that felling wedges are handy. These wedges must be of plastic, or aluminum or wood so that contact won't ruin the chain (Fig. 5-12).

Your felling is not limited to the length of your guide bar. Figure 5-13 shows the technique for taking down a tree up to double the size of your bar. I would recommend, if you have

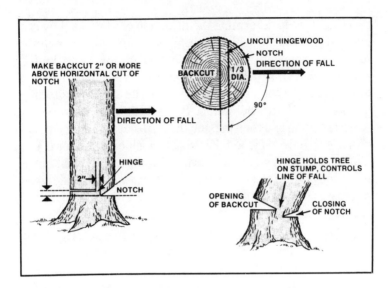

Fig. 5-10. Felling cuts.

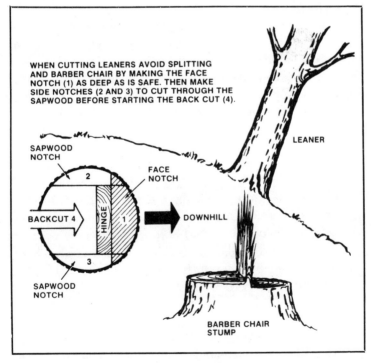

Fig. 5-11. The proper technique for cutting leaners.

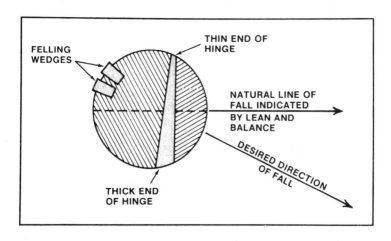

Fig. 5-12. Felling a tree away from the natural line of fall, using wedges.

little or no experience, that you stick to trees of moderate size (smaller than the guide bar diameter) for at least your first season's cutting.

After the tree is down, you will need to limb it. Often, half the firewood in a tree is in the limbs, especially if you're cleaning up a woodlot to get rid of especially branchy wolf trees and such. If at all possible, limbing could be done with the guide bar on the side opposite that on which you are standing. But never limb from a downhill direction. Until you've seen a 3-foot diameter oak rolling down a steep hillside as limbing is finished, you can't really appreciate the power behind the thing. Several tons of wood can tend to flatten you out more than you would wish (Fig. 5-14).

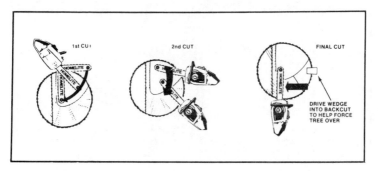

Fig. 5-13. Felling a tree up to twice the diameter of your bar length.

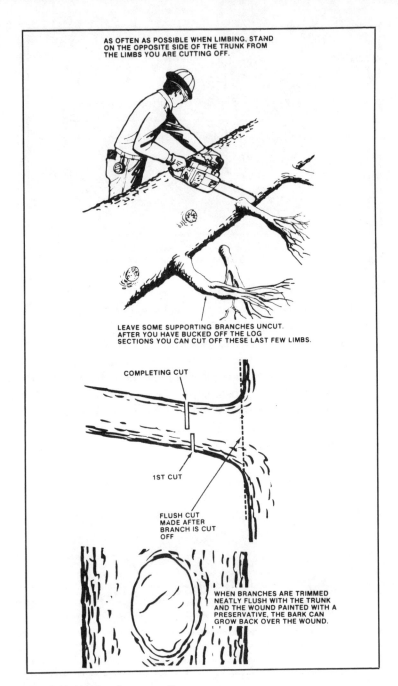

AS OFTEN AS POSSIBLE WHEN LIMBING, STAND ON THE OPPOSITE SIDE OF THE TRUNK FROM THE LIMBS YOU ARE CUTTING OFF.

LEAVE SOME SUPPORTING BRANCHES UNCUT. AFTER YOU HAVE BUCKED OFF THE LOG SECTIONS YOU CAN CUT OFF THESE LAST FEW LIMBS.

COMPLETING CUT

1ST CUT

FLUSH CUT MADE AFTER BRANCH IS CUT OFF

WHEN BRANCHES ARE TRIMMED NEATLY FLUSH WITH THE TRUNK AND THE WOUND PAINTED WITH A PRESERVATIVE, THE BARK CAN GROW BACK OVER THE WOUND.

Fig. 5-14. Limbing done correctly.

You might consider, too, leaving a few branches on the underside of the tree. They will tend to serve as natural sawbucks and keep the tree off the ground as you get around to bucking it.

BUCKING A TREE

Bucking is the act of cutting the tree into usable lengths. It is done after limbing, but you don't have to cut everything to stove size in the woods. Much depends on your schedule. I tend to cut, or buck, trees to lengths that will fit easily in my pickup (about 8 feet long), and then bring them home for the splitting and bucking to stove length. Still, there are times when stove length bucking is essential.

Again, always buck from the uphill side of a log. You will need to learn to judge stresses on a log, as the stress can pinch the bar and lock your saw in place. As with most everything else that can go wrong, this happens even to experts. If the log tends to sag as it is cut, you will need to come up from underneath, using the top of the guide bar to finish the cut. To prevent splitting, you may wish to finish the buck from below anyway, on larger logs. Those splintered ends can be a pain when it comes time to feed a log to the fire.

SPLITTING LOGS

For *splitting*, the average wood burner needs no more than an axe, a splitting maul and two or three heavy splitting wedges. There are many mechanical splitters on the market but, to be honest, if you're using less than 10 cords of wood each year, I don't see the real cost benefit in buying one. First, the *hydraulic rams* are too expensive, with even the smallest models starting at over $500. Other models, of which the best and cheapest seem to be the screw type, take too long to set up and aren't particularly cheap.

Pick a splitting hammer or maul to fit you. Mine is 8 pounds with a 32-inch handle, though I do have a 6 pound model that gets used occasionally. Splitting wedges should weigh in at least at four pounds, with five or more preferred. If you plan to use an axe for splitting, get one with the heaviest head you can find. Find a model that spreads at the *poll* as much as possible. The poll is the flat back of the head. Never use an axe to drive splitting wedges, as that is about the surest and fastest way I know of to ruin the relatively soft metal of the poll. Use a sledge or splitting maul.

Most logs will pop right open with a mild swing of the axe or maul, but knotty wood and larger log sections will force you to resort to the wedges or to more than a single blow. You might first want to try a technique known as "clover-leafing." In any case, clover-leafing is nothing more than going around the log and splitting off the bark side first, thereby reducing the size of the log that must be split.

Most often, you will simply want to look for the radiating cracks coming from the center of the log and strike as near as possible to the largest of those. Logs up to 2 feet in diameter, and sometimes more, will often pop right open on the first, second or third swing when hit correctly

Logs split a bit more easily if they are first stood on a section of log to reduce ground resilience. This also helps to prevent your swinging right on through the log and down into the ground, possibly striking a rock with the axe or maul blade. Green wood, in most every case, splits more easily than does seasoned wood. Split wood seasons more rapidly than does unsplit. Splitting size is up to you. My cousin's husband prefers not to split anything for his large stove unless it is over about 16 inches in diameter, while I tend to prefer to split anything over a foot in diameter. Having a good selection of different sizes is the idea, so that the stove can be properly filled.

Once the splitting is done, the wood needs to be stored and seasoned. Wood can be stacked in rows, with trees or stakes at rows end, and then covered with plastic to keep water out. It can be chimney-stacked (two logs in each direction on each layer at 90 degree angles) for faster seasoning.

One of the difficulties a novice wood burner often faces is telling when the wood is well enough seasoned to burn well, without giving off huge amounts of creosote. Actually, with hardwood the process is simple. Swing two pieces together. If they make a clunk, the wood is still too wet. If the

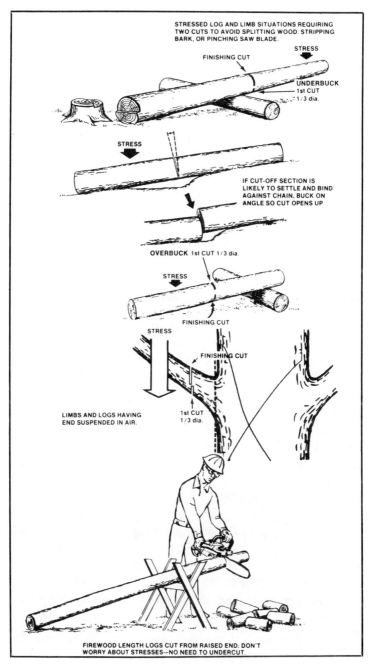

STRESSED LOG AND LIMB SITUATIONS REQUIRING TWO CUTS TO AVOID SPLITTING WOOD. STRIPPING BARK, OR PINCHING SAW BLADE.

FINISHING CUT

STRESS

UNDERBUCK 1st CUT 1/3 dia.

STRESS

IF CUT-OFF SECTION IS LIKELY TO SETTLE AND BIND AGAINST CHAIN, BUCK ON ANGLE SO CUT OPENS UP

OVERBUCK 1st CUT 1/3 dia.

STRESS

FINISHING CUT

STRESS

FINISHING CUT

FINISHING CUT

LIMBS AND LOGS HAVING END SUSPENDED IN AIR.

1st CUT 1/3 dia.

FIREWOOD LENGTH LOGS CUT FROM RAISED END: DON'T WORRY ABOUT STRESSES--NO NEED TO UNDERCUT.

Fig. 5-15. Bucking logs in different stress positions.

167

wood makes a clear, cracking sound much like 10 pins in a bowling alley, it is ready.

CHIMNEY CLEANING

One of the more important, and too often ignored, facets of wood burning safety is the cleaning of the chimney. The frequency that any chimney will need cleaning varies, as the use and type of stove determines in large part the amount of buildup of *pyrolignous acids* (called creosote), as does the types of wood burned. Too, a clogged chimney will often cut down on stove efficiency, so that a good cleaning can help save you wood, as well as reduce the chances of a chimney fire.

Chimney fires are unpleasant, even when they do not become severe enough to burn down the house. Stovepipes turn a cherry red and flaming debris will shoot out the top of the chimney. Such debris can ignite the roof or even surrounding trees and brush.

In no case should a chimney go without a cleaning each year, and with certain types of woods and stoves cleaning every six months is needed. Airtight stoves by their very nature keep chimney temperatures down and add to creosote formation, so that buildup is more rapid. The burning of green wood and softwood has been thought to also add to the buildup, though there is now some controversy over that point. The simplest way to find out if your chimney needs cleaning is to check. Slip the stovepipe out of the flue and see if there is a buildup of ¼-inch or more of creosote. If there is, the chimney needs cleaning.

For the job, you have a choice of tools. You can either use an old burlap sack stuffed with rags, or one of the more modern cleaning brush systems, with flexible fiberglass handles in, usually, 3-foot sections attached to wire brushes sized and shaped to fit your flue(s). In addition, you will need a flashlight and a wire brush, a vacuum cleaner and a dust pan and, probably, a 1-inch putty knife with a rather stiff blade.

First, clean the stove of all ashes. Lay newspaper or a cloth around it to catch any mess you might now make. Use the wire brush and putty knife to clean soot and creosote off the internal surfaces of the stove. If your stove is the airtight type that has a baffle system, use the putty knife and the wire brush for cleaning. Take the stovepipe down and take it outdoors for its cleaning. Use the flue brush to clean the stovepipe. Remove the damper, if there is one, to finish the job properly.

Some chimneys have cleanout doors and some don't. In either case, seal the flues with masking tape and newspaper, and go up on the roof with your cleaning gear. It is at this point you will begin to appreciate the commercially available outfit. The brush is inserted a couple of feet down from the top of the chimney, with the first section of rod attached. Another section is attached, and then another, until the bottom of the chimney is reached. You then simply scrub up and down until the walls of the flue are clean. Remove the rod, a section at a time. Wear gloves, old clothing and non-slip shoes for this job as it tends to get a bit dirty.

Once that's done, you can remove the accumulated mess from the cleanout door. If there is no cleanout door, it is best to use a shop vacuum slipped through the flue and down into the mess to remove it, Do not use a household vacuum as the fine particles will get through the filter and will probably eventually ruin the motor.

For the stuffed bag process, you slightly overstuff the bag in relation to flue size. Tie ropes to each end, lowering one down so someone at the flue can grab. The bag is then hauled back and forth to cut the buildup. This doesn't do as good a job as the flue brush will. You may wish to get hold of some old tire chains to help cut the harder buildups of creosote. The job will still not be as good as you could do with the wire brush, but it will be better.

Of course, the easiest way to get your chimney cleaned is to hire a professional. And it's also the most expensive. The brush kits go for about $55 to $75 depending on flue size and the number of brushes needed, but they are well worth it.

CHIMNEY PROBLEMS

A good cleaning will often solve a slow fire or a bad smoking problem, as the flue area can be reduced by too much of creosote. But other factors can add problems and fill your house with smoke.

A too short chimney, or obstructions inside of 10 or 12 feet, can cause a downdraft or a slow draft, and allow the stove to smoke. A quick check suffices here. All you need do is measure the chimney to see that it rises at least 2 feet above anything within 10 feet (3 feet above on a flat roof). Trees may have grown up since the chimney was installed, or it may simply have been built too short to work properly.

Smoking can also be caused by wind drafts. The only cure for this is to add a cap to the chimney to keep the drafts out. Caps are available commercially, or you can build your own. The simplest cap is a heavy piece of slate set on four bricks at the corners of the chimney top. I would also add a piece of hardware cloth mesh to keep out birds. This is placed under the bricks and should never be mortared in place since it must be removed to clean the chimney.

Other problems stem from leaks in the chimney, either to the outdoors, or into the house. These can be dangerous as they may pass sparks as well as smoke. It is advisable to make repairs as soon as possible.

For masonry chimneys leaking smoke, you make up a bag stuffed with newspaper or straw and place a board, about ½-inch smaller on two sides than the chimney flue, at the base of the bag. Both are tied firmly together. A rope is dropped down the chimney and everything is pulled to the bottom. Another rope is tied to the top of the bag—for a bag, use a plastic feed sack—and run out the top of the chimney before it is pulled down. Now make up a fairly heavy mix of fire clay mortar—usually fire clay mortar is used in a slurry form, but here it needs to be thicker. Pour this down the chimney and start pulling the bag up. A good flashlight is essential to see when more mortar must be added. Continue adding mortar until the bag reaches the top of the chimney.

In most cases, the above treatment will easily seal cracks in chimneys lined with flue liners, though for rock chimneys or other unlined chimneys, several treatments over a period of weeks may be needed. In such cases, if the flue is large enough, it makes more sense to install either a liner of 24 gauge stove pipe, or one of the metal chimneys.

HOT AIR HEATING

Warm or *hot air heat* is among the most popular kinds for a very simple reason. It is fast acting, relatively efficient and is reasonably cheap to install at least compared to hot water heating systems. It does cost more than baseboard electric heat (Fig. 5-16). A central furnace is not essential for warm air heat, as circulator heaters designed to use fuel oil or kerosene are available in sizes larger enough to heat four or five rooms, if properly placed (and if the room layout allows

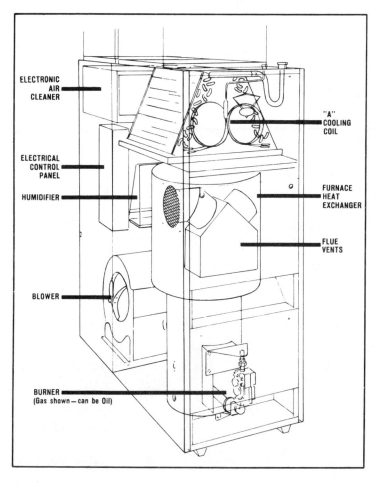

Fig. 5-16. Modern forced warm air furnaces can offer humidity control and electronic air filtration.

good air circulation). Gas fired units for individual rooms are also available and can be had in models that recess in the walls (Fig. 5-17).

Central heating systems are most practical for those who want even heat throughout a house, and in such cases a forced air system is better than a gravity system. I've lived with both and would never have a gravity system again if the choice was mine. The gravity units tend to be more expensive. The forced air heating system consists of the furnace, ducting and registers, controlled by a thermostat. The largest problem with forced air heat is breaking it into zones so that unused, or little used, areas are not heated as heavily as other rooms. Zoning usually requires fairly expensive work and materials. With forced air systems it is best to shut off registers in little used rooms, or to adjust them so that the air flow is quite low, if the room must be kept from freezing. Return air ducts carry cooler air back to the furnace to be heated and recirculated (Fig. 5-18).

For those rich enough to afford air conditioning, most modern forced air furnaces can be readily adapted to accept the cooling coils. The ducting is already in place, cutting installation costs significantly.

Select a furnace with provision for use of washable or replaceable filters, and also select a humidifier to match the furnace output. The humidifier is a relatively inexpensive addition to the system. Until you've lived with a dry house with forced air heat, you don't really know what nasal discomfort can be.

Place warm air supply registers along outside walls, low on the wall or in the baseboard. You probably will have to use floor registers if the house you are to heat is being remodeled. Otherwise, you would have to tear out many walls to place the ducting (tearing out walls will often still be necessary for heating second floors).

In most cases, each room with a warm air supply register will also have a return register, though a single, centrally located return is often enough for a small house. Cold air return location is not critical, so registers can easily be placed where furniture or rugs can't cut off air flow. It's best,

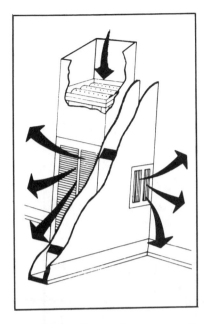

Fig. 5-17. Vertical furnaces for small space installation are readily available. This counterflow type emits warm air at the bottom.

though, to keep them a room's width away from the supply registers.

If your home doesn't have a basement, warm air furnaces designed for hanging from ceiling joists are available, as are small models to fit into a space no larger than the average closet. When installing such a furnace, make sure you leave enough space so the furnace can be serviced in the future.

In general, furnaces for forced warm air heating use either coal, wood, oil or gas for fuel, though it has been sometime since I've seen a coal furnace. Most of the wood furnaces I've seen lately are multi-fuel units. When the wood load burns out, the furnace automatically switches to either gas or oil. More and more companies are entering the wood furnace field as fuel costs continue their inexorable rise. There is more research being done, and a wider choice available now than ever before.

HOT WATER HEATING

At one time, *hot water heat* was something of an aristocrat of heating systems. The water is heated in a boiler and

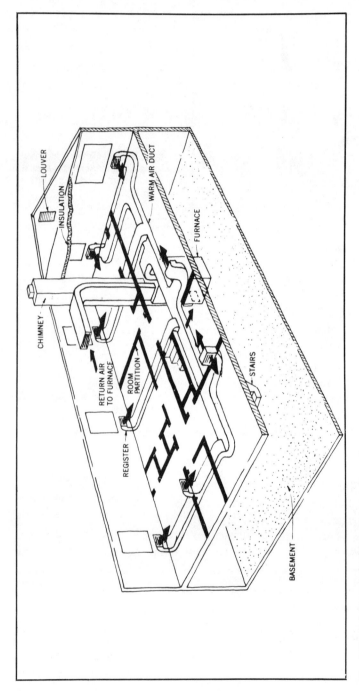

Fig. 5-18. A fairly standard forced warm air system.

then circulated throughout a system of pipes to radiators or convectors.

Boiler cost and installation is more expensive than hot air heating, so few such systems (comparatively speaking) are installed these days. Too, it takes longer for the heat to transfer to room air, so response to temperature changes is more gradual. There is no way to install cooling coils on hot water systems. About the only advantage such a system offers is the possibility of installing coils in the boiler to allow hot water to be heated. Still, the advantage is slight since any family using much hot water will usually need a booster system during the months when the heat isn't in use (Fig. 5-19).

ELECTRIC HEATING

Several forms of *electric heat* are available, and there are definite advantages to electricity as a heat source. It is the

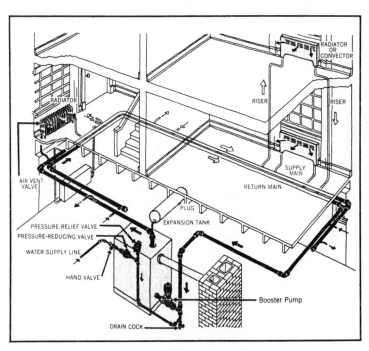

Fig. 5-19. A two-pipe forced hot water system, which is more efficient than a single pipe system since warm and cool water do not mix.

cleanest of all fuels and, at the home heat unit, it is 100 percent efficient. The problem tends to come with the fact that the production of electricity is nowhere near 100 percent efficient. Fuel costs can rapidly get out of line. I've heard of all-electric houses where the electric bill in winter was well above an already outrageous mortgage payment. Much depends on the cost of electricity in your area as to the desirability of installing electric heat. It can be made more desirable if used as a backup to a wood heat system, so that the electricity doesn't cut in unless the fires are out.

Most electrical heating units seen today are the baseboard resistance type, though *heat pumps*, central and floor furnaces and heating cable are available. The heat pump is popular in areas of moderate temperature and provides both heating and cooling capacity. The unit takes heat from the outside air in winter and brings it into the house, while reversing the procedure in summer. Heat pumps use less electricity than do electric resistance heaters and are a form of forced air system. The primary disadvantage is that, at this moment, they do not work at all well in really cold climates.

Resistance heating units for wall installation are also available. They provide good heat sources for areas where baseboard style installations are not practical (Fig. 5-20).

OIL AND GAS BURNERS

Oil *burners* are of two types. If lighted number 1 grade fuel oil is used, the burner will be a pot-type or vaporizing burner, while number 2 fuel oil is used in gun and rotary style burners. Number 2 fuel oil is a bit less expensive than number 1, and also provides a slight amount more heat value per gallon.

Pot, or vaporizing, oil burners work by vaporizing the fuel in a pot which contains a pool of oil. Heat from the burner flame serves to do the vaporizing. In most such burners, there is a pilot light or electric arc used to light the fuel manually (Fig. 5-21).

Atomizing (rotary and gun) oil burners have pumps that force the oil through a special nozzle, while a fan blows air into the atomized oil. An electric spark ignites the mixture

Fig. 5-20. An electric wall unit.

automatically. The gun type atomizing oil burner is the most popular for home use (Fig. 5-22).

Gas is often used in urban homes and is piped right into the home, while bottled gas (*propane*) is used in rural homes. Despite a lot of noise in the past few years about the shortage of gas supplies coming up, it remains a popular fuel and is about the least expensive of fuels (except for wood) in most areas of the country. Gas is flowed to a burner head at low pressure and is ignited by a pilot light or electric arc. Any gas burner with a pilot light must be equipped with a safety valve that cuts off the gas flow if the pilot light goes out (Fig. 5-23).

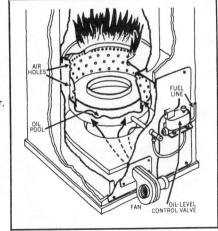

Fig. 5-21. A vaporizing burner.

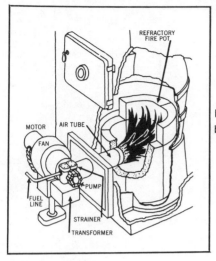

Fig. 5-22. A gun style atomizing burner.

SOLAR HEATING

The use of *solar energy* to heat is still in developmental stages. I have seen little change in price, except up, for active solar energy systems. The problem of cost is com-

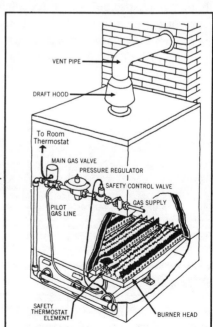

Fig. 5-23. A typical gas burner.

pounded in most areas by a need for a backup heating system, using conventional fuels for times when the sun doesn't shine for three or four days. Passive solar energy systems, and passive supplemental solar energy systems, are generally more practical.

In virtually all areas of the country, some form of solar energy may prove practical. Naturally, the South tends to get the best of it.

For you to consider the practicality of solar energy, you will need to know the number of degree days in your locale. Degree days are simply the number of degrees below 65 degrees F. multiplied by the number of days when the average temperature stays below 65. The greater the number of degree days, the larger solar collectors must be to provide adequate heat. As an example, Birmingham, Alabama averages about 2551 degree days each year, while Portland, Maine, has about 7511. A solar heat system in Portland, then, would need about three times as much collector area at a minimum as would one built for use in Birmingham.

If you intend to buy manufactured equipment, the maker will be able to supply the necessary figures to allow you to determine the correct size of the collectors. Collectors are set at an angle to gather the sun. Each latitude requires a different angle, though most have an allowable margin of plus or minus 10 degrees. Usually, the collectors are designed to be set at the angle equal to a locale's latitude.

House design becomes very important for full-sized solar collector installation. The roof pitch and the amount of pitched roof affect the possibility of installing system.

For active solar systems, redesign of existing houses is possible and may soon prove worthwhile. There are now literally hundreds of firms carrying one or more types of solar heating systems. See Appendix B.

Passive solar energy systems are the simplest of all and require little, if any, care after installation. Essentially, they are care-free because there are no moving parts to break or wear out. Heat production is generally a lot lower than active systems, but the lower overall cost and care for the passive systems may well offset any large heat needs. The floors,

179

walls, ceilings and other areas of the house as used in passive solar heating can become heat sinks, storing the energy during periods of sunshine and releasing it during the night.

Windows and Oil Drums As Heat Collectors

Probably the simplest heat collector is a series of south-facing windows. During the day, drapes are left open so that the house heats up. At night, the insulated drapes are closed to cut down heat loss. Expense is minimal, but the actual heating possibilities are not high, especially in northern areas. Other forms of solar collectors are easily made, and many can be bought.

One form you can easily make, if you have the space, involves oil drums filled with water. Stacked on their sides, with the end facing the sun painted black, these drums will fill with heat during the day. At night, a shutter or other device closes off the exterior face of the drums. A drape can then be pulled to allow the interior ends of the drums to radiate heat to the house.

Lean-To Solar Collectors

Lean-to solar collectors placed under windows are reasonably easy to construct and can serve as heat source supplements. If enough are used, they may well cut down daytime heat requirements to almost nothing. Determine, first, your latitude. Again, these collectors are best placed on a south or southeast facing wall. The collector itself is simple to construct once you know the angle you need. A plywood box in a triangular shape is really all it is, though the sun facing side is covered with either heavy black plastic (which requires more bracing) or dark colored transluscent fiberglass sheeting of the kind made by Filon. Make the box about three window widths wide and frame it so that the center third is directly under the window sill. The floors and side of the box are of plywood, and it will last longer of if you use bricks or concrete blocks to prevent actual ground contact. Walls and floors are of two layers of plywood, on 2 by 4 studs, with insulation between.

You will need to get some metal ducting to form a sort of

chimney at the top center of the collector, cutting out enough of the middle piece of fiberglass sheet so that the chimney fits there, and into the window when opened. The box is used to keep from having to cut through the wall. It will prevent normal window use during the winter, but not too many of us keep windows open at that time of year. Insulate the chimney box well. Make sure the openings at the collector and any space around the chimney box at the window are sealed and insulated as needed.

The collector is left open during the day and closed with a plywood shutter at night, so that any build-up heat is retained and moved into the house. If the collector starts to deliver cool or cold air, it is a simple matter to either seal the chimney box open, temporarily, or to remove the box until the sun reappears.

Solar heat of the passive sort can be inexpensive. But it just isn't too efficient in terms of area of collector and heat retention. Some commercial manufacturers make more complex and more efficient units, and these are worth checking out. I suggest that if you write the firms in Appendix B, you ask whether their devices are active or passive and go from there.

6

Wiring

Wiring principles and practices differ little from area to area, though codes as to who can do what and what sort of check is required do vary widely. Before starting any home wiring job, whether it is on a new house or during renovation, it is best that you check carefully over local codes to see what is allowable and what isn't. In most areas, if you do improper work or do work you're not allowed to do, the building inspector can refuse a certificate of occupancy for a home, or even cancel one already in effect. In other cases, you might be forced to rip out an entire wiring job and reinstall it, or have it reinstalled.

Much depends on your use of electricity, of course, but under-planning, resulting in under-wiring is probably the biggest mistake made in building or renovating a home today. Extra capacity, above and beyond present needs, is always a good idea even with energy as expensive as it is today. For modern homes, even for those of who wish the simple life and expect to use very few appliances, at least a 100 ampere service is needed. In fact, the National Electrical Code recommends at least that and most local codes will require it. Much better is 150 ampere service. For those who will have electric hot water heaters, electric ranges and many appliances plus, possibly, a workshop, a 200 ampere service is an even better idea. It is simpler and cheaper to install the larger service panel and entrance wiring at the beginning than to go back later and change things over.

PLANNING

Figure 6-1 shows the possibilities for appliance setup on planned circuits, while Fig. 6-2 shows floor sketches for a more or less typical six room house, illustrating where the circuits would be run. To meet code requirements, you will need grounded circuits for all new construction and for additions to grounded circuits already in existence. There will need to be two 20 ampere appliance circuits for the kitchen and dining room, and one for any laundry room you may put in. These appliance circuits must be independent of lighting circuits. Wall outlets should be located at least every 12 feet, so you don't have to run a maze of extension cords.

For appliance circuits of 20 ampere capacity, the total carrying capacity in watts is 2400. You will need to make sure that no more appliances are added to any such circuit once that figure is reached. Figure 6-1 gives some typical wattages to help with your figuring.

The circuit numbers in Fig. 6-2 are as follows: circuits one through five supply all the lighting for the house and all convenience outlets, except for those in the kitchen, dining room and laundry. Set them up to supply no less than one 20 ampere circuit for every 500 feet of floor space. The appliance circuits are numbers six and seven, and are both 20 ampere capacity. There would be another for any laundry area, and no lights are installed on them.

The variety of circuits can be great. The drawings show appliance circuits, with number 9 used as the circuit for any fuel-fired heating gear. For a central air conditioning, a 240-volt circuit would be needed, and that would be 10 to 12. From this point, your needs would probably vary a great deal from those shown, but they do give an indication of what can be done.

Six circuits could run from a sub-panel for more efficient service, and on farms a more or less centrally located yardpole is probably a good idea. From the main panel on the yardpole, a 100 ampere sub-panel could be installed in the main barn, and then circuits could run from it to other buildings as needed.

Your planning should consist of not only figuring the loads to be carried, but should continue on to the drawing of diagrams showing the locations of outlets lights, and appliances, with wire runs to these and to wall switches. This will help you determine completely the number of boxes needed, the numbers and types of switches and so on. At this point, you should already know if you need to buy permits and what codes must be followed. The next step is a check with your local power company to see what costs will be for their end of the installation, and to see just how much of the installation they will do. Usually, the local utility will make the installation of the meter, and all wiring leading to it, but you may have to set up the yardpole yourself.

SERVICE CABLE

Two types of material are used to install an electric service: *entrance cable* and *conduit* through which wire is run. Service cable is cheaper and easier to work with than conduit. Today, most areas allow its use. Some don't and local codes will probably superseded the National Electrical Code (NEC), so a check is needed. There are two types of service cable, *armored* and *unarmored*.

First, set the entrance panel in place and attach. Any service entrance panel should be located as near the heaviest sources of electrical use as possible, usually the kitchen. The entrance head is then attached to your building at least 10 feet above the ground. The outer cover must now be stripped from the entrance cable for at least 3 feet so that it can be run through the entrance head. Allow enough length for connections to the power lines.

The service cable is then run down the side of the building, using straps at 4-foot intervals to hold it in place (Fig. 6-3). Watertight connectors attach the cable to the meter socket. Drill a hole through the building within a foot of the location of the service panel, and feed the cable through. The black wire of the cable connects to the left

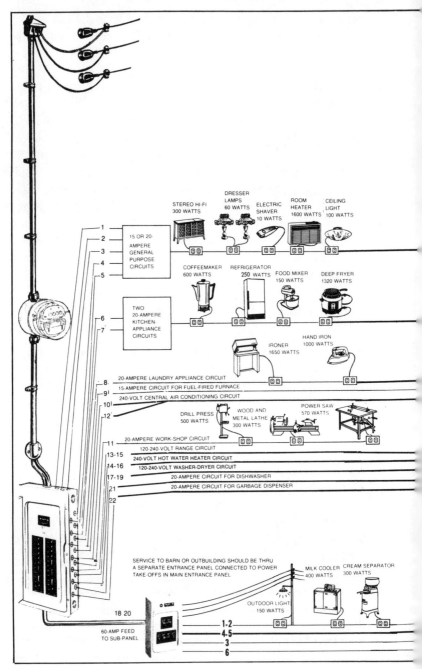

Fig. 6-1. Appliance setup.

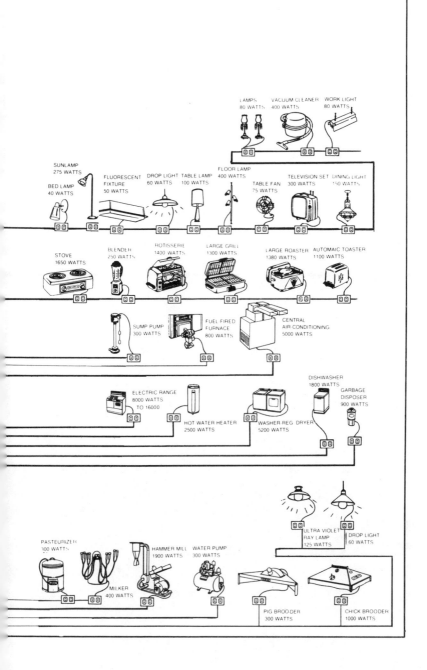

LAMPS
80 WATTS

VACUUM CLEANER
400 WATTS

WORK LIGHT
80 WATTS

SUNLAMP
275 WATTS

BED LAMP
40 WATTS

FLUORESCENT
FIXTURE
50 WATTS

DROP LIGHT
60 WATTS

TABLE LAMP
100 WATTS

FLOOR LAMP
400 WATTS

TABLE FAN
75 WATTS

TELEVISION SET
300 WATTS

DINING LIGHT
150 WATTS

STOVE
1650 WATTS

BLENDER
250 WATTS

ROTISSERIE
1400 WATTS

LARGE GRILL
1300 WATTS

LARGE ROASTER
1380 WATTS

AUTOMAIC TOASTER
1100 WATTS

SUMP PUMP
300 WATTS

FUEL FIRED
FURNACE
800 WATTS

CENTRAL
AIR CONDITIONING
5000 WATTS

ELECTRIC RANGE
8000 WATTS
TO 16000

HOT WATER HEATER
2500 WATTS

WASHER-REG DRYER
5200 WATTS

DISHWASHER
1800 WATTS

GARBAGE
DISPOSER
900 WATTS

ULTRA VIOLET
RAY LAMP
125 WATTS

DROP LIGHT
60 WATTS

PASTEURIZER
300 WATTS

HAMMER MILL
1900 WATTS

WATER PUMP
300 WATTS

MILKER
400 WATTS

PIG BROODER
300 WATTS

CHICK BROODER
1000 WATTS

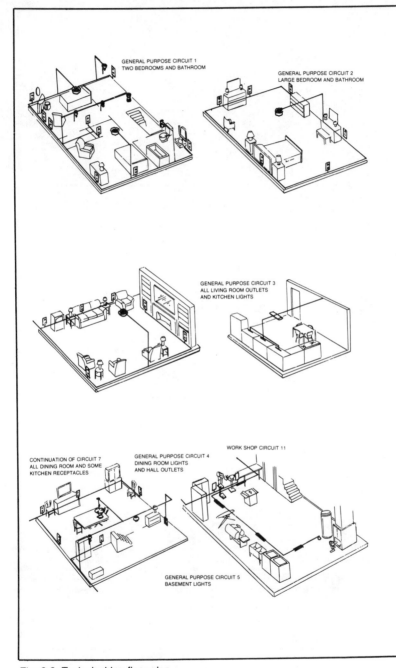

Fig. 6-2. Typical wiring floor plan.

188

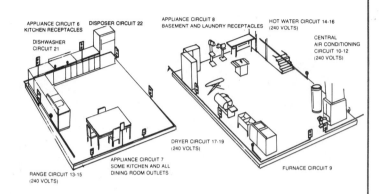

APPLIANCE CIRCUIT 6
KITCHEN RECEPTACLES

DISPOSER CIRCUIT 22

DISHWASHER
CIRCUIT 21

APPLIANCE CIRCUIT 8
BASEMENT AND LAUNDRY RECEPTACLES

HOT WATER CIRCUIT 14-16
(240 VOLTS)

CENTRAL
AIR CONDITIONING
CIRCUIT 10-12
(240 VOLTS)

DRYER CIRCUIT 17-19
(240 VOLTS)

RANGE CIRCUIT 13-15
(240 VOLTS)

APPLIANCE CIRCUIT 7
SOME KITCHEN AND ALL
DINING ROOM OUTLETS

FURNACE CIRCUIT 9

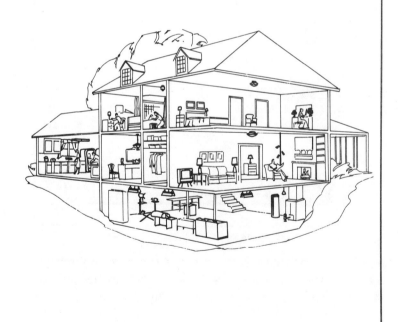

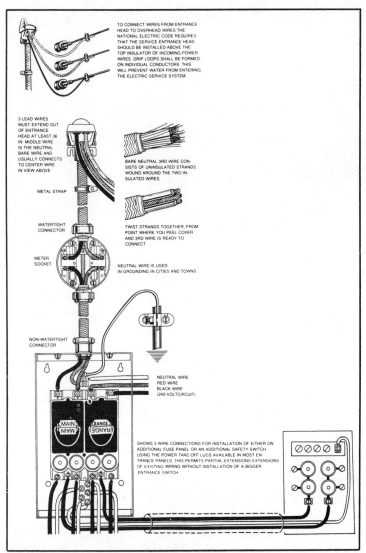

TO CONNECT WIRES FROM ENTRANCE HEAD TO OVERHEAD WIRES THE NATIONAL ELECTRIC CODE REQUIRES THAT THE SERVICE ENTRANCE HEAD SHOULD BE INSTALLED ABOVE THE TOP INSULATOR OF INCOMING POWER WIRES. DRIP LOOPS SHALL BE FORMED ON INDIVIDUAL CONDUCTORS. THIS WILL PREVENT WATER FROM ENTERING THE ELECTRIC SERVICE SYSTEM

3 LEAD WIRES MUST EXTEND OUT OF ENTRANCE HEAD AT LEAST 36 IN. MIDDLE WIRE IS THE NEUTRAL BARE WIRE AND USUALLY CONNECTS TO CENTER WIRE IN VIEW ABOVE

BARE NEUTRAL 3RD WIRE CONSISTS OF UNINSULATED STRANDS WOUND AROUND THE TWO INSULATED WIRES

METAL STRAP

WATERTIGHT CONNECTOR

TWIST STRANDS TOGETHER, FROM POINT WHERE YOU PEEL COVER AND 3RD WIRE IS READY TO CONNECT

METER SOCKET

NEUTRAL WIRE IS USED IN GROUNDING IN CITIES AND TOWNS

NON-WATERTIGHT CONNECTOR

NEUTRAL WIRE
RED WIRE
BLACK WIRE
(240-VOLT CIRCUIT)

MAIN

RANGE

SHOWS 3-WIRE CONNECTIONS FOR INSTALLATION OF EITHER ON ADDITIONAL FUSE PANEL OR AN ADDITIONAL SAFETY SWITCH USING THE POWER TAKE-OFF LUGS AVAILABLE IN MOST ENTRANCE PANELS. THIS PERMITS PARTIAL EXTENSIONS EXTENSIONS OF EXISTING WIRING WITHOUT INSTALLATION OF A BIGGER ENTRANCE SWITCH

Fig. 6-3. Entrance cable and service panel.

terminal of the main disconnect, and red wire to the right terminal. The third wire is the bare neutral wire and goes to the neutral strip. In cities, this neutral strip would be grounded by connecting it to the water pipe system, but out in the boondocks we need to do things another way. Using a number 4 copper grounding wire, tap off the overhead neutral wire and drive a copper rod at least ½ inch in diameter and 8 feet long into the ground. The rod must be located at least 2 feet from any building, and must be driven at least 1 foot below the surface. The ground wire is attached with a clamp. Proper grounding is essential to a safe electrical system (Fig. 6-4).

I'm assuming here that everyone will be using circuit breakers, as fuses can drive you nuts when overloads occur. They tend never to be available in the right sizes, and also present a temptation to use too large a fuse in a circuit that overloads often, which is dangerous. Circuit breakers cost more but are, as far as I am concerned, safer and more convenient. In the long run, especially you use many electric motors with high start up draw down, you could save money with circuit breakers, as they can just be flipped back once the circuit cools down. No circuit breaker should be reset, or fuse replaced, until you check and see what caused it to blow in the first place.

In your service panel, you will find two strips. One is connected to the white wire of the entrance cable and one to the black wire. The black wire is the hot wire. Connect white wires to the side of the circuit breaker bus bar for neutral and the black wire to the circuit breaker. Snap it in place. Always work with the main disconnect off if the meter is in place and power flowing. No one should ever work on a live circuit. Always match white wires to white and black to black.

SERVICE CONDUIT

If you live in an area where service conduit is required, you will need a hacksaw, screwdriver, hammer, pliers and a chance to rent a conduit bender. The size of the conduit is determined by the size of the wires run through it. Three wire service will require one red wire, one white wire, and one black wire in appropriate sizes for your energy requirements. For 200 ampere (or 150 ampere) service, you will be using three number 1/0 or 2/0 wires, which will require a conduit 2 inches in diameter.

Again, the service entrance head must be at least 10 feet above the ground. Metal straps are used to connect the

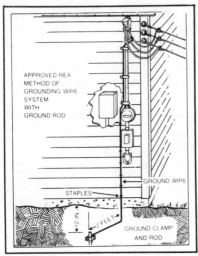

Fig. 6-4. Grounding
the electrical service.

conduit at 4-foot intervals, and conduit connectors are used on the meter socket.

Once the conduit is in place, the wires must be inserted. This is done from the meter up by pushing the wires through the top hub of the meter until they extend at least 3 feet out of the service entrance head. Now the wires are fed down through the bottom hub of the meter to the entrance ell. The ell will have a screw-on cover, which must be removed so you can turn the wires and push them into the house.

From this point, connections are the same as for service entrance cable. If conduit or armored cable were to be used for every circuit in the house—totally unlikely today—you would have a grounded system. Since you don't, follow the same grounding procedure as you did for the service entrance cable.

A SIMPLE WIRING SYSTEM

Figure 6-5 shows the basics of a wiring system, illustrating the ways black and white wires must be connected. Wire nuts are used to make connections—all wiring connections must be made in boxes, and the boxes must all be covered in some way, either with a wall plate or an appliance such as a light fixture—so soldering is not needed. White is hooked to white and black to black in all cases, except for an exception I will cover in a bit.

NM AND NMC TYPE CABLE

Cable sizes are determined by the capacity needed for the circuit. For indoor use you will find yourself handling two primary types of *non-metallic sheathed* cable. A cable is nothing more than two or more wires grouped together and covered by extra insulation. Basically, you'll work with either type NM or type NMC cable in appropriate sizes for circuit load carrying capacity. Usually, type NM is called *Romex* and is suitable for use in dry locations. Each wire is insulated. Then spiral wound paper is wrapped about them, with an outer sheather of plastic. Type NMC is a dual purpose cable since it is suitable for wet or dry locations. Usually, the individual wires are solidly embedded in plastic. Use only copper wire and cable. While there is still some controversy over the use of aluminum wire, I don't like it and feel it is not as safe as copper (Fig. 6-6).

BOXES

Again, all connections in wire runs must be made in boxes. A look at the kinds available can almost give you a headache. *Octagon* boxes are usually used for fixtures or junction boxes, while rectangular boxes are used to house receptacles and switches. There are a variety of ways to install the boxes. Bar hangers are probably best for octagonal boxes when installed in ceilings, as they provide excellent support for light fixtures. Switch boxes can be nailed through or may have plates on them to nail to the studs. All boxes must be firmly attached to the building's framework and not just set in wallboard or paneling (Fig. 6-7).

Boxes are now available in galvanized metal and in plastic. They come in a variety of depths, too. Box size is determined by the number of wires in it. Check your local codes for the various numbers of connections that may be made in any one box of any one size. Proceed from there in selecting the ones you need.

WIRING TECHNIQUES

Wiring is not difficult, but it must be done correctly. Home wiring is absolutely no place to kid around. Never

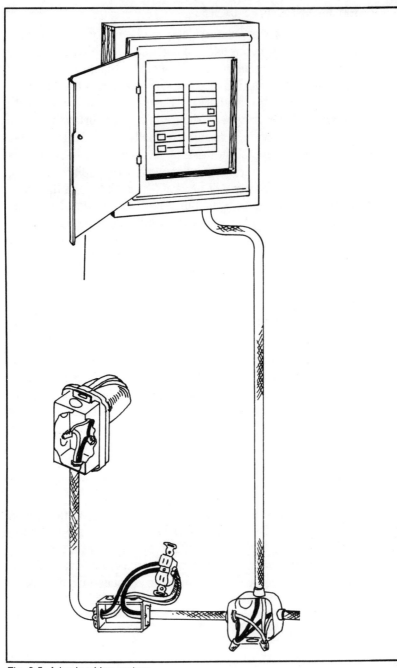

Fig. 6-5. A basic wiring system.

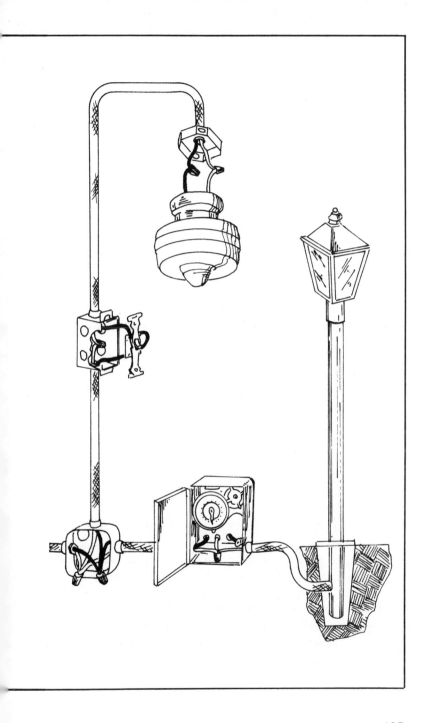

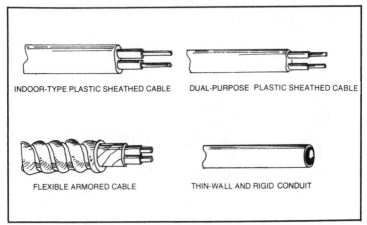

Fig. 6-6. Types of cable.

work on a live circuit. Use care. Neatness counts in wiring for a very simple reason. A neat fitting junction, switch or other appliance with be a safely wired one, assuming you've gotten white to white and black to black.

At boxes, pull about 8 inches of cable through, so you will have enough with which to work and not so much you have to chop some off. Not being able to get a switch far enough out of a box to screw down the terminals is a pain. Having to cut off 6 inches of good copper wire at each outlet can be very expensive at today's prices for cable. Strip about 1 inch of wire when you are getting ready to screw down the terminals. I prefer to use a pair of needle nose pliers to make an open-ended loop in the stripped end; then place this on the terminal screw, with the open end of the loop in the direction the screw turns. As the screw turns down, it will close up the loop and make a good tight connection. Today, too, some switches and receptacles are available with push-in terminals. There is some variation in the exact amount of wire to be stripped, so follow the manufacturer's directions and simply insert the wire. The connection is made.

It is best to use wire strippers, but you can use an electrician's knife (or any other kind of sharp knife). If you use a knife, make sure to taper the cut insulation to the stripped portion. Also, make sure not to nick the wire and thus weaken it.

Nonmetallic sheathed cable is subject to mechanical damage, so all codes require that you provide some form of protection where such damage is likely. You can use either wiring staples or clamps to anchor the wire. For the average person, the clamps offer less chance to nick the cable insulation, though I've been using staples for nearly 20 years with no trouble. Bends must be gentle. The NEC states that any bend in a cable must be of such size that if extended to a full circle, the diameter of the circle would be at least 10 times the diameter of the cable. Cable must be supported, in new construction, at intervals no greater than 4 ½ feet, and within a foot of entering any box.

Where cable must run over ceiling joists or other framing members, as in attics, it should be protected by 1-inch wood guard strips nailed on each side of the cable. Cable can also be run through holes bored in joists or studs.

For new construction, the wires are run to the boxes, which are mounted so that where needed their surfaces will be flush with the finished wall. Do not though, install the switches or receptacles until after the finished wall is on, unless the room is to be paneled only. While dry wall construction is much neater than plaster used to be, the tapers and painters are sure to leave a few drips and splotches. It is a lot easier to just clean the boxes (Fig. 6-8).

Working With Old Construction

If you've bought an old farmhouse with poor or no wiring, the work really starts. A quick examination will probably show that the wiring, if it exists, is inadequate beyond belief for today's purposes. I can't even remember the number of 10-room and larger houses I've seen with 30 ampere entrance panels over the years.

Again, locate the place of probable heaviest use, and install 150 or 200 ampere service panel. Now, check the old wiring for the condition of the insulation, grounding and so on. The odds are good that if the system is 20 years or more old, it is of the ungrounded kind. In many areas this makes it legal for you to go ahead and add ungrounded additions. Do not do it. Take out the old, ungrounded receptacles and

STEEL OUTLET OR SWITCH BOXES WITH WALL MOUNTING BRACKET.

USE STEEL BOXES FOR SWITCH, RECEPTACLE AND BRACKET OUTLETS IN THE HOME.

FUSE DEVICES—DESIGNED TO PROTECT LOW AMPERE CAPACITY MOTORS ON APPLIANCES. POWER TOOLS. ETC.

OCTAGON BOXES FOR USE WITH FIXTURE OR JUNCTION OUTLETS. AVAILABLE IN STEEL WITH CABLE CLAMPS.

AT LEFT. BEVELED CORNER BOX. FITS INTO WALL OPENING IN OLD BUILDINGS. HAS CLAMPS FOR LOOM OR NON-METALLIC SHEATHED CABLE. NO CONNECTOR NEEDED. SIDE-BRACKET BOX (CENTER) USED WITH COVER (RIGHT) IN NEW WORK. WHEREVER EXTRA SPACE IS NEEDED FOR WIRES.

CONVERTS FUSE BOX INTO AUTOMATIC CIRCUIT BREAKER.

PLUG AND CARTRIDGE FUSES WITH SAFETY VALVES TO PROTECT WIRES AGAINST OVERLOADS.

CLOCK OUTLET WITH HANGAR.

DRYER OR RANGE PIGTAILS AND RECEPTACLES.

BAKELITE DUPLEX WALL OUTLET AND PLATE.

PORCELAIN PULL CHAIN OUTLET WITH RECEPTACLE.

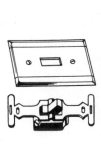

BAKELITE TOGGLE SWITCH AND PLATE FITS ANY STANDARD SWITCH BOX.

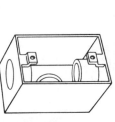

WEATHERPROOF RECEPTACLES, SWITCHES AND BOXES FOR OUTDOOR USE.

Fig. 6-7. Boxes and other wiring devices.

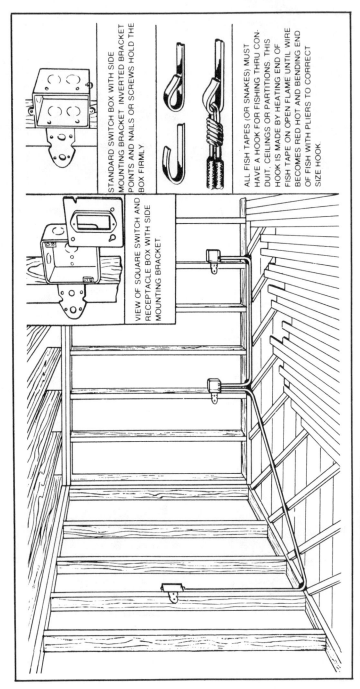

STANDARD SWITCH BOX WITH SIDE MOUNTING BRACKET INVERTED BRACKET POINTS AND NAILS OR SCREWS HOLD THE BOX FIRMLY

ALL FISH TAPES (OR SNAKES) MUST HAVE A HOOK FOR FISHING THRU CONDUIT, CEILINGS OR PARTITIONS. THIS HOOK IS MADE BY HEATING END OF FISH TAPE ON OPEN FLAME UNTIL WIRE BECOMES RED HOT AND BENDING END OF FISH WITH PLIERS TO CORRECT SIZE HOOK.

VIEW OF SQUARE SWITCH AND RECEPTACLE BOX WITH SIDE MOUNTING BRACKET

Fig. 6-8. You can run conduit across subfloors.

replace with modern wire and receptacles. This is the easy part, for nine times out of 10 you can do the job by simply attaching the new wire to the old and pulling it through the wall, floor or ceiling.

It is the addition of new circuits that provides the work, and the work is far from all simple wiring. Wire may have to be fished, naturally, and there's a special tool for this job. But at times obstacles in the wall or ceiling are going to force you to tear out chunks of plaster, often making holes large enough to allow you to insert a drill in the wall and bore holes in sole plates and studs. This sort of mess is pretty close to unavoidable if you're to do a good job. Sooner or later after the rewiring is done, you will pick up a fair amount of skill at repairing holes in plaster.

A couple of different boxes are made to aid in adding on wiring. The "Grip-Tite" box has side clamps that are tightened after the cable is pulled through. It does a good job of securing the box without having to nail it to a stud. Metal box supports are slipped in beside an ordinary box and the tabs bent to hold the box firmly in place. Of the two, I tend to prefer the "Grip-Tite."

Sound your walls for studs—this is almost impossible with plaster walls. If you can locate the studs, you can get ready to rewire. If not, remove the baseboard and, about 2 or 3 inches up from the floor, drill a series of small holes until you hit the studs. Keeping the holes 2 inches apart will assure that sooner or later you hit a stud. Once the stud is located, select the spot for your box. Try to stay about 4 to 5 inches from the studs on old construction. Switches are best located from 48 inches from the floor. If you are planning on wall lights, place the openings for those from 66 to 70 inches above floor level.

Light switches are always placed on the side of the door away from the hinges, never on the hinged side. You should use the largest size switch box (depth) possible, which means the standard 2½ inch. Use a template you make by tracing around the box to mark the spot for the wall opening. Drill holes at least ½ inch in diameter at each corner of your drawing, and use a compass saw to cut the wallboard or plaster and lath. If you are cutting really old walls, or

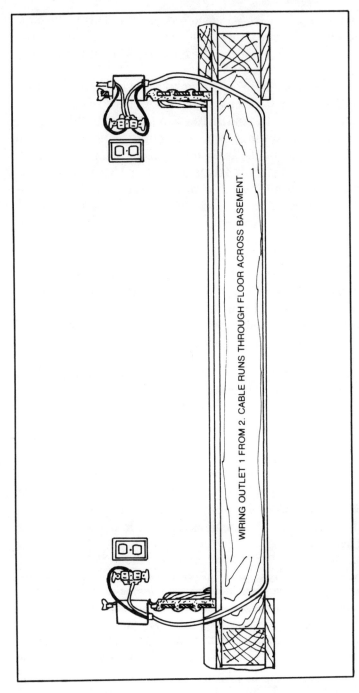

WIRING OUTLET 1 FROM 2. CABLE RUNS THROUGH FLOOR ACROSS BASEMENT.

Fig. 6-9. Wiring new outlets from the basement.

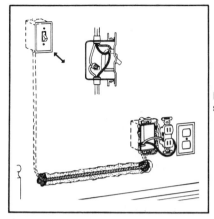

Fig. 6-10. Wiring from a wall switch to a wall outlet.

wallboard, place one hand alongside the cut being made to provide some support and keep from breaking off material you don't want to have to replace. Insert the box, after the cable is run, and install the cable locknut before locking the box in place.

Ceiling boxes in old construction can be a bit difficult if no attic access allows you to get to things. The cable is fished, and then the hole for the box is cut from a template made from the box. The box hanger must then have its locknut removed and a wire run through the threaded stud. It is then inserted in the cut hole at an angle, and the wire is pulled to center the hanger. The cable is now connected and the threaded locknut reinstalled, after the hanger wire is removed. Tightening the locknut draws the unit tight to the ceiling (Figs. 6-9 through 6-12).

Three and Four-Way Switches

Especially with outbuildings, the control of lights from several points can be a great thing. A three-way switch

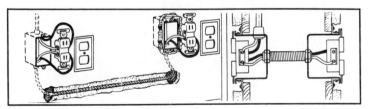

Fig. 6-11. Wiring from one outlet to another.

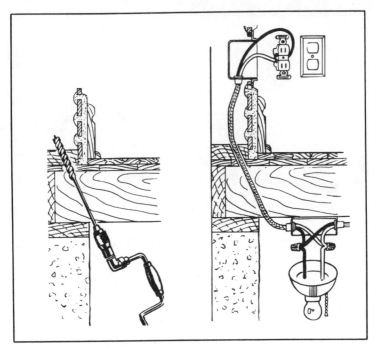

Fig. 6-12. Running wire through a floor.

easy to light a long hall from either end, or light the tool shed from house or shed. It is with three and four-way switches that you may have to connect black to white wires, but in all such cases the white wire from the switches must be painted black to avoid later confusion (Figs. 6-13 through 6-15). Four-way switches allow light control from three separate points, and such a circuit requires two three-way switches as well as a four-way (Fig. 6-16). Other changes and additions to lighting and receptacle circuits are possible, as shown in Figs. 6-17 through 6-24.

Major Appliances

Electric water heaters, ranges and dryers as well as certain large room air conditioners require 240 volt circuits with much heavier than usual cable. An electric range will require a separate number 6 cable run from a 50 ampere circuit breaker. It's usually best to use a heavy duty wall

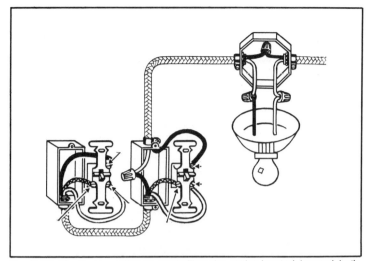

Fig. 6-13. Three-way switches controlling the outlet located beyond both switches.

receptacle, as shown in Fig. 6-25, because this allows easier movement of the range for cleaning or replacement than does wiring it directly to the entrance panel. An electric water heater might typically be wired in as shown in Fig. 6-26.

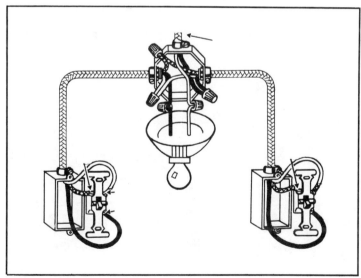

Fig. 6-14. Three-way switches controlling the outlet located between the switches.

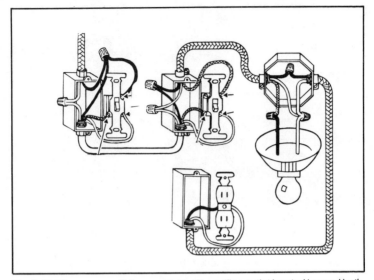

Fig. 6-15. Three-way switches controlling the ceiling outlet located beyond both switches. The receptacle is always hot.

Yardpole Line

As I've said before, where several buildings are to be served, a central, or nearly central, distributing device is better than trying to run everything from the house service

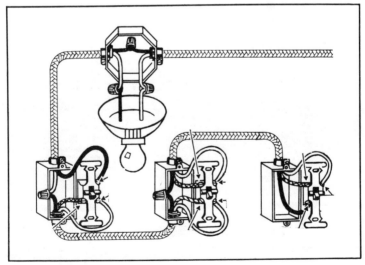

Fig. 6-16. Installing four-way switches.

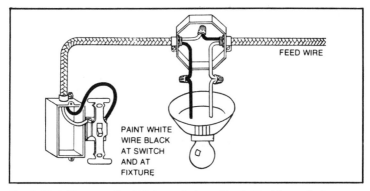

Fig. 6-17. Adding a wall switch to control a ceiling light at the end of a run.

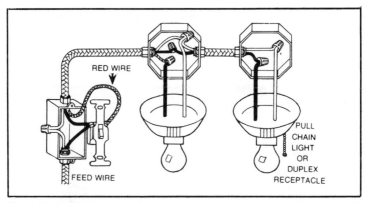

Fig. 6-18. Installation of two ceiling lights on the same line, with one controlled by a switch.

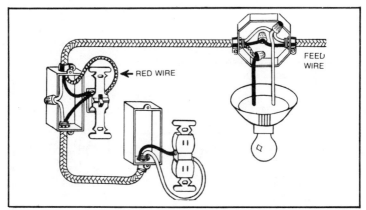

Fig. 6-19. Adding a switch and convenience outlet beyond the existing ceiling light.

207

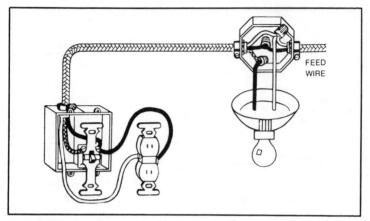

Fig. 6-20. Adding a switch and convenience outlet in one outlet box beyond the existing ceiling light.

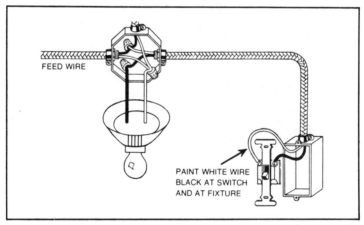

Fig. 6-21. Adding a wall switch to control a ceiling light in the middle of a run.

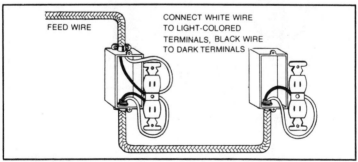

Fig. 6-22. Adding new convenience outlets beyond old convenience outlets.

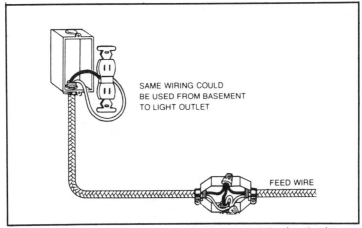

SAME WIRING COULD
BE USED FROM BASEMENT
TO LIGHT OUTLET

FEED WIRE

Fig. 6-23. Adding a new convenience outlet from an existing junction box.

panel. Figure 6-7 shows a typical installation, but you could easily find an exception in your area. This drawing shows both metered and unmetered wires running through the same conduit, which will occasionally violate a code or, if not a code, the sensibilities of a utility company. It is best to check first.

The *yardpole* line must be grounded and must use non-ferrous metal no less than ½ inch and 8 feet long, with the rod located at least 2 feet from the pole, and its top driven a foot

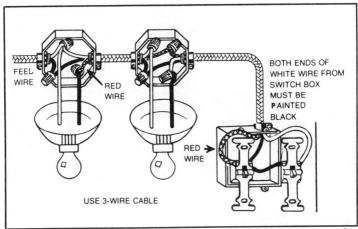

FEED WIRE

RED WIRE

BOTH ENDS OF
WHITE WIRE FROM
SWITCH BOX
MUST BE
PAINTED
BLACK

RED WIRE

USE 3-WIRE CABLE

Fig. 6-24. Installing a new ceiling outlet and two new switch outlets from the existing ceiling outlet.

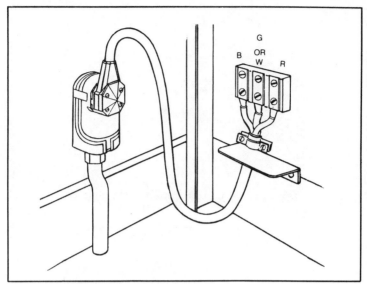

Fig. 6-25. Typical electric range or dryer hookup.

or more into the ground. The ground is connected to the so-called neutral wire at the top of the pole. The grounding wire will be number 6 copper, fastened every 6 inches down

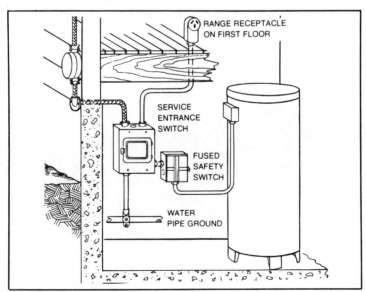

Fig. 6-26. Typical water heater installation.

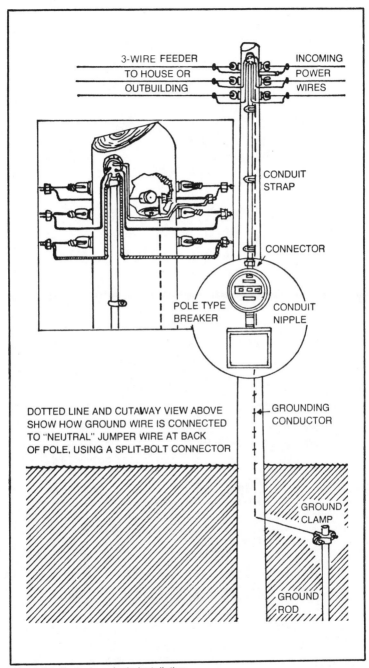

3-WIRE FEEDER
TO HOUSE OR
OUTBUILDING

INCOMING
POWER
WIRES

CONDUIT
STRAP

CONNECTOR

POLE TYPE
BREAKER

CONDUIT
NIPPLE

DOTTED LINE AND CUTAWAY VIEW ABOVE
SHOW HOW GROUND WIRE IS CONNECTED
TO "NEUTRAL" JUMPER WIRE AT BACK
OF POLE, USING A SPLIT-BOLT CONNECTOR

GROUNDING
CONDUCTOR

GROUND
CLAMP

GROUND
ROD

Fig. 6-27. Typical yardpole installation.

211

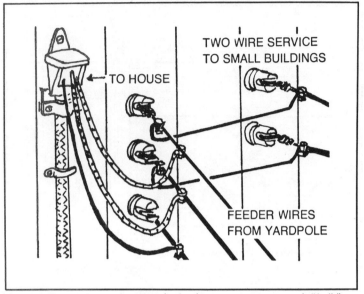

Fig. 6-28. Three-wire service tapped to feed two-wire service to a small building.

the pole. All circuits branching from the yardpole must be at least 10 feet clear of trees, roofs and other obstructions.

Once the feeders to the main buildings are in place, it is possible to run two wire service to other outbuildings where

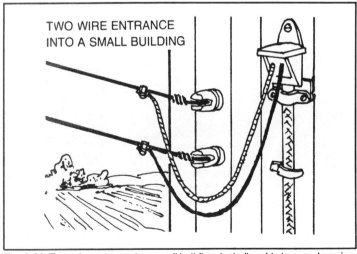

Fig. 6-29. Two-wire entrance to a small building, including drip loop and service head which are both required.

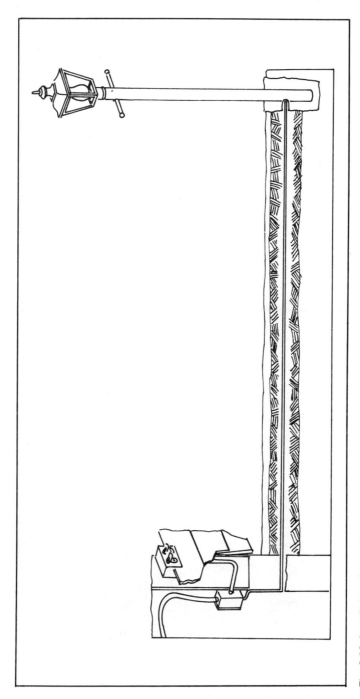

Fig. 6-30. Installation of a yard light.

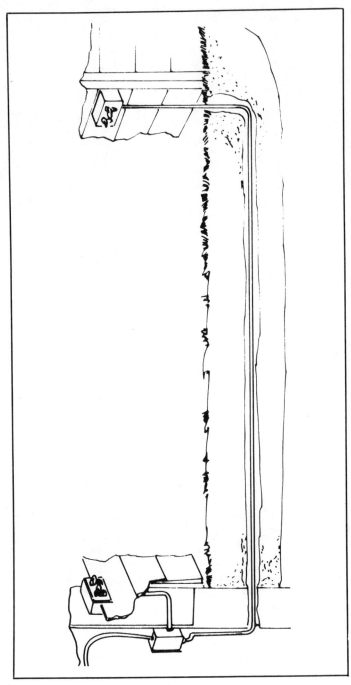

Fig. 6-31. Installation of outdoor outlets, one on the outside of the house and the other running underground to a garage or other outbuilding.

the power needs are limited to lights and the possible occasional use of tools like a small electric drill. Figure 6-28 shows how to tap two wire service from a three wire service. This sort of tap can be used only in outbuildings where the anticipated load on the circuit is less than 3500 watts. No motor over half a horsepower can be used.

Use number 8 wire for two wire service, so that it will be heavy enough to withstand wind, rain and icing (Fig. 6-29). Space insulators on buildings so that they are at least a foot apart. Make sure the wires clear the ground by 18 feet over driveways and 10 feet over foot paths.

Underground Wiring

Wiring to outbuildings can also be run underground, but a check of local codes will be needed to make sure of the type of wire to use. Some localities still specify that the wiring must be done through conduit, while a few allow the use of NMC cable. There is a type UF underground feeder that may also be legal in your area. In any case, any bends and the resulting upright sections to the surface should be protected with conduit. While some outdoor wiring is safe enough at a depth of 2 feet, on farms where there is a chance of heavier equipment moving over the area, I would go down at least 3 feet. Wires placed between layers of sand are less likely to be damaged. The wire should be laid loosely in the trench, as tension could result in damage. In fact, allowing the wire to slither around the trench is a good idea. (Figs. 6-30 and 6-31).

7

Fences and Gates

Farm fencing differs in many ways from urban fencing, for it must do more jobs and, often, do them longer. Too, farm fence runs are likely to be a great deal longer and, thus, more expensive and time consuming to erect.

Good fences may not actually make good neighbors, but in some cases good neighbors would ease life for themselves and others by putting up fences. We could do the same ourselves. Last year it never occurred to me to fence my garden. When my neighbor turned his flock of chickens out, I never realized that my tomato crop could be gone. But it was. Those foul fowl would peck out one side of a partially ripe tomato and the rest would rot.

This year a light fence will keep them out. I don't much care about the rabbits nibbling the lettuce, as that is cheap enough to plant extra for the animals. The birds can have the sunflowers. But I want my tomatoes.

REASONS FOR FENCES

A well built fence will serve its purpose for many years, becoming a pleasure to look at even if the style is totally utilitarian. It should go up at reasonable cost and with some semblance of ease. A poorly built fence will look shoddy, will not serve its intended uses well, and will be the source of extra work as long as it stands. The choice is really up to the person who erects the fence as proper planning and material selection, along with good construction practices, can make almost any fence long lasting and secure.

The purposes of fences are nearly as varied as the people who erect them. A farmer may wish a single or double strand wire electric fence to keep a few hogs from straying on to the road or someone else's property. Someone trying to save on heating bills may erect a high fence as a windbreak. Others may wish to add cachet to the home, distinguishing it even further from any nearby. A horseman or horsewoman may wish to erect a high and strong stallion fence or a lower, but nearly as strong, fence for foals, geldings or mares.

Fences can serve to keep children in, and other people out, or they can insure privacy when cooking or sunbathing in the back yard. They can also do little more than mark boundary lines to prevent squabbles.

Fences suitable for one purpose may be totally out of the question for others. As an example, barbed wire, fine for cattle, is among the worst of all possible choices for horses. A cow which runs up to a barbed wire fence will usually just stand there waiting. A horse, physically and psychologically a much different sort of animal, will most often panic, with major cuts resulting as it struggles to get away—cuts that may too often be bad enough to force the owner to destroy the animal.

Thus, a careful determination of the type of fence to be used is needed. For decorative purposes, the choices and materials are extremely wide, particularly if no children need to be protected. Farm fences must suit the jobs to be done. Windbreak fences must be of especially sturdy materials to constantly withstand winter wind loads without collapsing. Almost any fence with solid panels, in fact, must be constructed to withstand expected wind loadings. Material selection and fence type both have a bearing on the ease of erection; the more materials and the stronger the fence must be, the harder you will find it to erect as there will be much more work involved.

Fence construction is hard enough work, and expensive enough, that it pays all of us to do the job only once. Old and new materials can be used, but a selection of those materials that are known for long life is wise. Proper setting of posts is imperative both for present and future strength. Proper post size for different jobs is essential to a long lasting fence.

Using incorrect materials and coupling them with poor erection techniques will provide a fence that could well fall down in a single year, and one that will surely not last half a decade. For very little greater expense and almost no extra work, it is easily possible to erect a fence that will stand 20, 30 or more years unless damaged by mechanical accident. About all you have to do is keep up the paint, if the fence is painted. Today's pressure treated woods start out a rather sickly green, but in about two to three years age to a fine silver gray, with no need for any painting. Check for pulled nails or staples every couple of years, and other very minor maintenance chores. A poorly built fence will require almost constant maintenance if it is to last even five years.

Simply put, doing it right is easier, if not at the outset, then over the long term, and will eventually be cheaper as less repair and replacement is needed. That's what this book is all about. Modern and traditional fences should be erected with first class methods and the best materials affordable. This may not solve all your fencing problems, but those it doesn't solve should be easier to resolve.

No matter how much money and effort you plan to put into fence erection, much of it may well be wasted if the early steps, planning for uses and layout, are slighted as they so often are. In some cases, for those of us not building fences every day or week, it will be essential to back off and look at even small construction details well in advance of actual building. It is quite possible to make small mistakes that can ruin both the appearance and durability of any type of fence.

FENCE USES

The basic style of any fence must conform to its needed function. There is little sense in erecting a chicken wire fence and expecting the lines to hold mares or stallions.

There is even less sense in erecting a garden fence of heavy duty chain mesh to keep out a few rabbits, squirrels or raccoons. You're not likely to be able to keep out raccoons in any case.

If the primary purpose of a fence is decorative, it needs less overall strength than does one that must hold animals, or one to deter theft. Construction techniques do not differ all that much for the two types. A decorative fence that falls over in two years is of no more value than a utility fence that is knocked down the first time a goat hits a post. In some cases, possibly in most residential cases, fencing may be dual purpose. You'll want it to keep your children safe on your property and out of danger from traffic or other hazards. At the same time, you'll probably want the fence to be attractive in order to please yourself, possibly to please your neighbors, and surely to enhance the value of your home.

Farm fencing is seldom thought of as an aesthetic need, unless the farm is a commercial horse or cattle selling operation. Even then, the most attractive fencing is usually reserved for use in the areas around the home and main selling barns. The reasons for not worrying about attractiveness in areas away from public view are not hard to imagine in this day of ever leaping inflation. First, quality fencing is expensive, whether attractive or not, but attractive fence of good quality is even more expensive. Second, in the usual case, attractive fencing requires more attention to detail and is a bit harder to erect. It takes more time, if you are doing it yourself, and costs more money if you are hiring it done.

Only you know to what uses you will put a fence. If you are holding stallions in paddocks, the need for sturdy fences is much greater than if you're holding, say, geldings on large pastures. Both fences must be sturdy, but one must be a fair amount sturdier. Selecting a fence to keep a small dog in a yard seems simple. If that dog is female, how high need the fence be to keep neighborhood males out in times of estrus for your female? If your dog is one of the breeds used for attack, defense and general protection, how much fence is legally required to protect the general public?

Again, these questions will vary from person to person and from area to area, as will the answers. If you chain a dog, you may need only a small fence to keep wandering children away. If the dog roams your yard and is a large breed, you could be forced to erect a high chain link fence. If you keep a female in heat indoors, you may need only a small fence to keep it in your yard at other times, and to keep neighboring mutts at bay.

Again, keeping children within the confines of a yard depends in large part on the child's inquisitiveness and to some degree on his or her mechanical aptitude and climbing ability. Too, the type of fence used may well depend on your perception of the neighborhood in which you live.

Each situation requires an individual answer that you must consider carefully to keep from wasting money and time, and to keep from *not* doing the job you wish to do. A fence that will hold adult bovines of any type may, and almost surely will, be inadequate for calves. A fence that holds range-bred adult horses can damage foals. A fence that does a fine job of holding cows or horses will not be "pig proof." Pigs are renowned for their ability to scoot through many types of fencing.

Think about the fence you need. Then draw a rough layout, possibly with some rough fence design drawings. Use graph paper to help with the layout.

FENCE DESIGN

Probably the best way to show fence design and layout is to use a hypothetical example, though the land described lies outside my window now. Consider a small house set to the front of a 220 foot by 410 foot plot, with the house actually sitting 60 feet back from the road. Forty feet behind the house the land drops, steeply, going some 310 feet to and just over a small creek. A few trees are actually on the property, and it is surrounded by woods on 2½ sides. The plot is almost a perfect rectangle, which generally makes a fencing job a lot easier.

Assume for our example that a fence is needed to enclose a gelding, in the rear of the house, with the pasture being brought up on the wide side of the lawn (the house sits about 25 feet in from the property line on one side) so the horse will have a bit more level ground to roam in bad weather. A bit more than 1½ acres is to be enclosed in this manner. The front yard will be enclosed with a decorative fence, while a garden plot of about 50 by 100 feet will be set in no less than 15 feet from the road. Three types of fence, then, are to be needed.

Layout

The first chore is to bring out the graph paper and make rough drawings of the above perimeters. That's easily done, but then we take the drawings outdoors, with at least a 25-foot tape measure (another person is also a great help). The property stakes are located, and the problems start. The first property line marker brings us right on through a 30-inch diameter white oak that adds greatly to the overall attractiveness of the yard. Two black locusts and several tulip poplars on down that property line would force a fence set right on the line to zig and zag pretty badly, so the first step is to measure in about 8 feet before setting the first corner stake for the fence. While it is possible to fence directly up to large trees, the root system can give you fits when posthole digging is done. Too, it's possible to damage a valuable tree cutting through roots.

Crossing the small creek will present another type of problem, as it will drop away under the fence at least 30 inches on one end and possibly as much as 6 inches more on the other end. This is solved by using special water gates, but requires some thought as to type. The steep slope of the land will also require some special fencing techniques.

Another large oak interferes with pasture fencing at the rear of the house, so it is again dropped back to keep from tapping into the root system. Once this side of the fence is designed, we get to the L corner to lead out onto the flattest portion of the property, and a run of about 100 feet before coming up against the start of the garden fencing (one portion of this side will also join with the decorative fencing around the front yard). The garden rectangle is easily figured, for the ground is almost perfectly flat here. Ideally, we would prefer to locate the garden further back where the ground still has a slight slope, but the fencing complications to gain enough level or near level room for the horse add too greatly to the expense if that is done.

The decorative fencing will now form an upside down "U" in front of the house, though the side with the garden and pasture will be finished differently than will the side against the woods. The garden fence must keep small animals out, while the pasture fence will keep a large, though gentle, animal in. The other fence attractively shows the approximate property limits. In some areas it pays to be exceptionally careful while running a fence line. Setting it inside one's own property line may cause you to lose a few feet of property, while setting it on another person's property can cause a legal problem and result in you losing your fence job.

Choosing Materials

Once the layout is determined, the time comes to decide on materials. This is a local decision in many instances as several materials are usually available to do any fencing job. Various metals and woods can be had, and in most cases at least two of each will do a fine job for any fence need you can imagine. Cost, to a point, should be one determining factor, while appearance is another, assuming pretty much equal utility and durability.

Availability and local pricing of wood or other materials can cause major variations in the price of any fence job, as can the amount of labor you are able or willing to provide. One type of fence that is greatly popular here, for both decorative and other uses, is the *zig zag* split rail of pine or oak. Pine of several types is easily found, as is oak. Ease of erection is great. The need for postholes is negligible, except for some corners and at gates.

Durability is fair, but repairs are simple. The bottom rail lies directly on the ground, so rot can be expected to destroy it, and the rail above it, rather quickly, usually well within five years.

Utility is also great. This type of rail fence will provide an attractive setting for many house styles (not the more formal styles, of course), while also providing enough height and strength to keep in large animals. Keeping out smaller animals is accomplished by running 2 or 3 foot high chicken wire around the interior, stapled or wired to a rail every few feet.

While there are not many postholes to dig, the need for splitting the rails is present. Such a project requires time and space to store the logs to be split, as well as the strength and energy to take care of the splitting and stacking of the rails. If those two things are to be found, though, this may well be the cheapest form of fencing in many areas of the country.

A strong consideration, then, for our example, must be given to split rail zigzag fencing. Other forms of fencing may do nearly as well for most other factors, but this fence will provide a unified look and will be cheap, though a lot of work.

Locust abounds in my area, so for the split rail zigzag sections of the fence, we will consider the use of locust for bottom rails, increasing fence life from under five years (probably three or so, if pine or oak is used as bottom rail material) to about 10 to 15 years. The sections of fence done in zigzag style will be those for decorative and garden purposes. The horse fencing will be three rail *post and rail* fence, of pressure treated wood, with handmade sections to prevent problems at the creek sections. Garden fence will be lined inside with chicken wire 36 inches high to keep small animals at bay. There is little point in trying to keep deer out of local gardens. Fencing for such purposes would have to be at least 7 feet high, making the cost prohibitive. The best bet is to put in a 3 or 4-foot high fence and hope.

Pressure treated lumber such as Koppers Company's brands, *Wolmanized* and *Outdoor*, are ideal for strong permanent fencing. The processes to impregnate these fence woods, usually made of pine, have been in existence for decades, with test stakes from 1934 showing no deterioration as yet. Cost is higher than plain pine, of course, and is even higher than treating pine at home. The difference is in the life span of the wood. Home treatments seldom get more than a few gallons of preservative into the wood fibers, where pressure treating can force the wood to absorb some 20 to 40 times more of the chemicals.

Of course, *redwood* and *cedar* are fine fencing woods, too. The biggest problem in both cases tends to be the overall price of such woods in certain areas of the country. In my present locale, the price is about double that of pressure treated pine, so such an option is too luxurious. In other areas of the United States and Canada I understand there is almost no price differential, though in certain places the differential is even greater. West Coast sites generally have the lowest redwood prices, while transport costs really run things up when you go East.

DETERMINING THE AMOUNT OF FENCING NEEDED

With the decisions made as to type of fencing and approximate shape of the fences, the time comes to take a tape measure in hand and walk the fence line to find out just how much material will actually be needed. A tape at least 25 feet long is essential, and for longer fence lines a 100-foot tape is better. Using a 25-foot tape, I carry a small hammer and a dozen or so plastic tent pegs to mark and hold the end of the tape when working alone. At this point, absolute accuracy isn't essential. Remember, though, if you're out as little as 8 feet overall, you could end up buying an extra panel of fence.

Our theoretical example is going to require 296 feet of zigzag fencing for the garden (perimeter minus 4 feet for the gate). From this point, the post and rail fence will extend 340 feet down the back, 210 feet across the back, and about 300 feet up the hill, then across behind the house about 100 feet, and up 50 feet to meet the garden fence. More zigzag fence will extend from the post and rail to the front of the lawn, about 100 feet, and then across about 25 feet to complete the decorative venture.

Thus, we end up with 421 feet of zigzag fencing and 990 feet of post and rail fencing, plus 296 feet of chicken wire to line the garden fence. We will also need two gate posts of heavy enough construction for the garden fence gate, two gate posts for a 10-foot gate for the horse, plus the gates, and also six corner posts for the post and rail fencing.

The zigzag fencing is a bit harder to figure, as the changes of direction cause a loss of length, as does the 6-inch overlap at each end. The posts should be cut no less than twelve feet long, and split into rails of that length, allowing no less than ten feet of actual length, which will give a more or less normal 8-foot panel when set at an angle. Heights vary. Normally, a 3-foot high section of zigzag will require eight or 10 rails. Thus, our 296 feet, plus the decorative sections, will have to have some 53 sections, needing between 424 and 530 rails. That's a lot of log splitting!

The 990 feet of post and rail fence, in locally available 10-foot panels, will require 99 sections. At this time, the post and rail fence needs, minus a gate but plus the extra eight posts, would run about $1500. The zigzag can be done for nothing except the gas to run a chain saw if you have access to forested land, or for very little if you can find someone willing to sell 12-inch to 18-inch pine on the stump for you to cut and haul yourself. Don't go much over 18 inches in diameter as the splitting increases in difficulty as the tree grows in girth.

The chicken wire adds probably $40 to $50 to the job, as do the two needed gates. Cost will vary widely depending on the type of gates chosen; you can even buy hardware kits and make the gates of locally available rough cut boards to bring prices down more.

PLANNING FOR YOUR FENCING NEEDS

Total cost for about two acres of not very complex fencing then will be about $1700 to $1800 or so. Even with climbing inflation rates, this sort of a job isn't at all cheap, so the need for good basic planning and the use of the best construction methods is easily seen. If you do all the work yourself, the savings are huge. Considering getting someone else to build zigzag fence is not rational. The labor-intensive cutting and splitting would run the cost of that type of fence above even the most expensive of other types. If you hire someone else to put in the post and rail fence, the cost will rise about a dollar a foot, possibly as much as $1.50.

Essentially these types of fencing are suitable for most suburban and rural areas as decorative, garden and large livestock fence styles. Urban and suburban areas will have different requirements. You may wish to use a chain link style to keep intruders and trespassers from your property. Vertical board fences will provide privacy and protection, too. Gates will probably need to be higher and sturdier, often with locks installed. Keeping children in the yard and others out may be the major job of these fence types, while some people I know are now considering their fences as first lines of protection against thieves.

You must plan for *your* needs. There are literally hundreds of examples of different fence types found in stores, catalogs and newspaper ads. Look them over. Consider your needs. Build to suit those needs. If you build well, your fences will do the job needed for many years to come.

Don't make the mistake of considering only wood fence because of the industrial look of *chain link* metal styles. Today's chain link fencing comes in attractive colors, vinyl coated to prevent rust. Many manufacturers have set the links up so that strips of wood can be slipped through, in many patterns, or simply vertically or horizontally, to give a more attractive appearance than was available a few years ago.

In fact, most metal fence styles are now available with vinyl coatings. Colors vary, though dark green seems very popular. Vinyl coated fence should easily outlast non-coated by quite some time, while providing a more attractive appearance. It would, actually, be a fine alternative to the chicken wire garden fence lining used in our example, allowing the split rail fence to be eliminated from that area, while still having an attractive look.

Fence erection covers many chores. Probably the simplest of all is the split rail, so that will be our first style covered. Just lay the rails on the ground and spike or wire them at the junctions. The fence goes up very quickly, once the splitting is done. Split rail fence jobs may even take off some of that winter weight we all managed to put on; there is hard labor involved.

RAIL FENCES

Actually, rail fences need not be of only the zigzag type used by Abe Lincoln and other 18th and 19th century farmers. Felling smaller trees and using them as posts to be notched for rails allows us to form a really rustic appearing post and rail fence, with less actual labor involved. For example, each 10-foot panel will need one post, cut for the three rails, instead of eight to 10 rails for the zigzag styles. You will have to dig postholes for this type of fence, but you can rent power posthole diggers, or augers, to cut down on the work there. Log splitters just don't work on 12-foot lengths.

The main reasons for erecting either type of rail fence usually revolve around cost. Commercially produced posts and rails are expensive. A single 10-foot cedar rail will cost upwards of five dollars, and the posts are usually a dollar or two more than the rails. Small gates can cost at least $25, often well up into the $50 range for larger ones. Even pressure treated rail fences are expensive, compared to the home split models. A single 10-foot panel will almost never sell for less than $15.

The simplest cure is to build your own, as our ancestors did. The work is easier today since we have chain saws. Of course, splitting rails is still hand work and hard work. Not everything comes easy, even today.

Selecting Wood

The wood for your split rail fencing must have two qualities, one of utmost importance and the other a great aid to ease of splitting and overall construction. First, because wood finishes are not used on this type of fence, the wood must be durable in contact with the ground and the air so you will not have to replace the ground rail every year or two. The second quality is one you will pay a good bit of attention to if you wish to have any energy left after splitting your rails. Use a type of wood that splits fairly easily and in a straight line. This last need just about totally cuts out the use of woods such as sycamore, elm, hickory and gum.

The first requirement brings to mind woods such as cedar, redwood, post (yellow) locust and white oak. Most oaks are not durable in contact with the ground, so they are to be avoided for ground rail or post use. Most maples are in the same category and won't split straight anyway. Maple of most kinds is fairly easy to split, but the grain is not straight enough to work well for this kind of fence. The ropy barked post locust is a fine choice in many areas of the country, though you will want to look out for the thorns.

Locust is a resinous hardwood and lasts, almost as long as it is reputed to last, when in contact with the ground. Cedar is often easily found in small sizes in many areas. White cedar, actually *arborvitae*, is now often classed as a weed since it tends to take over pasture land. Where locust or cedar is not easily found, consider using white or yellow pine for ground rails or posts. Avoid hemlocks and firs for in-ground use as they rot very quickly. Redwood is almost never available for the cutting or for stumpage fees, so we can forget that for our present purposes. White oak will do almost as well as locust and will split well if you make it a point to select straight trees with branches starting well up on the trunk.

Locating Trees

Once you have decided the type of wood you must use, you will need to locate trees to fell for the fence. What works well and cheaply in one area may not be at all sensible in another. Here a lot of cordwood is cut, for stumpage fees, so it's possible to check with a landowner and pay him the stumpage fee for fence wood (usually pine). There are many acres of fairly straight 6 to 16-inch pines to be cut in this locale, nearly ideal for split rail fences. Present stumpage fees run about $8 or so a cord, but you would have to work out just how many trees of whatever size would make up a cord in your individual deal. Too, it's sometimes possible to clear fence rows for the trees on them. You might spend some time searching out road-widening crews at work. Today most of the wood they fell goes through big chippers and is dumped or sold very cheaply to paper makers.

Size Considerations

Once the trees are located, you have come to the time to select for size. Trees for split rails should be no larger than

18 inches at the butt. Cut into 12-foot lengths. That is about all the tree most people, in pairs, are going to be able to handle without a lot of special logging gear. In fact, 18 inchers should be split at least once right where they drop. The thicker the tree you drop, the harder it will be to get accurate splits over any length, for the more likely the tree is to have overgrown knots or other grain deformities.

The next selection, for ease of splitting, involves a bit more than size. Opt for trees with few low branches and the straightest looking trunks. None of your splits are likely to be dead straight, but a lot of extra crooks and curls just add to problems. Even easily split wood such as white pine and locust can be a real hassle if there are many knots.

Tools

Now lay out the tools you will take into the cutting site. You will need a small truck. A good chain saw is required. If you're going to be doing a lot of cutting, forget the 12 and 14-inch homeowner's models and go for a low end of the line pro model. My Homelite 360 tends to be a shoulder breaker when I'm up in a tree cutting off limbs, but for the other work I do, it is close to ideal.

Have at least three soft wedges for felling. You can either buy plastic or aluminum wedges or cut some from oak, locust or hickory. A splitting maul of at least 8 pounds is essential. You need no less than three splitting wedges, and preferably five, weighing five pounds or more each. Three wedges usually snap open any 12-foot long pine, but occasionally they will hang up. That is when the extras are handy.

Felling Trees

Felling larger trees is not a job for those with little or no experience. If you fall in this category, start with the smaller stuff until you have gained a good idea of just what forces and reactions are likely. Even a small tree—say 1 foot in diameter and 30 or so feet high—weighs as much as a ton. Once that much weight starts to go, you had better know where it is going so you can be someplace else.

General felling safety involves, first, clearing brush and detritus that is liable to trip you away from the base of the tree, and from two escape paths at 45 degree angles to the rear of your cut. Then you check to make sure the tree you're dropping won't hang up in another. You make a notch in the direction you wish the tree to fall, coming in about one-third the distance through the trunk. An accurate match of top and bottom cuts in the notch aids accuracy. You will, of course, check for branch growth on the tree, so that you'll be notching on the side with the heaviest growth, as that will be the tree's natural direction of fall. Keep all observers well out of the way, and don't fell any trees when unaccompanied children are around.

Bring the back cut in about 2 inches above the lower cut on your notch. On larger trees, you may wish to use the felling wedges to help guide the tree over. In some cases, you'll want to use them to help drive the tree over instead of cutting too far through the hinge wood. When felling trees, you must always leave enough wood to serve as a hinge, or the tree is liable to kick back strongly when it hits the ground.

Once the tree starts to go, use your escape path, getting well out of the way of any kickback. If the tree hangs up your chain saw as it starts to go, leave the saw and scat. Saws can be replaced. Most of the time a trapped saw will have little or no damage done to it anyway, beyond a possible mangled chain, handle or guide bar.

Bucking Operation

When bucking the trees into splitting lengths, after limbing, always buck from the uphill side, if any. Limb in the same manner and, whenever possible, do your limbing on the side opposite the one you stand on.

Posts for a 4-foot high fence need to be at least 6 feet long, though 7 is better, a consideration for the bucking operation. Rails for a total split rail fence should be 12 feet long, though you may get by with 11. A 12-foot rail laid in a zigzag pattern will give about an 8-foot straight line fence panel, allowing for end overhangs. Rails for post and rail fences can be 8 or 10 feet long as you desire.

Styles

We've already covered the basics of planning this sort of fence so you should, by now, have an idea of how many rails you will need to complete the job. Actually, there are really three types of fence for which the trees you're cutting will provide suitable material. Zigzag rail on rail fence requires about the greatest number of rails, but very few posts. Some corners may be braced with double posts and, of course, gates require posts. Usually the rails are either spiked to each other, or tied together at junctions using baling or fence wire in figure-eight loops. Type two of split rail fence is similar to the zigzag but is built in a straight line, with rails alternately laid one atop the other. The end of a rail from one panel, for instance, will support the end of a rail from another panel, leaving a rail's width between rails, just as in zigzag fencing. Fewer rails are required because of the straight line of the fence, not the rail-on-rail erection. Such a fence is supported by posts at each panel junction, usually with the posts tied together at the top in some manner, either with wire, or with a board set across and nailed to the tops of both posts.

The third style of rail fence is similar to commercial post and rail fences, though rougher in finish. The posts are bored to take the cut down ends of the split rails, with the bore holes being cut large enough to accept the ends of two rails, one from each side. This fence need not be any more roughly finished than the commercial versions, though selecting small, round trees and peeling them adds to the work needed. Such a modification, though, might well suit those living in suburban areas where the neighbors are likely to get upset if something appears too rustic. Post and rail fencing requires a bit more work per post, but fewer rails are needed, with the actual number being determined by the rails per panel you decide to incorporate in your fence. At a minimum, I would look for two rails in fences not over 3½ feet high, while anything over that height should have at least three rails. Five-foot high fences should at least make the builder consider adding a fourth rail.

Splitting

Once the fence design is determined, you will have a good idea of the number of rails needed as well as posts, if any. Start by felling a few less trees than you expect to need. You may be surprised at the number of rails to come from one tree.

Start the split by swinging the splitting hammer, wedge end, into the end of the log. This gives a slot for driving the first wedge. Drive that first wedge into the end of the log until a split extends about 2 feet along. Insert the second wedge into the split and drive it home. Depending on the wood used, the size of the log, the grain and so on, two wedges should do for most splits up to about 10 feet. A third will be needed for 12-foot long logs, and possibly a fourth and fifth for longer, thicker or denser logs. Keep going until the log splits in half.

From this point, the number of splits needed will depend on the use you have for the wood (posts or rails), the size you wish the pieces to be. Generally, a rail should be a triangle or rectangle about 4 to 5 inches across its thickest parts. Variations of several inches are probable, but try to hold them to the large side to prevent weakness of the rails. Posts are made a bit thicker. If the more formal post and rail fence is made, the posts should be at least twice the thickness of the rails, before the rails are cut down to fit the post slots. This prevents weakening of the posts when boring the slots with your chain saw. Trimming down rail ends is a good idea, but should not be carried to extremes unless you wish the rail to snap off near the post the first or second time it gets a good bump.

Gate posts should be longer and thicker than line posts, as should end posts. The end post must support rails coming in at an angle, while the gate post suffers from the stresses of gate weight (always heavier than a few motionless rails), and the opening and closing of the gate.

Digging Postholes

Once the rails are cut and laid out along the fence line, it is time to dig the postholes. When building this sort of fence,

I find it best not to dig postholes in advance of laying out the materials (in the two styles where postholes are needed). Size variations caused by splitting, and by possible missed long length measurements in the woods, can force the postholes to be switched around, a bit of extra work that almost no one will appreciate. Using a hand posthole digger is the cheapest way to do the work, and is fine if you're only putting in a few sections of fence. For larger fencing jobs, try to rent a posthole auger. While this adds to the cost, it will surely cut down on time spent digging (and energy).

Postholes are best dug so that at least one-third the length of the post is in the ground, and should be about ½ foot deeper than the portion to be buried. This extra 6 inches of hole should be filled with gravel or small rocks to allow for water drainage below the surface. Gate posts need to sink down a foot or so more than do fence posts, while corner posts should be set in 6 inches more.

Concrete or other forms of bracing, as well as preservatives, can be applied before erection if you desire. Gates for this rustic form of fencing will be covered later. See Table 7-1.

For your rails, look for a wood with good durability in contact with air. The rating should be no less than fair, with good or higher preferred. For posts, select a wood with moderate or higher durability in contact with the ground. If you can tie all that in with woods having good or great splitting ease, you should end up erecting a long lasting fence with the least possible effort.

WOOD FENCES

There are many different and correct ways to set poles for wood fences and many variations on the theme of fillers for the panels, starting from the basic board and moving on to a wide array of designs before slipping back to rails. All of the good techniques have in common sturdiness and durability, whether the section being put in is board or otherwise.

The post is the heart of any fence design. The best boards or rails are of no use if the proper size and wood type posts are not set to the correct depth, using the procedures

Table 7-1. Some Facts on Various Types of Woods.

WOOD DURABILITY DURABILITY IN CONTACT WITH:			
WOOD TYPE	AIR	GROUND	SPLITTING EASE
Arborvitae	very high	very high	great
Ash	fair	poor	good
Birch	fair	poor	moderate
Cedar, red	very high	very high	great
Cedar, white	very high	very high	great
Fir, Douglas	good	moderate	good
Fir, white	good	poor	good
Hemlock	fair	poor	good
Locust	very high	very high	good
Maple	fair	poor	good
Oak, red	good	poor	good
Oak, white	high	moderate	good
Pine, sugar	high	moderate	good
Pine, white	high	moderate	great
Poplar	fair	poor	great
Redwood	very high	very high	great
Spruce	fair	low	good.

most likely to give long lasting results. Because pressure treated woods are becoming so popular and are generally reasonable in cost as well as exceptionally durable, it is time to take a longer look at the processes and chemicals involved in making the material so suitable to outdoor use.

Applying Preservatives

As a start, let's look at three methods of applying preservatives to fence material (in this case, dry pine). Assume your fence will be 80 feet long, with 4 by 4 posts and 1 by 6 boards 6 feet long. Simply brushing on preservative allows about one-twentieth the amount to soak in as does pressure treatment, while a homemade dip vat will give treatment to a depth of, possibly, ¼ inch, using a bit more than one-fifth as much as does pressure application.

It may not seem to make much difference in the life of the wood on first thought, but with a protection depth maximum of ¼ inch or so, your fence is going to soon have rot problems. Any wood exposed to weather will eventually check and crack to a depth greater than ¼ inch. When that happens to brush or dip treated wood, rot soon sets in.

Pressure treatment drives the chemicals right to the sapwood. In the case of our Wolmanized Wood example, chromated *copper arsenate* is used to preserve the wood, with 0.25 pounds of chemicals per cubic foot used for wood not in contact with the ground. Wood coming in contact with the ground is more heavily treated, with 0.4 pounds per cubic foot (Fig. 7-1).

Characteristically, woods treated in this manner are a light to medium shade of green. The chemicals, once in the wood and dried, do not leach out and are not a hazard. The two major causes of wood rot are fungi and insects, especially termites. *Fungus* is a plant with a liking for wood fibers; fungi grow very well in the presence of moisture. Termites like to chomp on wood's cellulose fibers, and may do their work either above ground or below. They work mostly below ground in temperate climates. Wood to be treated is placed in a pressure chamber. The chemicals are forced deep into the fibers, making the wood inedible to both fungi and termites.

The treatment is so effective that wood in use for four decades shows no failures. There is now some use of pressure treated woods for foundations in frame homes. To receive approvals from banks and the various government agencies who get involved in home building today, such materials must be able to prove a good degree of durability. It is reasonably safe to assume a properly treated wood fence or

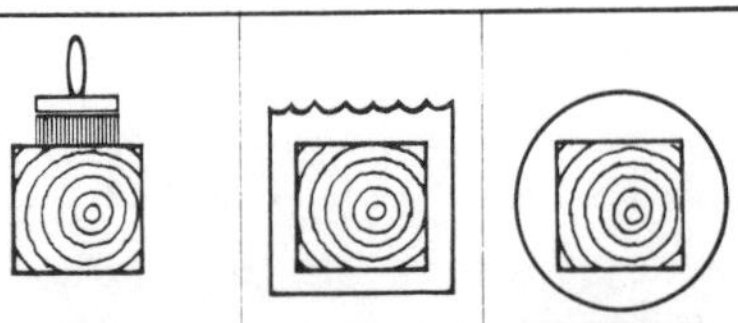

Methods of Treating Wood and Their Effectiveness in Ground Contact Applications	Brush Treatment	Dip Treatment	Pressure Treatment
Protection	Surface with Slight Penetration	1/10" to 1/8" Penetration	Sapwood Treated
Average amount solution required to treat 80-foot fence, made from 4 x 4 posts and 1" x 6" x 6' boards	6 Gal.	23 Gal.	120 Gal.
Average added years service over untreated wood in ground contact	1 to 3 Years	5 to 10 Years	Lifetime Protection

*Untreated wood typically lasts 2 to 5 years. Quantities based on treating dry pine.

Fig. 7-1. Chemical retention under different wood treatments.

other structure will come quite close to living up to the claims made for it.

Home dip treatments do not provide the same degree of protection, though dip and soak is a much better method than is simple brush-on treatment. Dip treatments will use about 23 gallons of preservative for our fence example. This is nearly four times as much as can be applied by brush, though less than one-fifth the 120 gallons the wood absorbs under pressure.

According to Koppers Company, life expectancy for a brush treated fence does not exceed that of untreated wood by very much, ranging from one to three years, while dip treatment will give a five to 10-year life. Much depends on the type of wood used, though, and the methods of installation.

Wood Types

Treated woods are most commonly pines and firs simply because they are, throughout almost all the United States and Canada, the most readily available. When wood is to be pressure treated for use in fences or in other applications, the ease of availability and the ease of workability are paramount. When untreated wood is to be used for fences, especially for posts, the more common pines and firs are among the fastest to deteriorate. A much more careful selection of material, with both eyes aimed at durability in contact with the ground, is essential to a long lasting job. Some of the woods recommended for such use are hard to work with. *Locust* posts, with a natural, untreated life of about 10 to 15 years, are much like cast iron once they are seasoned. Predrilling is best. White oak, not for use as posts but excellent for boards, is easier to nail, as far as driving goes, but it has a bad tendency to split when nailed. It is also best predrilled. Oak, too, has a very bad tendency to warp and crack as it dries. Anyone buying locally cut material to use in fencing is well advised to stack the materials properly to dry, and then to allow several months to pass before actual use.

Redwood and cedar (heartwoods) are among the most durable of all untreated woods. Actually cypress is about the only other that comes close, and it is expensive and hard to locate in many areas. Both cedar and redwood have the ease of workability of the pines and firs. Some pines, such as yellow, are a bit harder to work than others and will provide you with a true lifetime fence if carefully installed.

The only unfortunate features of the cedars and redwood come with availability and price. In most areas of the country either wood can be easily obtained most of the time, but there are times of shortages. At those times the already high prices rise even more. Some areas of the country see no shortages and much lower prices. My brother informs me that he found, on moving to San Diego, that heart redwood there costs little more, if any, than does pine and fir in New York. I assume transport is the main reason. With the rising cost of fuel, the cost of moving West Coast materials to the East Coast has more than doubled in a very short period of time.

Naturally, costs of other woods will vary a lot, too, depending on the distance from point of origin to user. One of the reasons pressure treated woods remain relatively low in price is simply because the processor has to pay for shipping on just the chemicals. The wood can be cut, milled and treated from locally available species of trees. Again, local prices for labor and fuel will have a lot to do with the final price. Untreated rough sawn pine in Sullivan County, New York, is more than double the price of the same wood in Bedford County, Virginia.

When planning your fence, all such problems of durability and price must be kept in mind if the job is to be a good and lasting one. There seems little, if any, point to doing a shoddy fencing job, as even that will cost a fair amount of money and require a lot of time and labor. A bit more money, and not much more time and effort, will add up to a fine looking, long lived fence (Figs. 7-2 through 7-13).

FENCE TOOLS

Tools for most styles of fencing are not very exotic; nor are they really hard to use. Still, most of us start out quite unfamiliar with the few tools needed to run a fence line before

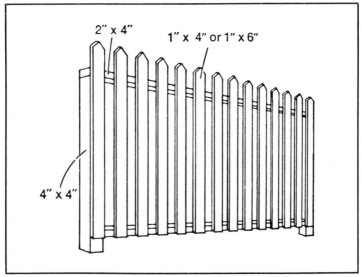

Fig. 7-2. Picket fence.

erecting the fence, or at least with their use in such situations. There are a few shortcuts to aid speed when two or more people are working, and when just one person is doing the setting, tamping, cutting and nailing. Such familiarity can be gained as we go along, but a fair knowledge at the outset

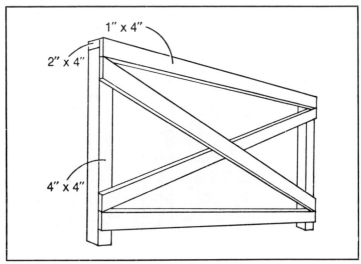

Fig. 7-3. Post and rail fence.

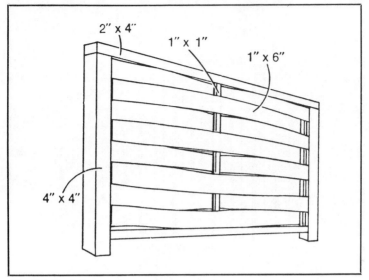

Fig. 7-4. Basketweave fence.

can add to both speed and overall fence quality and appearance.

Masons's cord is a primary tool, and one for which no other type of twine is quite as suitable. It is cotton and fairly

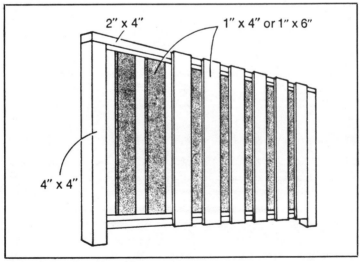

Fig. 7-5. Board and board fence.

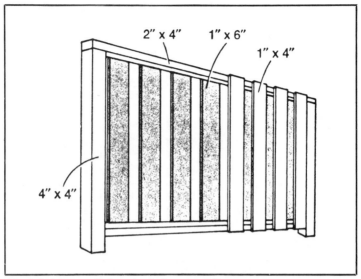

Fig. 7-6. A fence with boards of alternate widths.

smooth surfaced. The few extra cents it costs over and above other less strong and smooth cords is a sensible expenditure. You can then make sure the cord is tight, firm and won't stretch out, letting the posts push out of line or the line level

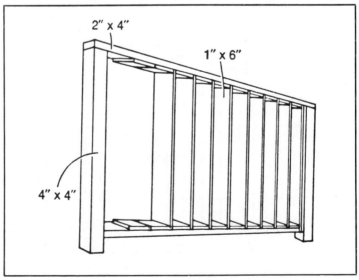

Fig. 7-7. Louver fence.

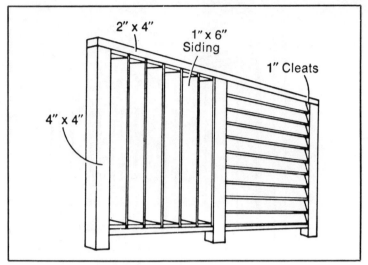

Fig. 7-8. Fence with alternate louvers.

sag and drop its reading. Furry twines, no matter how strong, should never be used.

Levels

Line levels are nothing more than simple levels with hooks to attach to the mason's cord. For areas where the top

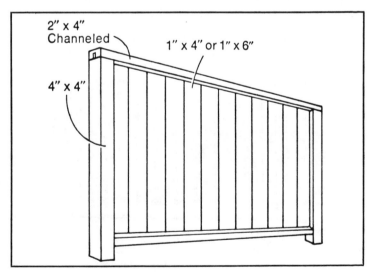

Fig. 7-9. Channel panel fence.

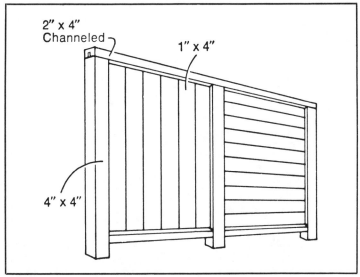

Fig. 7-10. A fence with vertical and horizontal panels.

rail or board must be level, these are essential (most fences will not have level rails or posts or boards, though). For sites where level boards would look decidedly odd, they can be dispensed with.

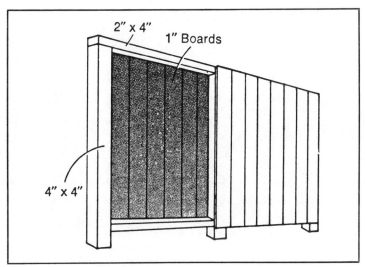

Fig. 7-11. A fence with alternate panels.

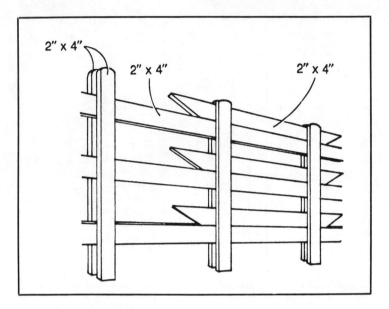

Fig. 7-12. Shaped ends fence.

We are all familiar with the basic bubble style levels. For most larger fence jobs two sizes are exceptionally handy, the 2-foot size for getting in restricted areas and the 2-foot size for getting in restricted areas and the 4-foot model for

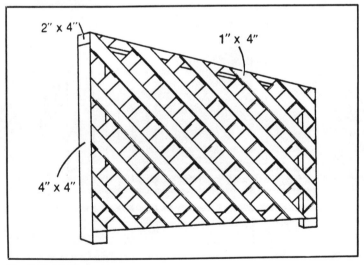

Fig. 7-13. Trellis fence.

greatest accuracy. In no case is a cheap level a savings. Their accuracy is not dependable from the outset, and those few that are accurate at the start will lose accuracy with only mild knocks and drops. In my own case, the two levels, a Stanley 24-inch aluminum 100 Plus and a PowerKraft (Montgomery Ward) 84-3878 mahogany 48-incher, more than serve well. Both are top quality and have survived bounces and jounces without a loss of accuracy. While the wood level is actually a mason's model, it serves very well for other uses. Wood tends to expand and contract less does metal with temperature changes.

Chain Saws

Saws can be more of a problem when the fence is located some distance from a power source. My primary wood slicing tool is a Craftsman 7 ¼-inch circular saw with two horsepower rating, but beyond 50 feet from the house it is not too useful. Extension cords must increase in size as distance grows, which can add greatly to the expense for such a cord. Many fence posts are 4 inches or more in thickness, forcing a double cut with a small circular saw. In such cases, boards should probably be cut to fit, after the posts are installed and careful measurements taken, with the circular saw at the power site and then carted to the erection site. Posts can be cut to fit with a chain saw.

A chain saw is primarily a rough cutting tool, and certain precautions are needed to get better than average accuracy. First, have the chain sharpened by machine. The machine will do a better job of sharpening both sets of teeth to the same degree and at the same angle. This keeps the saw from pulling left or right, which can ruin an otherwise good looking job. Keep an extra chain on hand. Once the first chain begins to drop off its finely sharpened edge, chains should be changed. Finally, keep a close eye on chain adjustment as a loose chain causes inaccuracy in the cut and can be slung off too easily, marring the surface of the wood.

Use the smallest possible bar on your chain saw as the smaller bars are generally a bit easier to guide with accuracy. My Homelite 360 is equipped with a short 16-inch bar for such work, as well as limbing and bucking small firewood logs.

Tape Measure and Hammers

A good tape measure is also an essential tool. Nothing less than 25 feet is of much use for fence work (unless you're putting up a single panel). The Stanley PowerLock, which has a rather stiff first 7 feet so one person can make long measurements horizontally, is a fine tool.

Hammers are needed even for unnailed fences. Those post and rail fences with precut holes and rail ends will often be a very tight fit so that some sort of smooth faced hammer is essential to driving the rails all the way into the posts. I use a 3 pound Craftsman engineer's hammer for such work. Nailing hammers come in a wide variety of styles, weights and sizes. Too many people attempt to do every job with a single 16-ounce claw hammer. For most nailing jobs, that may well be fine. For fence nailing, framing and other heavy jobs, a heavier hammer actually saves effort. For most people, something on the order of a 20-ounce framing hammer would be good. For people more accustomed to nailing in heavy material, I would recommend at least a 22-ouncer or even a 28-ounce one.

Handsaws

Handsaws for fine cuts are great things to have. Too many people today try to depend totally on power saws, when there would actually be less effort required to use a good eight or 10 point (to the inch) crosscut saw for smooth finish cuts. There is no carting of a dozen pounds of power saw and 50 feet of extension cord and no changing blades. Just mark, cut and nail. Good miter boxes are also of exceptional value when you're installing board fence with compound or other miter cuts. These tend to be expensive (some run well up over $125) but can often be rented, which is handy as you will probably often need a capacity for boards 6 inches and maybe even a bit more in width.

Posthole Diggers and Tamping Bars

Posthole diggers are necessary for permanent fences and come in three styles known as "no pain," "moderate ache" and "ouch." In other words, you can get a posthole auger that works off a tractor's power takeoff, one that is held by one or two operators and has its own motor, or you can get a hand posthole digger. The variation in price is very wide, with good hand posthole diggers selling for not much more than $15 and good tractor power takeoff models going for well over five hundred. The motorized mid-sizes are usually to be found in larger rental companies' stores.

Tamping bars are another type of tool that may not be very familiar to most people. It is simply a steel or iron bar with a semi-bladed end and a blunt end. The tool is used to tamp down dirt around fence poles.

POST SETTING

Probably the single most important job in assuring that your fence will last as long as possible is the work done in setting your posts. Siting the postholes has already been covered, but some study of the actual sites may save later problems. Those holes set in low-lying areas likely to become flooded are the ones where troubles are probable. Constant soaking is not good for even treated wood. Ditching is one possibility for curing poor drainage, but aesthetically and practically it just isn't always possible. The post just has to stay wet as long as the ground stays wet. In other cases, where the ground is clayey and holds water too well, adding to the gravel in the bottom of the posthole can help solve such problems.

During the design phases of your fence projects, you will need to look at posthole depths as related to post lengths. Posts must increase in size as fence height grows, and the amount of post buried in the ground also increases in length. Paneled fences, especially those designed as windbreaks with solid or almost solid filler materials, need larger posts, buried more deeply than do most other types of fence. In general, one-third of the post length should be inserted in the posthole, and the posthole is best made no less than twice the diameter of the post. This oversize hole allows movement for positioning and also makes tamping any earth fill a lot easier. Too, it increases the capacity for concrete around the post should you be setting your posts that way, thus making for a more solid fence. Dig postholes to the corrent depth—mark a hand posthole digger with a piece of tape at the correct distance up one handle so you won't have to measure the depth of each hole as you dig—and tamp in at least 6 inches of gravel or broken rock in the bottom. If the ground is exceptionally damp, tamp in a foot or more of gravel. Make sure you allow for the lost depth when digging the posthole (Fig. 7-14).

Set the post in the hole and tack on two braces before leveling or plumbing. Pour concrete if that's being used and allow it to set before completing the fill job. Concrete should set at least 24 hours before the final dirt fill is tamped on top of it. Three days is actually a better way to get a good cure, but it is often too much time if you are in any kind of a rush.

End posts are to be about 25 percent larger than line posts. Gate posts should be that large, or larger, depending on the size and weight of the gate to be hung. Even if the rest of the fence line is set in tamped earth, end posts and gate posts should be set in concrete to prevent stress wobbles over the years. For fences over 3½ feet high, set end posts 6 inches deeper than line posts and gate posts from 6 to 12 inches deeper. Don't forget to get longer posts to allow for the extra depth (Fig. 7-15). Before filling, each post should be plumbed as closely to dead vertical as possible.

LAYING OUT BOARD FENCES

For board fences, use either galvanized or aluminum nails so that staining won't be a problem. The nails should be three times the length of the board being nailed to the post. In other words, nine or 10 penny nails for 1-inch boards, 20 penny nails for 2-inch boards and so on.

The simplest way to lay out a board fence and keep the intervals between boards identical is to measure and mark the top board elevation along each post (this must be done

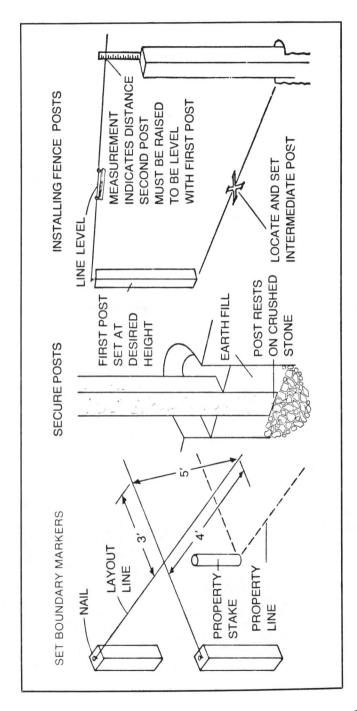

INSTALLING FENCE POSTS

LINE LEVEL

MEASUREMENT INDICATES DISTANCE SECOND POST MUST BE RAISED TO BE LEVEL WITH FIRST POST

LOCATE AND SET INTERMEDIATE POST

SECURE POSTS

FIRST POST SET AT DESIRED HEIGHT

EARTH FILL

POST RESTS ON CRUSHED STONE

SET BOUNDARY MARKERS

NAIL

LAYOUT LINE

3'

5'

4'

PROPERTY STAKE

PROPERTY LINE

Fig. 7-14. Proper methods for spotting, securing and installing fence posts.

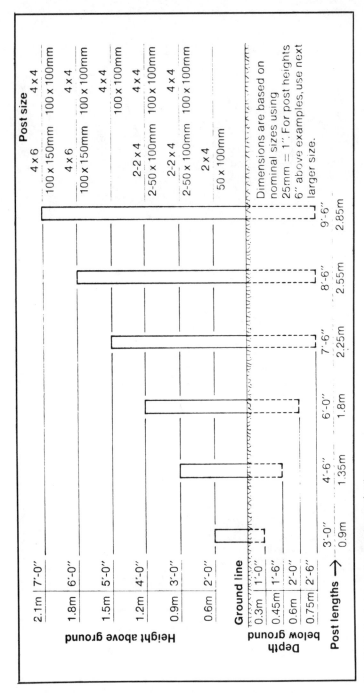

Fig. 7-15. Post size and embedment depths.

250

individually). Then nail up each top board. Do the first panel according to measurements taken on the posts, as this is the place to make any changes. Now, take a straight board and mark the intervals, and do the same with a second such board. With two people working along the fence, it is now a simple matter to hold each end of the board being nailed against the correct mark on this "story" board, and nail it in place. If you're working alone, a bit more complex work is required to assure accuracy.

Make two triangles with at least a 3-foot leg on the ground for support. On the vertical leg of the triangle, to face the post, mark the intervals. Nail a section of 2 by 4 along the bottom line of the board position. These braces are 6 to 12 inches inside the posts. The boards are then set on the 2 by 4's and the whole works are moved close up against the posts where the boards are now automatically positioned for nailing. Making the triangle braces is a bit of work, but it saves putting a single nail in one board end, running to the other and putting in a single nail, then returning to the first end, finishing the nailing, and going to the final end and finishing. If two nails are placed in the first end, the board will probably be out of line. Using a single nail may require some nail pulling and board rearrangement to get each one at exactly the right height. It is much simpler to make and use the braces.

These techniques will give you a basic board fence from lumber you cut yourself. There are other ways to make board fences, though the post setting remains the same. Essentially, using fence brackets simplifies this sort of fence even more. Teco produces a fence bracket that is simply nailed to the post, one at the end of each board. The boards are then inserted in the brackets and either nailed or left loose as you wish. Nails are supplied with the brackets. The brackets do two things. First, the board fence becomes a simple one-man job. Second, the boards become easily replaceable items should they be damaged or warped too badly. Just nail each bracket at its appropriate height, insert and nail the boards and that's it. The brackets and the nails are galvanized (Fig. 7-16).

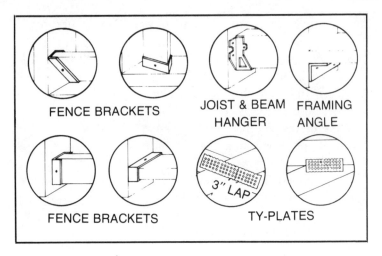

Fig. 7-16. Galvanized metal fence brackets make the job easier and allow more freedom of design.

ERECTING POST AND RAIL FENCES

Post and rail fences are even easier to erect than are board fences, but there is one technique that can save a great deal of time and aggravation. Simply do not tamp or finish fill around the posts until the rails are inserted in their holes. Trying to get rails some 8 inches longer than the distance between posts into their holes after the fence has been set in concrete or solidly tamped in place is a fine way to go crazy. Get a rough plumb on the posts, brace them, insert the posts, replumb to a finer degree and fill, tamp and go on about your business. It is possible to replace broken rails, but usually you'll need to cut the rails so that little more than 2 inches is left to be inserted in each rail hole in the posts. This will allow the rail to move back into one hole far enough to clear the other. Cut carefully so that the pushing back is a real forcing back. If such replacements are made, either drill a hole through the post, into the rail and insert a dowel, or drive a nail through the two so the rail can't be easily jarred loose.

Any cut ends of pressure treated or otherwise treated wood should be retreated. Obviously, we're not going to have the facilities to pressure treat wood at home. It is by far the best to buy such material as close to the actual sizes needed so little, or no, cutting is needed. When cuts are made, brush on several coats of preservative as recommended by the supplier of your brand of wood, or dip the ends and leave them soaking in dry weather for at least 24 hours for longest lasting results.

As we go along, we'll move beyond the simple board and post and rail fences. The above procedures, combined with your choice of finishes (pressure treated wood, redwood and cedar do not have to be otherwise finished unless you wish to) will provide a good, basic fence system that will last a long time.

Pressure treated wood, redwood and cedar weather to a gray color as time passes. Painting such woods is felt by many to detract from overall appearance, but the biggest drawback seems to me to be the need for repainting every few years. Why add to the work needed when such fencing will have a fine natural look if left as is, and will not have its durability affected at all? See Figs. 7-17 and 7-18.

EQUINE FENCING

With the many special purposes fences serve in today's world, it is virtually impossible to cover them all. Still, there are several important uses that are adaptable to the needs of many people. With the number of horses in the United States rapidly approaching 10 million, and the number of people climbing almost as steadily, the need for *equine fencing* is great. Too many horses, though, are confined by fence that is more likely to do a great deal of harm than to simply prevent problems. The reasons for such fences are simple—economy and a lack of knowledge about the basics of equine psychology.

By nature, almost all horses want to roam. Should your horse amble over into your neighbor's prized vegetable or flower garden, into the path of a speeding car, onto a school playground, into an open feed shed, or any of a dozen other areas, the price of horse ownership can take a quantum leap almost immediately. Fences and horses go together in the modern world, to the point where well-built fences are an

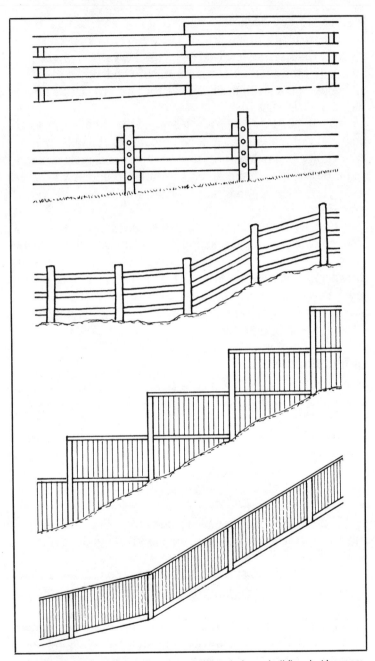

Fig. 7-17. Hillsides can present some problems in fence building, but here are five good ways to solve them.

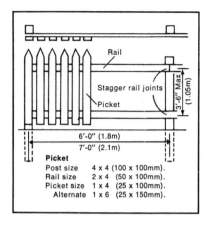

Fig. 7-18. The basic picket fence.

Picket
Post size	4 x 4 (100 x 100mm).
Rail size	2 x 4 (50 x 100mm).
Picket size	1 x 4 (25 x 100mm).
Alternate	1 x 6 (25 x 150mm).

essential of equine care, but one that receives far too little attention in the areas of styles, installation and care. Too often, there is not thought to see if wire needs restretching, a board needs replacing or a coat of whitewash is needed for pasture fences.

Because horse fencing has risen in price dramatically in recent years, the wallet is the deciding factor in fence design and construction, sometimes with tragic later consequences. Real fence costs must include the possible damage to the horse, the possible damage to other things and the need for care and replacement of the fence.

Equine fences serve to segregate mares and stallions, keep horses off too lush spring pastures and to keep foals out of pasture herds. Of course, protection in one form or another, either for the horse or for the general public, is of primary importance. Yet many fences of totally unsuitable materials present danger instead of protecting.

Barbed Wire

Today, *barbed wire* is still among the cheapest forms of fencing to be found. Based on the original outlay, it may look like the solution to keeping horses. It isn't. Barbed wire is probably the single worst material to use for fencing in horses.

While original costs for barbed wire may be as little as one-tenth that of board fencing, the continuing cost for valuable and loved animals is exceptionally high: foot-long chest cuts and bone deep hock slices. Horses hung up in barbed wire have a very strong tendency to struggle, entangling themselves even more and cutting themselves more deeply.

Barbed wire is particularly bad when used to fence the hot-blooded breeds such as Arabians and Thoroughbreds. Such animals will almost always panic when trapped, slicing themselves terribly in the struggle to get free. Range bred cold-blooded horses are also prone to panic when trapped, but they may sometimes stand for a longer time. I've seen an Appaloosa stallion that stood for well over an hour after becoming entangled while trying to leap a barbed wire fence to get to a mare. Still, no horse is going to stand forever, so that only luck can prevent major cuts, sometimes even death and, too often, crippling injury.

The more suitable types of horse fencing are not all that many. Basic requirements for equine fencing include strength; a certain degree of give, so a horse hitting the material won't feel as if it has run into a stone wall; durability; and expense somewhere close to within reason.

Stone and masonry walls fail on flexibility and expense. Too solid metal fencing is also to be avoided. Chain link fence too often is not only too solid but too expensive.

Mesh Fencing

Other types of *mesh fence* materials, sold as general farm or stock fencing, suffer from a variety of problems. Material weakness is one. Much farm fencing is down around 14 or even 18 gauge. Good horse fencing should be no lighter than about 12 ½ gauge. Mesh openings of most stock fencing is not correct for horses, either. Much fencing sold has mesh openings of 6 inches or more, while a good equine fence will have openings no more than 5 inches in the largest direction, with the best sizes being 4 inches and less. Rearing horses can too easily catch a hoof in the large openings, with resulting torn muscles or broken bones.

Special mesh fencing for horses has been developed and is probably the best and most easily erected choice for those who can afford the price. As with all else, the price is going to vary with distance shipped, the cost of posts in an area and the cost of installation. *Diamond mesh* is among the best known styles and provides about equal strength to four-board fence, with more give should a horse hit it running at a good clip. The diamond mesh pattern is so tight it is almost impossible for a horse to get hung up in the material. It is tight enough to keep children and small animals out of paddock areas where they might cause or receive damage. Diamond mesh fencing has been in use some 35 or more years, and the present versions are galvanized to keep down rust problems. Two grades are produced, one using 12 ½ gauge wire and the other 14 gauge. The lighter gauge wire is strong enough for most use since the wires are so closely wound. It comes in 165-foot rolls, either 50 or 58 inches in height (Fig. 7-19).

All wire fencing for horses should be installed with some addition to make it more visible, and diamond mesh is no exception. In most cases, the added portion takes the part of a 1 by 6-inch board along the top of the fence. This board is probably best made of pine, though many people do use oak. Unfortunately, when oak breaks it has a great tendency to form long spear-like projections which could impale a horse. Pine is more likely to snap off in just a ragged edge. While a breaking pine board might cut and scrape your horse, the odds on its getting impaled are greatly reduced.

Rubber-Nylon Fencing

Another form of flexible and strong horse fencing is called rubber-nylon. This material is cut from wider strips of conveyor belt material and then stapled to fence posts, usually in four strips, much as would be done with a board fence. It has great strength and exceptional give, so that injury chances are cut way down. Too, it is fairly economical and quite durable if installed correctly.

Rubber-nylon fencing does require one step, or one of several steps, to prevent possible problems with horses that are cribbers. Cribbers, or stump suckers, are horses with a habit of chewing or sucking wood or other fence or stable materials. The buildup of nylon threads in the large colon of a horse could eventually lead to some rather nasty difficulties, so the use of a non-toxic latex coating on the cut edges of the

Fig. 7-19. Special mesh fencing for horses is always capped with a board to provide better visibility if the animal is startled.

fencing is a good idea. If you can't locate a non-toxic coating, then take a propane torch and go around the edges. This is much like sealing the ends of nylon rope, as you just heat until the strands shrivel. If neither method is used, then you will need to keep up a regular inspection and trimming program if you even suspect there's a cribber now in your pasture.

Electric Fencing

Electric fencing for horses is rather common these days. It serves best as a supplement to other types of fencing. As an example, a fenced paddock where children might reach through the main fence can be made safer by running an electric fence strand about 3 feet inside the main fence. For older, more stable horses, a single strand electric fence will often serve to keep things in place, though even the best natured horse may get frightened through the fence occasionally. Electric fence uses a very light wire (about 18 or 19 gauge most times), so that even running three or four strands doesn't provide much actual strength. Frisky or otherwise inattentive horses can go right through the wire before the shock has time to take effect. I used electric fence for months, all by itself, to hold a horse, but that was a 16-year-old gelding in rather poor shape.

For the settled horse, though, electric fence can be quite economical. A good fence charger costs from $30 to $60, while a half mile or so of wire will cost under $10. Insulators are reasonable in cost, and some types of fence post don't even require them. The posts can be driven and the wire run around a good sized pasture in just a couple of hours. Marking out temporary pasture is a good use for electric fence. If fiber glass or metal fence posts are used, you must attach some protective device to the top to keep the horse from hurting itself should it rear and come down on the post. A short chunk of 2 by 4 will serve if, with fiber glass T-shaped posts, you drill a 9/16-inch hole about halfway through the 2 by 4 and then force it down on top of the post. The large metal posts can be capped with the same material, but will need a 1-inch hole or so. Electric fence also makes a fine temporary fence when you're tearing out sections of fence for replacement.

As with all wire fences, you must provide some extra visibility. Either hand pie plates, pieces of cloth or other markers at 6 or 8-foot intervals.

The selection of an electric *fence charger* is a fairly simple job, though the choice is wide. You can get a 110 volt powered unit in a dozen different styles, or a battery powered unit for use where no electricity is readily available. Some will fence a 20-mile or longer perimeter if properly installed. One type of fence charger should be avoided—the *weedburner*. These things produce a surge shock of long duration and could, if conditions are not good, badly shock or kill a horse. In any case, the long duration shock is meant to keep weeds away from the fence line and could, in dry weather, be the cause of brush fires.

Electric fence is right up there at the top as far as ease of installation goes. First, drive a grounding rod into the ground near the spot where your wires will come outdoors from the charger. Follow the charger's manufacturer's directions as to length and type of ground rod. Place the posts with insulators, where needed, about 30 to 32 inches from the ground (about breast level on your horse). Place a stick through the center of the wire reel and run it from post to post. Connect the gate insulator on the same side of the fence as the line from the charger, which serves to cut off power to the fence when you open the gate. If you want the rest of the fence to stay live when the gate is open, put the gate insulator on the opposite side. Place or hang the charger in a dry sheltered area and ground it. Then run the power line and plug in the charger.

Wood Fencing

Wood fence for horses is more variable than other types. It is pretty much up to you as to what pattern you use in the building. Simple four-board fence is exceptionally popular and relatively easy to erect, but the configurations and designs are nearly endless. Post and rail—a minimum of three rails—is popular and widely used, though there may be more chance of a horse hanging a leg in such a fence design.

As with any wood fencing, you must take a check of locally available materials to determine the most economical in relation to the uses. There are, too, some changes that can be easily made in constructing equine board fencing that will provide greater safety and durability.

The first change over regular board fencing is a simple alternating of boards. Make sure no more than two boards end on any one post. This means using 16-foot long boards when post distances are 8 feet (about the maximum for good strength around horses). Also, I would heartily recommend the use of annular or screw shank galvanized nails for greatest holding power. For a final touch on this type of fence, run a nailer board up the board side of the fence, using two 12 or 14 penny annular shank nails every 10 inches or so. The board end side of the fence should be placed in the direction of any expected impact.

Impact can be great when a full-sized light horse even glances off a fence. After all, many so-called light horses actually weigh up to 1,300 pounds, and something that size at

30 or so miles per hour generates a fair amount of force. Thus, board fence is often built with offset posts to help in those areas where impact could come from either side. The posts are set to one side and then the other of your mason's line layout, with the boards actually being on the center line. Then nailer boards are put in place on those boards nailed on opposite sides of the posts.

Safety Measures

Equine fencing requires a few other cares not really essential to good decorative fencing jobs. First, all dropped nails and other fragments *must* be picked up since a horse could too easily ingest one while grazing. Second, any coating, such as paint, must be evaluated for toxicity. Again, the cribbing horse is the problem. A lead-based paint, or a paint with some other leachable toxic element, could cause problems of a severe nature. Finally, and especially in areas where foals may be kept, it is not a good idea to leave a great deal of distance between the bottom board, or wire, and the ground. Keeping a bottom board within 4 inches of the ground is probably best. Most fences have their bottoms well above this level to make trimming the grass underneath an easy chore, but equine fencing must look to a more important problem. A horse that lies down and gets a leg caught is cast and, in such a condition, can panic and do itself a great deal of harm. Foals are more likely to become cast and to panic. Keep the fence down where it is difficult if not impossible for a hoof to slip underneath (Figs. 7-20 through 7-23).

We have got the horses penned and other types of board fence up and ready. But there is no way in or out. We will need gates.

TYPES OF GATES

Good gates are essential to a strong fence and can be of any style, though the most attractive are those that match the fence style. Of course, for residential fences gates are easily bought in the same style as fencing. Farm gates are another matter, especially if you're doing all the work yourself, from cutting the logs to splitting them and so on.

Gate posts are at least 25 percent larger than regular line posts and are set more deeply. Pintles are screwed into the gate post and the hinges hung on those. If you've bought one of the metal farm gates, the pintles are supplied. They are of a simple type—just an L-shaped bar with one end threaded. In fact, most farm gates use something close to this form of hinging as it tends to be simple and sturdy.

Farm gates should never be less than 10 feet wide, and 12 feet is better. All gates should be placed so that any equipment brought through has ample room to turn on the other side of the gate.

Pole gates for rail fences can be made easily by setting double poles in the fence line at each side of the gate opening. These poles have shorter pole sections run from one to the other and spiked in place. Poles, at least 2 feet wider than the gate opening, are slid over these crosspieces and the opening is closed. While such a gate is a bit time consuming to open for vehicles, they are cheap, easy to make, and allow you to just drop the top pole or two and step over the rest if a person is going through.

Barbed wire fences usually use the commercially made metal gates, but occasionally what is known as a *Texas gate* will be inserted. A Texas gate is nothing more than a section

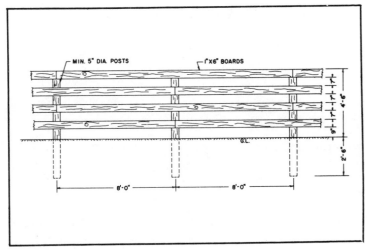

Fig. 7-20. A four-board fence for horses.

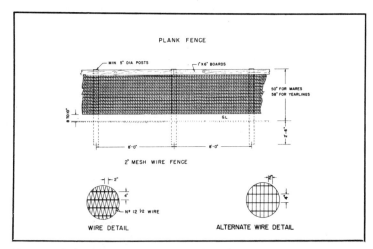

Fig. 7-21. Another view of a mesh fence for horses.

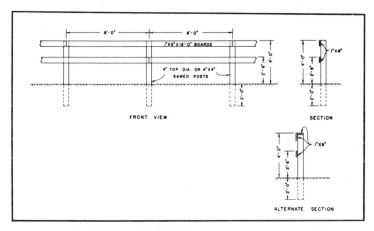

Fig. 7-22. Lightweight board fence for horses.

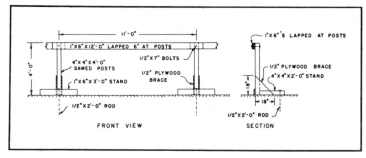

Fig. 7-23. A movable fence.

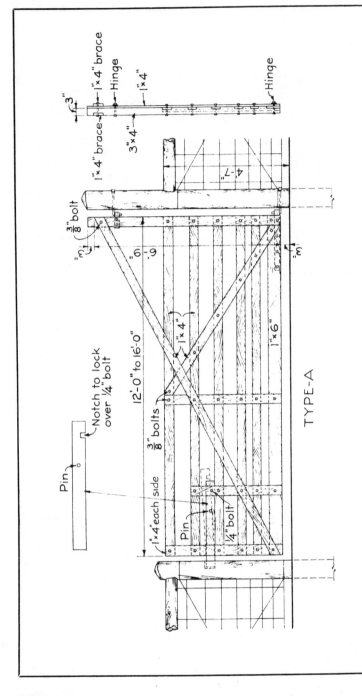

TYPE-A

3" bolt

1"×4" brace
Hinge
1"×4"

1"×4" brace
3"
3"×4"
Hinge

4'-7"

6'-9"

3"
3"

12'-0" to 16'-0"

Notch to lock
over ¼" bolt

1"×4"

Pin

1"×6"

3/8" bolts

1"×4" each side

Pin

¼" bolt

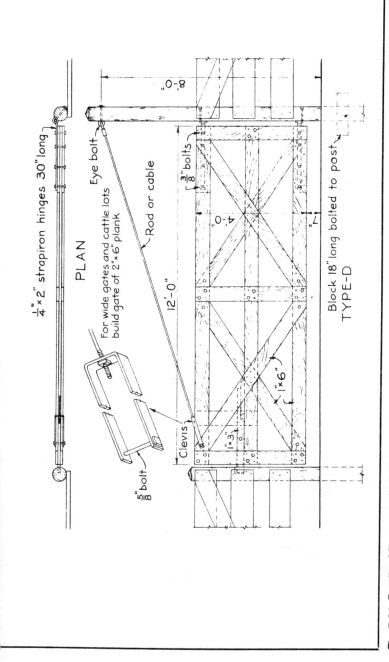

PLAN

$\frac{1}{4}$"×2" strapiron hinges 30" long

Eye bolt

Rod or cable

For wide gates and cattle lots build gate of 2"×6" plank.

Clevis

$\frac{5}{8}$" bolt

8'-0"

$\frac{3}{8}$" bolts

4'-0"

12'-0"

7"

1"×6"

1"×3"

Block 18" long bolted to post

TYPE-D

Fig. 7-24. Details of five types of wood gates and one style.

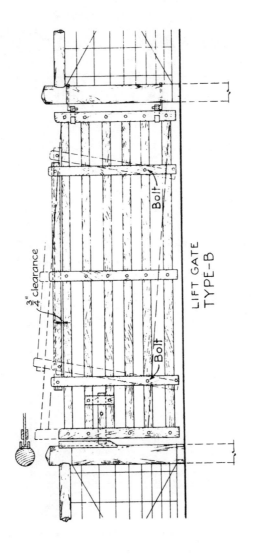

LIFT GATE
TYPE-B

Bolt

Bolt

$\frac{3}{4}"$ clearance

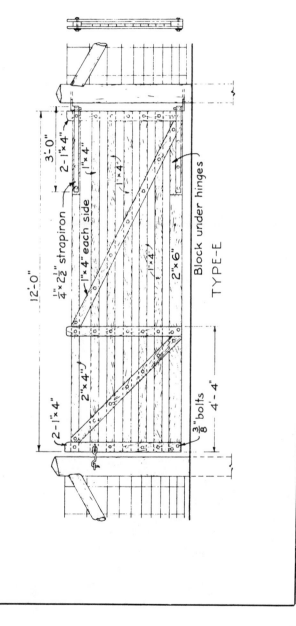

Fig. 7-24. Details of five types of wood gates & one style. (continued from 265).

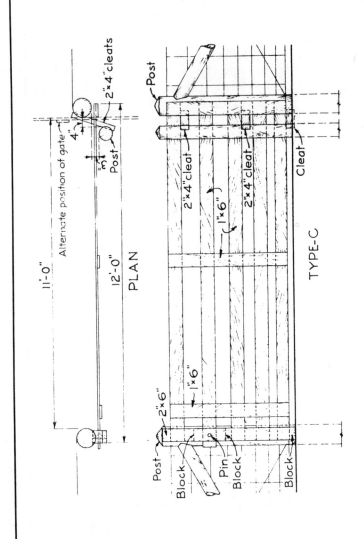

PLAN

11'-0"

Alternate position of gate

12'-0"

3"

4"

2"×4" cleats

Post

Post

TYPE-C

Post

2"×6"

1"×6"

2"×4" cleat

1"×6"

2"×4" cleat

2"×4" cleat

Cleat

Block

Pin

Block

Block

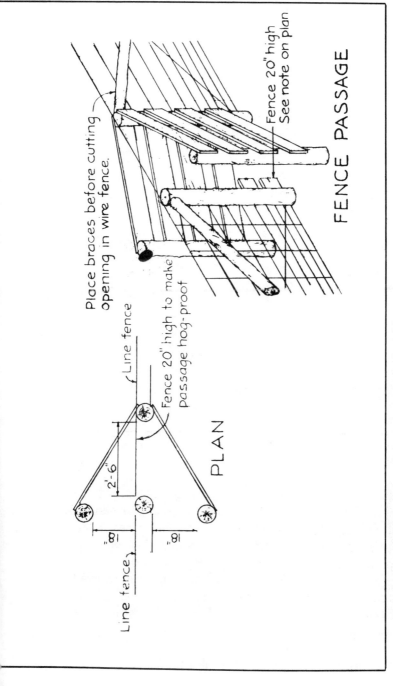

Place braces before cutting opening in wire fence.

Line fence

Fence 20" high to make passage hog-proof

Line fence

2'-6"

18" 18"

PLAN

FENCE PASSAGE

Fence 20" high See note on plan

Fig. 7-24. Details of five types of wood gates & one style. (continued from 267).

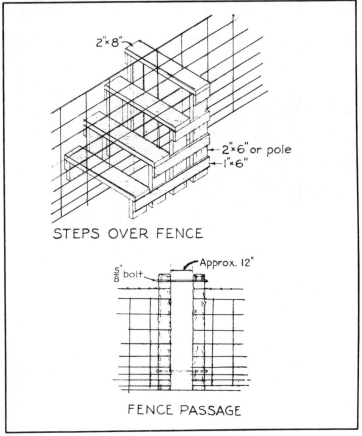

Fig. 7-24. Details of five types of wood gates & one style. (contined from 269).

of fence with an extra post not set in the ground, but tied or otherwise attached to the ground set pole on one side. It is lifted and rolled back out of the way when access is needed. Such gates should also have, at about the center point, spreader boards to keep the barbed wire apart.

Wood gates are easily built using readily available hardware from any farm store. You can go ahead and buy one of the kits sold by Montgomery Ward or Sears and make the job even simpler. These kits include hinges, pintles, corner braces, bolts and latch, and at present sell for less than $45. Wood gates in rustic style are probably your best bet for split rail fences that you make scratch, though pole bar gates can also be used.

Stiles are not gates, but they can be just as handy in areas where people, and not vehicles or animals, need to cross fences. Stiles are nothing more than roughly built stairs that extend through the fence, so that each side has a flight. They prevent wear and tear on the fence from people climbing over, under or through, but should not be used in areas where goats are kept. Goats negotiate them with ease, as if on a dare (Fig. 7-24).

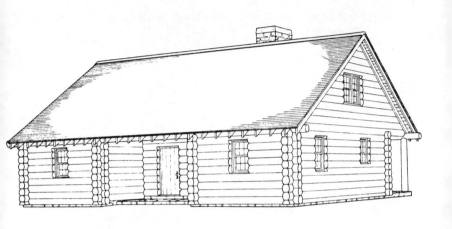

8

Tools and Vehicles
for the Homestead

Certainly no small farm or homestead will be complete without a wide variety of tools. There's probable no logical place to begin the list. At this moment I have two chain saws, three *bow saws*, four *carpenter's handsaws*, a *coping saw*, a *keyhole saw*, a *compass saw* and a *hacksaw* in my tool shed. And that doesn't count the new Stanley mid-price range *miter box* and *backsaw* in my basement (Fig. 8-1). In the past month and a half, I have used all but the coping saw, and that was used two months ago. In addition, I have three circular saws, so that I don't have to change blades for every different job that comes along.

SAWS

The list of saws needed and used in rural areas is large. I've already covered the chain saw pretty well in Chapter 5. The only really necessary remark here is a reminder to buy the best you can afford, whether new or used, and to care for it as the manufacturer recommends. If you do a lot of in-tree work, do as I did and also get a lighter saw, with about a 14-inch bar. If you have any plans at all to use wood heat, the chain saw is your starting point when buying wood saws.

Bow Saws

A companion to the chain saw is the bow saw. A bow saw has a simplicity that makes it attractive. It is very good for

Fig. 8-1. Miter box and backsaw.

cutting smaller logs into stove lengths, but it has another use
that I consider primary. I always carry a bow saw along when
cutting in the woods, since it can prove very handy for cutting
loose a hung-up chain saw. Sooner or later even the most
expert chain saw user is going to make a mistake in judging an
angle and either hang the saw up in the cut at a point where
wedges only get in the way, or drop a tree the wrong way.
The latter problem is handled by having escape paths cleared
and taking off when the tree begins to go, leaving the chain
saw behind. The first problem often requires a second and
third cut to relieve tension on the bar and chain of the chain
saw. It might be a lot less work to have a second chain saw on
hand with which to cut the first loose. But the extra saw gets
expensive, is a load to carry and isn't essential. The bowsaw
may be. Bow saws are cheap and have replaceable blades. A
smaller bow saw is also a handy tool when heavy pruning is
needed.

Handsaws

Handsaws come, basically, in two varieties—*rip* and
crosscut. My Nicholson ripsaw has six teeth to the inch, while
one of the Nicholson crosscut saws has eight and the other
12. The more teeth per inch, the smoother the cut you will
make, but the more work you will have to do to make the cut.
My fourth handsaw is also a crosscut, but with 10 teeth per

inch. It is an old Craftsman model that has been pretty badly battered during my travels over the past 15 years or so. For that reason, I use it to make cuts in wood that might have hidden nails or other debris which might harm the far more expensive Nicholson saws, which I try to keep in top condition. Keeping them in condition means hanging them up after each use, but not before all resin and dirt are removed with a kerosene-soaked rag. Then a light coat of any good oil is applied.

Handsaws of good quality cost much more now than they did some years ago. Like most carpentry tools, though, there is almost no chance of getting a good job from a poor tool. I can't see the sense in paying $10 or $11 for a saw that will last six months when $20 will buy one that will outlast me. Especially if you have a circular saw, you may feel no need for handsaws. If you do any work at all, you will sooner or later find the handsaw indispensable. First, circular saws have base plates that get in the way of cuts made right up to another surface. Second, the circular saw blade forces you to cut past the marks on angle cuts where two cuts meet. Stop early and finsh the cut with a handsaw. It is much neater and, if strength is needed, there are no extra cut lines to weaken the work (Fig. 8-2).

Hacksaws

Hacksaws are also handy tools, and the frame should be of top quality. Blades are available with 14, 16, 18 and occasionally more teeth per inch. In most cases, 18 teeth is a good rule of thumb. For really thin material, go for more teeth per inch if available. For heavier stock, use a blade with fewer teeth per inch. Since the blades are replaceable, top quality isn't essential, especially when you only need to make a few cuts in light, soft metal. In cases where heavy bar stock must be cut, go for top quality or most of your time will be spent replacing blades. Hacksaws are handy for cutting most metals and plastics, but they are not much good on wood (Fig. 8-3).

Keyhole, Compass and Coping Saws

Keyhole and compass saws are exceptionally handy when you are rewiring a house and doing remodeling jobs.

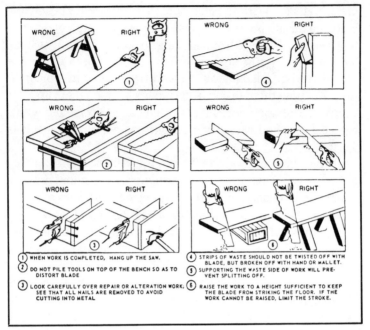

Fig. 8-2. Take proper care of your saw.

They are used to make small cutouts such as those used for wall receptacles and light switches. Holes are drilled at the corners of the box to be cut. The compass saw is then used to connect the holes. Keyhole saws can make slightly tighter curved cuts than can compass saws because of the thinner blades (Figs. 8-4 and 8-5).

Unless you're doing a lot of finish trim work, a coping saw probably won't be a necessity. Coping saws are used for tight curved cuts and are very handy for making coped joints in molding. They have little use otherwise outside of hobby work.

Fig. 8-3. A hacksaw with an adjustable frame.

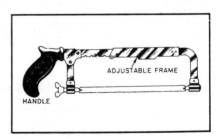

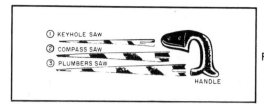

Fig. 8-4. Nested saws.

Crosscut Saws

For the true homesteader who doesn't wish to use a gasoline powered tool such as a chain saw, you will still be able to find one and two-man crosscut saws for felling trees. Most of the time the crosscut saws will have four cutting teeth to every raker tooth, with the cutting teeth extending out a bit past the raker teeth (these clean out the center of the kerf or sawcut). You may prefer such saws for felling timber (used with an axe), but expect to spend more time gathering your firewood and to be more tired when you come out of the woods (Fig. 8-6).

Circular Saws

Circular saws are one of the handiest tools for any type of building chore you are likely to run across. With different blades, they can be used to cut everything from 2 by 12s down to 1/16 inch paneling, and can move on to light metals and other materials. A good circular saw will last a long time, but the price variation can be tremendous. Saws are available for as little as $30 and for well over $300. In most cases, one

Fig. 8-5. Using a keyhole saw.

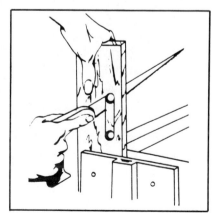

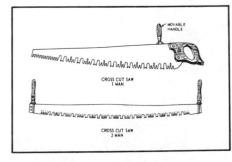

Fig. 8-6. One and two-man crosscut saws.

of the mid-range saws with about 2 horsepower will do about anything a homesteader, farmer or part-time carpenter will need. Such a saw will cost probably $65 to $85, with a 7½-inch blade, and extra blades can run from $3 on up past $20. I have two mid-range saws and one cheap one. The mid-range saws carry different blades, one combination and one rip, while the cheap saw carries a fine plywood blade. There is little point in paying for a lot of power and durability in a paneling saw, since the wood is light and quickly cut, even with the very fine teeth on the blade. Obviously, any electric tool should be UL listed, no matter the price range. It must be the type that either works with a grounded circuit or is double insulated.

Extra heavy duty worm drive circular saws are available and can be extremely handy when you are doing extensive framing work for a house and a barn, or several smaller buildings. Straight drive saws may overheat under such heavy use. I have never had a worm drive saw come close to overheating, no matter how heavy the use. To my knowledge, the only company making worm drive saws today is the Skil Corporation, and they are fine, professional tools. The price is high, compared to straight drive, but well worthwhile if you do a lot of framing timber cutting. I do not have a recent price list on hand, but a couple of years ago the smaller Skil worm drive model was up over $250. I doubt it has come down since then. Do not buy such a saw if you are only doing remodeling and repair. If you are starting from scratch and everything, or almost everything, has to be framed, give careful consideration to a worm drive circular saw. You could, in the long run, save money.

HAMMERS

The variety of hammers useful in repairs and general rural work is not quite as wide as the variety of saws, but still provides more than one item to add to your tool shopping list. My own hammer list includes a 28-ounce *framing hammer,* a 22-ounce framing hammer, a 16 ounce *carpenter's hammer,* a *brick hammer*, a 12-ounce *ball pein*, a 16-ounce ball pein, a 32-ounce ball pein, a 3 pound *engineer's hammer*, a 6-pound wood splitting maul, and two 8-pounders, as well as an 8-pound *sledge* and a *tack hammer*. About the only one I haven't used in recent months is the tack hammer. This far from exhausts the list of hammers to be found, but so far it is all for which I have found a need (Figs. 8-7 and 8-8).

You may ask why so many carpenter's hammers or claw hammers are needed. The answer is simple, since driving smaller nails with the 28-ounce hammer is rough on the wood. Trying to set 20 penny and larger nails with the 16-ounce hammer is something like a woodpecker trying to chop down a healthy tree. When nails move up to 12 penny size, I switch to the 22-ounce Stanley from the 16-ounce model. When the fasteners get up to 20 penny size, I move to the 28-ounce hammer. It takes less effort to drive nails if the proper size hammer is used. As to the three wood splitting mauls, I bought the 6-pounder years ago before I even knew they came in heavier sizes, so that is simply a mistake. Having two 8-pound mauls keeps me from having to stop wood splitting every time a handle breaks off. It is simpler to bring the new handles inside and work on them in the evening than to stop splitting while there is still light outdoors. I always keep at least two extra handles on hand, though, since it is possible to goof twice in a row. Occasionally, a handle will come up bad, with a knot or other defect right at the point where the handle enters the hammer head. Those handles snap on the first blow almost all the time (Fig. 8-9).

Sledges are useful when driving some types of wedges, for breaking up stone and concrete, and for driving small fence posts. Weights vary and can go as high as 20 or more pounds, but the most useful models are in the 8 to 10 pound range. If you get a chance, assuming it is possible to borrow

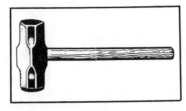

Fig. 8-7. Double faced sledge hammer.

one, try working for any length of time with a 20-pound sledge. You will see why I say lighter ones are more useful.

Engineer's hammers have pretty much the same uses as do sledge hammers. They are one-hand models with lighter heads and shorter handles (Fig. 8-10).

Soft face hammers are useful in many ways, and I forgot to include the two I have on my earlier list. Both are 16-ounce models. They are useful for spots where steel faced hammers would mar the work surface, and are used to drive plastic handled chisels, wood dowels and for forming and shaping metals.

Bricklayer's hammers have a flat striking surface, with beveled edges. The other side of the head has a sharp, hardened cutting edge (Fig. 8-11).

Ball pein hammers have a slightly crowned striking face and a round, ball shaped pein. Use these for striking chisels, riveting and shaping unhardened metals (Fig. 8-12).

Hammer Handles

Hammer handles vary in length and thickness with the size, weight and expected uses of the hammer. There is a variation in materials. You can buy most hammers with steel, fiberglass or wood handles. Steel is the strongest material and some handles are tubular, while others are solid. Steel is my least favorite handle material. Even with rubber grips,

Fig. 8-8. Wood maul.

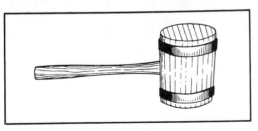

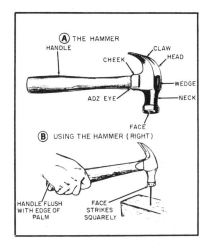

Fig. 8-9. The carpenter's hammer and its correct use.

the vibration is not dampened much, if at all. Fiber glass is next in strength and is my favorite, providing the hammer is fitted with a rubber grip. It is stronger than wood, so it is less likely to break, and the heads are less likely to loosen. A fiber-glass handle dampens vibrations about as well as wood. Wood is the least strong handle material, but it is usually the cheapest and always the easiest to replace. It is actually quite strong, particularly since today most hammer handles are of hickory or white oak (if you have a choice, go for the hickory). Some people prefer ash for splitting maul handles because it is a bit springier than either oak or hickory, but I have used in and do not find enough difference there to make up for the lower strength. Ash is not readily available in a lot of areas,

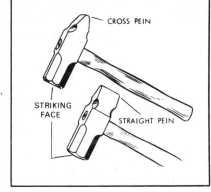

Fig. 8-10. Engineer's hammers.

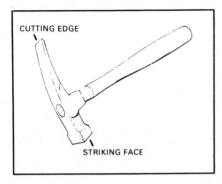

Fig. 8-11. Bricklayer's hammer.

so you might have to carve your own handle, which can be a chore.

Hammer Misuse

Hammer misuse is quite common. No hammer should be used to strike objects it is not designed to strike. This means that a claw hammer is not used to drive hardened steel masonry nails; nor is it used to break up brick or stone. It is also not used to pull deeply embedded large nails, unless you wish to make a near full-time hobby of replacing handles (Fig. 8-13). Sledges are not used to strike other sledges and mauls. The same holds true for wood splitting mauls, which also should never be used to strike concrete. Never use any sort of hammer, maul or sledge with a loose handle. Keep checking the faces of tools for chipping and cracking.

When using a wood splitting maul with wedges, notch the wood to be split with the maul before starting to drive the wedge. Then set the wedge in place and tap until it is firmly set in the log. Just sitting the wedge point in the notch can

Fig. 8-12. Ball pein hammer.

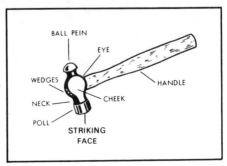

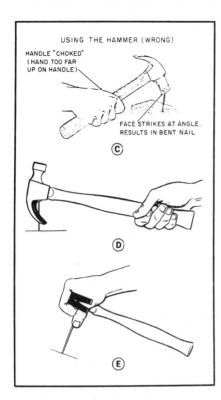

Fig. 8-13. Improper use of the carpenter's hammer.

cause the wedge to come, if you are lucky, zipping past your head at an incredible rate. I've had this happen, and though it is most common with green, frozen wood, it can happen with other kinds, too. The sensation is not pleasant even when the wedge misses, as most weigh around 5 pounds.

AXES

We will also include *hatchets* in this section, though in most cases I don't consider a hatchet a very handy tool (with the exception of specialized hatchets such as the shingling hatchet). A hatchet may be useful for splitting kindling, trimming limbs and driving stakes, but other tools will do the jobs as well or better. I prefer to split any kindling I have with a 3½-pound Stanley axe. The job goes more quickly, and the axe never hangs up in light wood as a hatchet is likely to do. A full swing isn't needed, since the heavier head will pull the axe through easily. I don't know how many axes I've got at the moment, but at least four of different patterns would be a good guess. Generally, head weights are under 4½ pounds, and the faces do not widen a great deal towards the *poll*. Wider polls would make them handier for splitting wood, but they in turn cut down on the handiness for trimming limbs. I prefer to split wood with a maul and wedges, though I do use an axe on lighter or less hard to split logs. If you wish to keep an axe for any length of time, do all your splitting on a section of log only, to keep the blade out of the ground. Also, do not use a maul, hammer or another axe to drive a stuck axe through a log. Split it apart with a maul and wedge instead (Fig. 8-14).

Sharpening an axe seems to be a problem for many people, and the biggest part of the problem seems to be involved with being in a hurry. High speed grinding wheels are out, as the heat buildup ruins the temper of the blade. When the cutting edge of the blade starts to dull, support the tool solidly. Use a file, and later a stone, to work the cutting edge back into shape. Restore the original contour of the cutting edge, starting 2 to 3 inches back from the edge with the file, and working to within ½ inch of the edge. Axes are usually fan-shaped. This is what you will be aiming for, but leave more thickness at the corners of the edge to keep them from splitting off. Now file the last ½ inch, feathering into the already filed portion. Use a *whetstone* to remove scratches, and then hone ½ inch back from the cutting edge to provide just about the shape shown in Fig. 8-15. Woodchoppers or splitter's, mauls are sharpened in pretty much the same manner, but the splitting edge is shaped to about a 70 degree angle.

I would avoid double bitted axes for most farm work. They may look professional, but they also require almost full professional skill and care to be safe and of much use.

MEASURING TOOLS

Measuring tools include such things as *framing squares, combination squares, levels* and *folding rules* as well as *tapes*. You will need levels only if you plan on building things such as sheds, barns, fences or houses, but the others are essential for just about any work where accuracy is demanded.

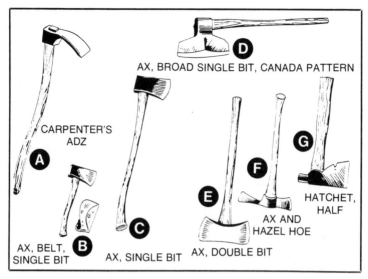

Fig. 8-14. Types of axes, adzes and hatchets.

We have already looked at the *rafter* or *framing* square in Chapter 2. There is little more to say here except to recommend that you get one of good quality, especially since even a top quality rafter square is reasonable in price (probably less than $7).

Combination squares are those small squares with sliding blades, and they serve a number of purposes. First, they provide a square for marking board cutoffs at 90 degree and 45 degree angles. Second, they can be used as a guide for marking a board to be ripped by holding the pencil or scribe on the end of the blade, set at the proper depth, and drawing the square along the board. Finally, most have levels set in

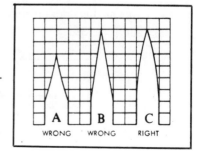

Fig. 8-15. Improper and proper shaping for sharpening an axe or hatchet.

the handle, and in a pinch these can be used, though they tend to quickly become more than a bit inaccurate because of the constant handling of the square. Again, the tool is inexpensive so it pays to buy for quality. I would not go overboard as to price, though, since the constant handling will soon cause the blade to rust. This messes up the markings, but does little for use as a cutoff marker.

Levels come in a multitude of price ranges, sizes and styles. Line levels are needed when laying out a building site and are made to just slip over the mason's twine to get the level of a foundation or other wall (Fig. 8-16). Standard levels come in lengths from about 1 foot to 6 feet. Your first check should be for quality. You will not have a need for top of the line models, but a good mid-range level is a far better buy than a $8 or $9 cheap one. The more expensive levels stand up to constant handling and the occasional drop, far better than the cheap ones can. They retain accuracy longer and have replaceable vials should those be cracked. For any extensive building work, I recommend that you consider getting 2-foot and 4-foot levels. The 4-foot model is great for longer surfaces, such as walls, and for plumbing door jambs. The 2-foot model is best used on windows and shorter surfaces. The longer the level, the greater the accuracy on irregular surfaces. But the tool must still be short enough to fit on the surface to be leveled (Fig. 8-17).

Folding rules soon become something like a second hand to carpenters and other builders. Most are 6 feet long. I have two Lufkin models in that length, and a Craftsman 8-foot model. These are most useful for measuring relatively short distances, especially when you're alone and need a stiff measuring tool to span a space.

For measuring longer spaces, a measuring tape is essential. The possibility of error when picking up and laying

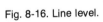 Fig. 8-16. Line level.

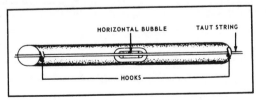

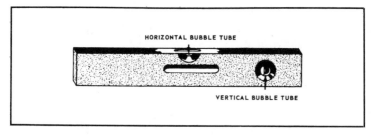

Fig. 8-17. Carpenter's level.

down a folding rule becomes too great after about 12 feet, so a tape at least 16 feet long is needed. I use a Stanley Power-lock, 25 feet long, as my basic measuring tape. For longer runs, such as along fence lines, I have a Lufkin 100-foot tape.

A sliding *T bevel* is also a handy tool. These bevels look a lot like a square and have a wood handle, along with a slotted metal blade that can be moved along and set at almost any angle. These are handiest when you don't know how, or don't want to take the time, to figure an angle on something like a jack rafter for a dormer. Use the sliding T bevel to determine the angle, clamp down the locknut and transfer the angle to your material.

TRUCKS

In any farm area, you will see a wide variety of truck types, from pickups and vans on up to tractor-trailer rigs. Most prevalent will be the pickup, as it often serves as a light hauler and as family transport. At the moment, I have a new Dodge, and it provides a good starting place for recommendations. First, I specified the slant six 225 cubic inch engine, which is the smallest Chrysler has available in full size pickups. This comes with four speed overdrive and I got, also, the 8-foot bed. I see no sense at all in pickups with shorter beds; nor do I like those with the sides of the bed set inside the fenders (this is usually an extra cost option and cuts down on carrying capacity). The truck is rated at half a ton, and with air shocks I've hauled as much as two tons over short distances. A step bumper makes the addition of a 2-inch trailer ball a simple matter, so that you can haul fertilizer spreaders and other such gear.

The only other extra on my vehicle is an AM radio. There is no power steering; nor are there power brakes, air conditioning or other such items. Part of the reason for not having power steering is the need to tell when the thing has been overloaded too far for driving safety. With power steering, you cannot tell if the front end is floating a bit. Air conditioning eats gas. I do regret not getting a sliding rear window, as that would improve ventilation for those hot and humid days.

As to the reasons for my engine choice, the first is gas mileage. With the overdrive, I pull about 21-22 miles per gallon on trips and about 17 to 18 around my hilly locale. Second, I have had a great deal of experience with the slant six and am pleased with its longevity. The power output is fine for engine size, and I have yet to fail getting a load somewhere for lack of power. I have friends who insist on getting pickups with 350 and 400 cubic inch engines. I can haul the same loads, albeit more slowly.

The 8-foot bed provides sufficient room for many kinds of hauling, since it will take a 4 by 8 sheet of plywood, flat, and will also hold, if the stuff is packed properly, about 50 bales of hay. My last pickup hauled alfalfa hay for my horse several times. Each time we got 50 bales on and transported it, in one case over 20 miles (Fig. 8-18).

Small pickups may be fine for your purposes, but I don't care for them. The load capacity is down too much for me. Generally, they are as well made, sometimes better, than the full size models. The tiny engines that provide such great gas mileage limit your hauling capacity, though. When it is time to bring in 3,500 pounds of fertilizer in a 500-pound spreader, you have to make two trips. Getting an extra five miles per gallon isn't much help if you have to retrace your tire tracks (Fig. 8-19).

Four wheel drive vehicles can be handy in some locales, but you should realize that these vehicles cut mileage to shreds. My brother's GMC provides a general use mileage of about 9 miles per gallon, while a friend's Chevy gives him about 10. Still, if you do a lot of rough country driving where getting stuck has to be a problem, it may pay you to select a four wheel drive vehicle.

Fig. 8-18. A truck for rough farm area work.

TILLERS AND TRACTORS

For most small farm and homestead purposes, a full size farming *tractor* is not too useful, though some of the smaller models such as the Ford Cadet may well be. In almost all cases, it will pay to study the land uses in your area and talk to those who have been there for some years before considering any sort of tractor purchase. There are so many new and used models to be found on the market that any sort of general advice about buying one is totally out of the question. Someone doing truck gardening will need a completely different type and size tractor than will someone farming a fair amount of grain or hay acreage.

Don't look for bright paint and fancy doodads in the used tractors. Check to see how many hours are on the meter, and to see how easily the tractor starts, shifts, and how well the power lift and power takeoff work. Check the tire condition, especially for cracks in the sidewalls, which tend to show the tires will need to be replaced soon and also show the vehicle has done a lot of sitting. See what equipment is available with the tractor, in line with your needs, and make sure the three point hitch is of a type that will mate easily with other brands of equipment.

In almost any instance I can think of, *lawn* or *garden tractors* are also a waste of money for small farms and for homesteads. Their prices are right up to the point where you can usually buy a good, used medium tractor with several pieces of equipment. If your layout is small enough for a garden tractor, it is probably small enough for a tiller.

Roto tillers of many brands are available, and the price varies with design and horsepower. Most common is the front tine 5 or 6 horsepower tiller, most of which can be bought at a quite reasonable price. Front tine tillers, though, force you to walk on the already tilled ground and also shake you to ribbons. They tend to be hard to control both for depth and direction if the ground isn't dead level and free of rocks. Rear tine tillers are more expensive, but allow you easy enough control to walk by the side of the tiller and use one hand to control the thing. They do, in my experience, a better job overall of breaking up the ground for planting. Still, the

Fig. 8-19. This little Dodge pickup has to be among the sturdiest of all vehicles.

price differential must be considered, since many rear tine tillers go for two to three times the cost of a similar front tine tiller. Many are also gear-driven instead of chain-driven, but to me that just adds complexity, should something break, and expensive.

Your best tiller bet is probably a used rear tine model with chain drive. Again, don't pay too much attention to the finish of the tiller. Look, instead, for broken tines and a clean, well-oiled chain. See that the controls are in good shape and the machine is easy starting.

Much of the accessory equipment for tillers and tractors will be poorly finished. The original finish may not have been poor, but many farmers simply let cultivators and plows drop in a spare field instead of storing them indoors. Thus you will see a lot of rust. This may or may not be a problem. If the rust interferes with the tool's working, reject it. Otherwise, it can more or less be ignored, though it would be a good idea to remove as much rust as possible and to store the machinery under a shed if at all possible. No matter where you store it, keep it well lubricated.

WRENCHES

Maintaining one's own gear is one of the lesser charms of homesteading, but is almost essential if you are to stand any chance of making a profit. Obviously, some really specialized types of equipment won't be too amenable to home maintenance, but most farm equipment is. Thus, a good set of mechanic's tools is needed. Check the machinery. There is no point in buying metric wrenches for English nuts. If you're working with inches, buy inch style wrenches.

Start with a moderate *socket set* of good, though not extreme, quality. Select a ½-inch drive and a ⅜-inch drive, with the ½-inch drive limited to larger nuts and bolts if you don't wish to duplicate. For a long time I work with ½-inch drive exclusively. If it is used gently on small nuts and bolts, things are fine. But it tends to be too easy to overtighten nuts under ½-inch or so in size, sometimes to the point of twisting off the heads.

Six and 12 point sockets in a good range are needed. I would start at ¼ inch and go on through about 1⅛ inches in

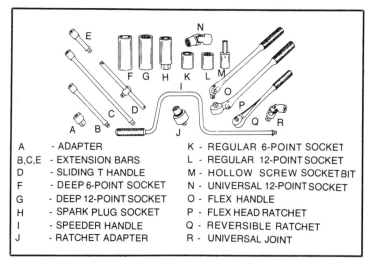

A	- ADAPTER	K -	REGULAR 6-POINT SOCKET
B,C,E	- EXTENSION BARS	L -	REGULAR 12-POINT SOCKET
D	- SLIDING T HANDLE	M -	HOLLOW SCREW SOCKET BIT
F	- DEEP 6-POINT SOCKET	N -	UNIVERSAL 12-POINT SOCKET
G	- DEEP 12-POINT SOCKET	O -	FLEX HANDLE
H	- SPARK PLUG SOCKET	P -	FLEX HEAD RATCHET
I	- SPEEDER HANDLE	Q -	REVERSIBLE RATCHET
J	- RATCHET ADAPTER	R -	UNIVERSAL JOINT

Fig. 8-20. Socket wrench set.

1/16-inch increments (less for any tiny wrenches) (Fig. 8-20).

Open end, combination and *box wrenches* are also needed. Look for good quality without going overboard. A professional mechanic using a wrench every day needs the absolute best, but a homesteader or farmer will usually need a particular wrench or socket once a month or so. Thus, the price paid for "pro" tools tends to be out of line. Brands offering good quality abound: Craftsman, S-K, Ward's, Bernzomatic and Crescent. Price is reasonable and quality is near the top. Most manufacturers now offer a lifetime guarantee (Figs. 8-21 and 8-22).

Fig. 8-21. Box wrenches.

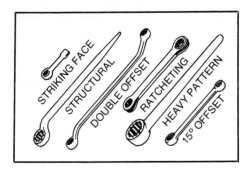

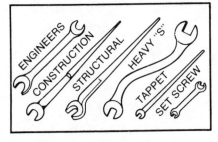

Fig. 8-22. Open end wrenches.

PLIERS

Pliers are exceptionally handy tools, though they are misused nearly as often as screwdrivers and hammers. Still, a good set of *grooved neck* pliers, a set of *slip joint* pliers, and a set of *locking* pliers are just about essential ingredients for any farmstead toolbox. Look for good quality and good finish. Forget the price. You do not need so many that you will go broke buying them. I like to have a medium and medium-large size of each type.

Fence pliers, or fence tools, are pliers that include a hammer face for redriving staples. They can be used as wire cutters and staple pullers. If you are building a new fence, drive the staples with a hammer.

Cutting pliers can be a linesman's type, side cutters or any of several others. They are handy, and I have five of varying designs and sizes. Go, again, for top quality (Fig. 8-23).

The specialty pliers such as *needle nose* are handy for many jobs, and should be picked up as needed. Again, the

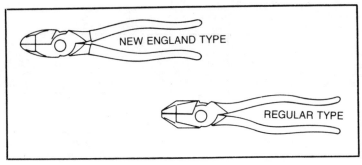

Fig. 8-23. Linesman's side cutting pliers.

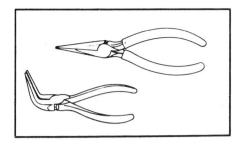

Fig. 8-24. Long nose pliers.

best are not extremely costly and few are needed, so you have no reason not to get the top of the line tools (Fig. 8-24).

SCREWDRIVERS AND SHOVELS

Select for quality here, as a poorly made *screwdriver* will tear up screws and make work much harder than is needed. Hardened steel tips and comfortable handles are the most important features to look for. If you expect to have a lot of frozen or hard-to-turn screws, select screwdrivers with square shanks so that an adjustable wrench can be used to provide added pressure. Tips sizes for standard screwdrivers should range from about ⅛ inch on up to ⅜ inch, while you should get all four Phillips sizes. Handle length can be important, but for most uses 6 inches will do quite well. Stubby screwdrivers help you to get in tight places, and offset models will allow use in even tighter sport.

Other tools for the farm or homestead abound, Without knowing your immediate situation, it is difficult to provide a list. You will probably need picks, shovels and posthole diggers, as well as brush clearing tools in most areas. As always, select for quality. I have one bush hook tool that is of light construction and is of little more use than a weed whip, while my second such tool is quite heavy and durable. There is nothing quite like swinging the hook into heavy brush to find the blade bending on contact with inch thick weed trees. For posthole diggers, I bought the best available, since the work is hard enough without having the tool break in use.

Shovels come in so many forms they can be confusing. I find a spade tip and long handled one handiest for work with dirt and gravel, while a scoop shovel is good for grains.

9

Raising Livestock

So far, we've covered much of the building and other things that may be required to start a small farm in a rural area. A lot of it must sound like hard work, and much of it surely is. Physical labor goes hand in hand with mental work when trying to make a go of it in rural areas, though. Raising livestock of any kind takes planning ahead, as well as a good understanding of the problems. The rewards follow, assuming nature doesn't get too nasty in the meantime.

SHEEP

Sheep are useful animals and have been around for quite a few years. They are also stupid animals and require more protection at certain times than do other animals. Especially for small farms, sheep can bring profits in two forms, wool and meat, as well as young lambs to sell as breeder stock or for other reasons. And it is with breeder stock we should start.

Ewes

Crossbreeds are considered the best, and you should look for *ewes* that are big boned and long bodied. Obviously, you will also want animals that are healthy. Yearling ewes, when bought, should weigh in at 100 to 110 pounds if bought in early spring. If bought in June, the weight should have reached 115 pounds. Lambs are usually born as twins. If you have twin ewes, mark them at the two week point after birth so they can be told apart. Keep an eye on them, and select the fastest growing of the two for your breeding program.

Rams

Rams are generally selected as purebreds, and it is best to locate one, or more, with already proven performance whenever possible. If performance is not proven, look for basically healthy, active and large rams, with yearlings in breeding condition weighing at least 200 pounds. Tests have shown that lambs sired by a particular ram will often average 10 pounds more at four months of age than those of another ram in the same flock.

Breeding

Breeding should be planned for the most profitable time, though that sometimes will mean extra work on your part, as well as a need for more barn facilities. Lambing time forces you to consider the weather, the feed available, the weather and overall barn space. A check with your local extension agent will give you a better idea as to the best lambing times for your particular locale. In general, late fall and early winter lambing is considered most profitable in terms of feed and weather. This avoids lambing in extreme cold, but also avoids the heat of summer which is hard on both ewes and new-born lambs. Of course, you must have a good supply of winter feed to carry you through. For colder areas, late winter and early spring lambing is considered best.

Ewes, like most animals other than man, are seasonal breeders and come in heat on an average of every 17 days. The ewe will stay in heat from 18 to 40 hours, and will then have a *gestation period* of 142 to 152 days before lambing.

Ewes will need protection from severe weather or bad weather changes in the month just before lambing is expected. Fresh drinking water is needed daily, and water temperature should never be allowed to drop below about 40 degrees. Keep the pregnant ewe from damp, musty barns and from muddy and wet areas around buildings. Once lambing is done, the ewe and her charges can usually, if all is well, be turned out onto fields. Experts say it is best to not turn them out on fields used for sheep grazing during the rest of the year. This cuts down on the chances they will pick up internal and external parasites. A balanced ration is needed, and a check should be maintained if you are not using a commercial feed already balanced. Most states have an agricultural or land grant college with a feed testing program which will help you out here. A lot of people tend to think the programs of extension agents and agricultural colleges are meant to help the large farmer only, but in my dealings with them that has not been the case. They make plans and programs available to almost anyone who asks. Many of the plans are suitable for small farmers, as are the programs.

As the lamb grows, it needs other treatment. At one month, you should treat for internal parasites, after making sure the spring pasture has grown enough for the ewe and lambs to be turned out. A too early turn out of the lambs can cut their growth rate drastically. The lamb should be continued on *creep feed*—this is a supplemental ration supplied in a box designed to keep the ewe out while letting the lambs in—and the ewe should still be getting half her daily grain ration for the first week.

During April or May shearing is done. After shearing is the time to cull your lambs. Nursing lambs are not sold at this time, but any cull ewes should be.

By the time summer arrives, you will still be checking weight gains in the lambs. When the gain drops below ½ pound a day, a change in handling is required. Such changes may include weaning lambs still with ewes on pasture and returning them to the barn for finish feeding. If the lambs are already in the barn, the feed needs checking, as does the internal parasite situation.

Two different forms of wormer should be used in the summer treatment. One type is used, and then two weeks later another is used. This keeps the parasites from building up a resistance to a particular substance. Some types of wormers get one, two or three types of parasite, but leave another pretty much alone. Each has different qualities.

Fall is the time to check buildings and feed supplies. It is also the time of year when feed prices are usually the lowest, so this is the best time to buy for the coming winter.

During breeding season, a single mature ram is expected to "settle" 25 to 30 ewes if the weather is warm, and as many as 40 in cooler weather. Generally, four rams are used for every 100 ewes, and the lambs are rotated every fourth day. A single ram is turned in with the ewes and left for 24 hours. Then the poor guy gets three days of rest before going back to work. Resting rams should be kept out of sight of the ewes in a shaded, cool area, on good graze with a supplemental grain ration of about ½ pound a day.

Pregnant ewes in good shape will gain about 10 pounds during the 3½ months after breeding. At the point where lambing is about to occur, ewes should have gained another 10 pounds. Six weeks earlier you should have started feeding ¼ pound of grain per day, with 4 pounds of hay a day in addition, if it is winter or pasture is poor. Keep an eye on the pasturing areas to make sure there are no ditches, broken fences, narrow gates or anything else that might cause the ewe to jump or squeeze through. Sheep panic easily, so it is best to remove the problems and not have stillborn lambs.

A month before lambing time, the ewes are again wormed and should be sheared at the head, around the udder and the dock. Lambs sometimes suffer from overeating disease. If you are worried about this, the ewes can be vaccinated against it—check with your veterinarian. As lambing times get closer, you will need to keep a close watch on your ewes with, finally, a check four times a day.

Lambing pens should be clean and dry and at least 5 feet on a side. When the lambs are born, the naval cord (for the lamb) is coated with iodine. Check the ewe's udder to see that she has milk, and make sure the lamb is nursed within the first hour.

On the day of lambing, give the ewe only water and fresh hay. No grain should be fed until the second day. The amount of time the ewe and her lambs will be kept in the lambing pen can vary from as little as a few hours to three or four days for weak twins. Once the lambs are strong and active, they can be turned out with their mother. Most often, they can be moved to a larger pen with a few other lambs and ewes for about 10 days. At this time, you can dock, castrate or vaccinate the lambs (the vaccination is for overeating disease). By this time, your ewes will need 1¼ pounds of grain, plus all the hay, either legume or grass, they will eat. Ewes with twins are kept away from those with singles, and the ewes with twins get 1½ pounds of grain per day. By the time four months have passed, you should have finished lambs weighing about 100 pounds to sell, if all goes well.

Feeding

Making any profit at all from raising lambs and sheep, whether for wool, meat or breeder stock, depends on the quality of the feed as well as other care. The feed must include a rather complex variety of protein, carbohydrates, minerals and vitamins. During normal grazing seasons, this assortment can be provided with pasture, salt and a mineral block.

Ewes will gain and lose weight over the year with, in some cases, weight losses actually promoting greater productivity and longer life if they come at the correct times. A mature ewe should gain weight just before and during the breeding season, so that three weeks before breeding it is wise to turn them on good pasture and present a small amount of grain to get them ready to gain. Clover pastures should be avoided before breeding and during breeding, as for some reason they tend to retard settling. Regular pasture will suffice until about six weeks after breeding, and then grain rations are to be fed. Weight gains in the last six weeks of pregnancy help prevent lambing paralysis and aid in providing adequate milk supply. For some reason, too, weight gains at this time also seem to aid the mothering instinct in the ewe. It is also at this time that the lamb gains most of its pre-birth weight.

Hay must be a good quality second or third cutting, so that the coarseness of the first cutting is avoided. What you would do in an area such as this, where last year no one got a second cutting of grass hays because of dry weather, is simply stick with the coarser first cutting or go to legume hays such as alfalfa. Legume hays are generally preferred, as they have from 50 to 100 percent more nutrients of most kinds than do grass hays.

Silage of finely chopped corn, grass or small grains can also be fed, but never feed moldy or frozen silage to sheep. Never feed with silage more than 24 hours out of the silo. If silage is used, you will need to add protein, calcium and vitamin supplements to the diet. Use two to three pounds of silage for each pound of hay recommended.

Grain for sheep usually means corn, though others can be used when the price is right. Shelled corn is considered the 100 percent marker, with ground ear corn at 91 percent and wheat at 98 percent (though it shouldn't make up more than half the grain ration). Barley is 96 percent as good as shelled corn, and oats are 85 percent as good.

Protein supplements can be supplied with soybean, cottonseed and linseed, as well as peanut meal. Simply compare the price and buy the cheapest.

Minerals in a complete mixture should be fed on a free choice basis. Normally, that means setting out mineral blocks and letting the sheep make their own decisions as to what is best for them. Usually, the blocks will have a salt base, and that is also fed free choice.

Water should be fresh and clean, with a nursing ewe given no less than two gallons a day. Keep the drinking area free of muddy areas, as sheep may well go for too long without drinking if the area is a mess.

I'm not going to tell you here how to shear a sheep. That is a skill best learned first-hand, as a properly sheared lamb is one without the nicks and cuts a novice is likely to add to its hide while trying to read instructions from a book.

Sheep raising is not the easiest of all livestock raising (raising rabbits probably is), but it is far from the hardest. I think horses may qualify here, as we will see soon. With sheep raising, there is a good chance of profit (Fig. 9-1).

CATTLE

I think I can safely assume that not many of you will want the information needed for a large beef or dairy operation.

Most likely on a small farm, one of two cows or steers will be raised for milk or beef. That eliminates the need to know all the details of crossbreeding, and also the need for storing huge quantities of feed to carry a large herd over the winter.

Breeds

Still, a look at the various breeds will give some idea of what is best for any intended purpose, as the idea of milking an Angus or butchering a Holstein is not all that efficient. Generally, cattle breeds belong to three classes: *British breeds, large breeds* and *dairy breeds.*

British breeds are *Angus, Hereford, Polled Hereford, Red Angus, Shorthorn* and *Devon.* They are medium-sized animals with a moderate rate of growth to maturity. Milk production is medium. They have good maternal qualities and reproduction rate is good. *Lincoln Red* and *South Devon* breeds are also British and are like those just listed, except for being slightly larger, while the *Red Poll* and *Milking Shorthorn* are the same as other British breeds except that milk production is higher.

Large (or Continental) breeds are *Charolais, Limousin, Chianina* and *Maine Anjou.* These are very large cattle and are later maturing than the British breeds, though they gain weight rapidly. These large breeds are marginal as milk cows, though the *Belbvieh, Simmental* and *Pinzgauer* produce more milk than the others. Calving problems can occur when a large breed bull is bred to a small cow.

Dairy breeds come in two sizes, large and small. The *Holstein* and *Brown Swiss* are large, late maturing cows, with heavy milk production and fast weight gains. *Jerseys, Guernseys* and *Ayrshires* are smaller earlier maturing with lower energy needs for heavy milk production, so that for most small farms they are the more practical milk cow breed.

There is actually a fourth breed classification, *Zebu,* and synthetic breeds containing *Brahman* genes. Such cattle are most useful in very hot areas where insects are a problem. While the growth rate is good and mature size is large, carcass quality is not as good as with the British and large breeds. The breeds are Brahman, *Santa Gertrudis, Brangus,*

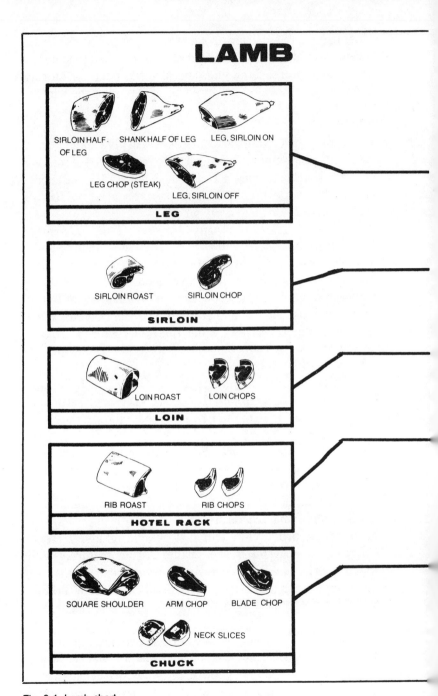

LAMB

SIRLOIN HALF OF LEG   SHANK HALF OF LEG   LEG, SIRLOIN ON

LEG CHOP (STEAK)   LEG, SIRLOIN OFF

LEG

SIRLOIN ROAST   SIRLOIN CHOP

SIRLOIN

LOIN ROAST   LOIN CHOPS

LOIN

RIB ROAST   RIB CHOPS

HOTEL RACK

SQUARE SHOULDER   ARM CHOP   BLADE CHOP

NECK SLICES

CHUCK

Fig. 9-1. Lamb chart.

304

CHART

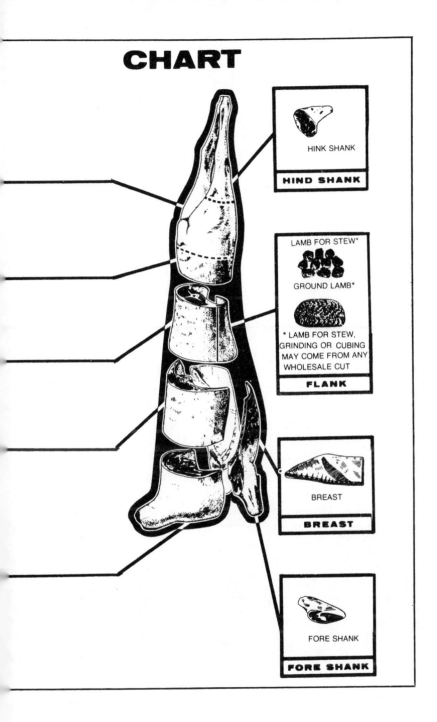

HINK SHANK

HIND SHANK

LAMB FOR STEW*

GROUND LAMB*

* LAMB FOR STEW,
GRINDING OR CUBING
MAY COME FROM ANY
WHOLESALE CUT

FLANK

BREAST

BREAST

FORE SHANK

FORE SHANK

Beefmaster and *Charbray*. Temperament among these breeds will vary.

As Table 9-1 shows, cattle size can vary a great deal depending on breed and crossbreeding practices. Crossing an Angus with a Hereford adds 50 pounds to the final weight of the steer, while crossing an Angus with a Charolais will add 225 pounds to the steer. Around here, with relatively small herds of a couple dozen or so cattle, the Angus is very popular as is the Angus/Charolais cross. Dairy herds in this area seem to consist mostly of Holsteins.

It generally pays to select a breed popular in your own locale, for at least two reasons. First, because the breed is popular, it is readily available and should be less costly than some other breed. Second, a breed becomes popular only because it does well in a particular locale. Unless you wish to be an experimenter, with the risk and cost that often entails, go with the crowd this time.

Beef and Dairy Cattle

Beef management and dairy or milk cow management differ quite a lot. Beef cattle breeds are generally more able to handle rough weather and require less overall care most of the time, as well as requiring less feed per pound of animal since they are not producing milk. In both cases, good pasture and easily available clean water are needed, so that is

Table 9-1. Expected Steer Weight At Low Choice and Crossbred Mature Cow Weight.

Breed	A	H	Sh	C	Si.	L	Ho.	J
Angus	1000	1050	1050	1225	1225	1125	1225	950
Hereford		1050	1075	1250	1250	1150	1250	975
Shorthorn			1050	1250	1250	1150	1250	975
Charolais				1400	1425	1325	1425	1100
Simmental					1400	1325	1425	1100
Limousin						1200	1325	1050
Holstein							1400	1150
Jersey								850

your first check. For beef cattle, you need little else other than good fences until finishing time when the animals are kept in a smaller enclosure and fed grain. American tastes do not extend to grass-fed beef these days, as it tends to be leaner and often tougher, without the fat marbling to add flavor and tenderness most people want. Usually, an animal to be slaughtered is grained for the last 30 days. Most dairy cows will need richer feed, usually with some grain in a daily ration. You will also want a milking shed for that twice a day chore, since milking a cow out in the rain isn't much fun for you or her. There will be a need for some sanitary facilities, even if you don't intend to sell any milk. The requirements for a class A dairy operation vary from state to state, but in every case they are quite touchy on the points of sanitation and general milk handling so as to prevent the spread of disease.

Keeping livestock for profit is a waste of time for the small farmer in most cases. The small farmer does not have enough land to profitably raise the numbers of cows, sheep, hogs or other animals to make a really attractive amount of money. The land required for a small herd can usually be used more profitably for other things. Keeping a dairy cow has another objection. The cow needs to be milked twice a day. That is an absolute and must be done, with all the required cleanup before and after the milking, plus a need for a place to store the milk. Still, a good milk cow will keep even a pretty large family in dairy products of all descriptions, from butter to milk, and there may well be some left over.

As far as beef cattle go, the need to milk the animals is removed, and the care is minimal compared to dairy cows. If you wish to raise a couple for meat for your freezer, select the breed you prefer and turn it out to pasture. Depending on the breed, it will mature so that you can finish-feed it in a reasonable length of time, and you can then have it killed and butchered. Rural areas have meat processors who do the job for you for a charge, per pound, and most of those I've met are reliable. The skills of a butcher are something not many of us have, even after learning to dress out a deer or other game animal. Some meat processors will also take over the finish feeding of the animal, if you wish, but this adds to the cost considerably. In addition to the butchering skills needed, few people have a freezer of the type intended to flash freeze large quantities of meat. If the meat isn't quickly frozen it may spoil, so the butcher's quick freezer is needed.

Right now, I believe meat processors in this area are charging 12 cents to about 18 cents a pound (finishweight) to butcher a carcass, after slaughter, and they keep the hide. Most beef animals will dress out at about 55 percent of live weight, so you can look for from 600 to 750 pounds of meat from a live weight steer of 100 to 1250 pounds. Feed costs will vary, as will the butchering charge, so it is really impossible to estimate what the per pound cost of meat will be for any steer. First, you have to buy the animal as a calf and then feed it. Right now feeder calves are going for a pretty good price, more than I used to pay for a pound of sirloin steak 15 years ago.(Fig. 9-2).

Feeding

Cattle are *ruminants*. They have an extra stomach, or *rumen*, which allows them to recall a meal and chew it over again before it reaches the second stomach. Cattle eat grass, grassy hays, legume hays and silage, as well as grains. Good pasture of fescue or orchard grass will hold a couple of cattle during, warm weather, but winter feeding of silage (usually chopped corn) is often needed. Winter feeding may also include hay. Finish feeding is most often done with corn, and should take place at least the last 14 days before slaughter. A month is better if you have the grain and time. You can determine the maturity of a steer simply by noting how fast it grows. When growth slows, finish-feed and take to the processor.

HOGS

Of all the four-legged animals likely to make money for a small farm *hogs* are the best. Feeder hogs bought young in the spring can be converted to cash and food before winter falls. But this requires tiresome care and expensive extra feeding. Hogs, though, are not grazing animals and must be fed in their pens daily. Still, they take little room and can provide some profit, as well as a good deal of sausage, chops and roasts (Fig. 9-3).

To raise pigs, you will need some shelter for them—the size, of course, depending on the number of pigs to be raised. Fencing must be sturdy and should have a board run at the base to prevent the pigs from rooting underneath and scattering. A bit of room to move around and root is also a good idea, and the *sty* itself should have an easily washed concrete floor, if at all possible. Pigs are no more dirty than other animals, but they are too often kept in conditions of filth, often to an extent that I am surprised that most of them don't die. A concrete floor in the sty helps cut down on accumulation from any walling they do and also helps keep down odors, which can be quite strong if not controlled.

Select healthy hogs of a breed, or cross, popular in your locale. Feed the hogs well for about six months, possibly less depending on the breed, and take them to your meat processor or sell them. The work is done and need not start again until spring.

RABBITS

Rabbits raised for meat at home require very little space and minimal equipment. If you live in an area where the climate is reasonably mild, *hutches* about 2 feet high can be placed outdoors. Generally, a hutch doesn't need to be more than 4 feet deep and about 2½ or 3 feet wide.

Figure 9-4 provides a plan for a two unit rabbit hutch of decent size that can be used almost anywhere. With addition of shelter and some form of heat it would be fine in cooler areas.

Using rabbits for home meat supply provides you with a fine-grained, white meat high in protein. Meat yield is quite high since only about 20 percent of the carcass is bone, and the skins have some market value. Most valuable is the skin from white rabbits because it can be dyed any color.

Young rabbits can be bought as breeding stock, or you can pay a little more and get older animals almost ready for breeding. Just weaned stock is cheaper, but the does aren't

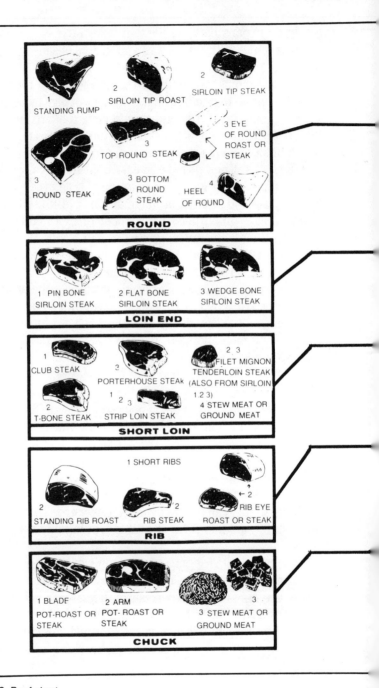

Fig. 9-2. Beef chart.

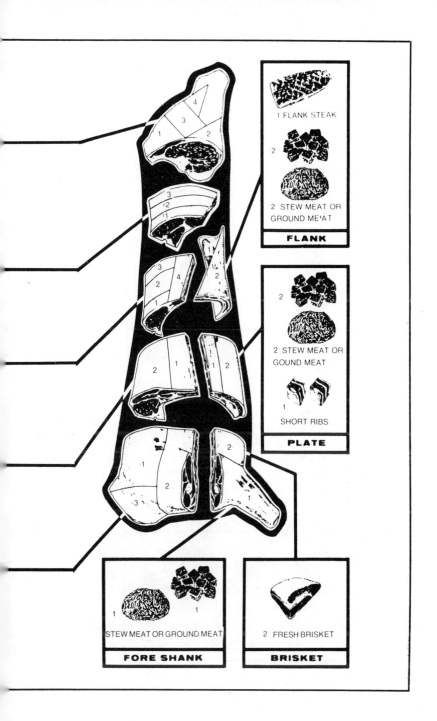

1 FLANK STEAK

2 STEW MEAT OR GROUND MEAT

FLANK

2 STEW MEAT OR GOUND MEAT

SHORT RIBS

PLATE

STEW MEAT OR GROUND MEAT

FORE SHANK

2 FRESH BRISKET

BRISKET

HAM

HAM SHANK PORTION   SMOKED HAM CENTER SLICE   HAM BUTT PORTION

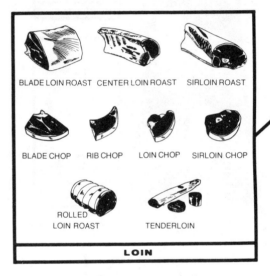

LOIN

BLADE LOIN ROAST   CENTER LOIN ROAST   SIRLOIN ROAST

BLADE CHOP   RIB CHOP   LOIN CHOP   SIRLOIN CHOP

ROLLED LOIN ROAST   TENDERLOIN

BOSTON BUTT

BOSTON BUTT   BLADE STEAK   ROLLED BOSTON BUTT

Fig. 9-3. Pork chart.

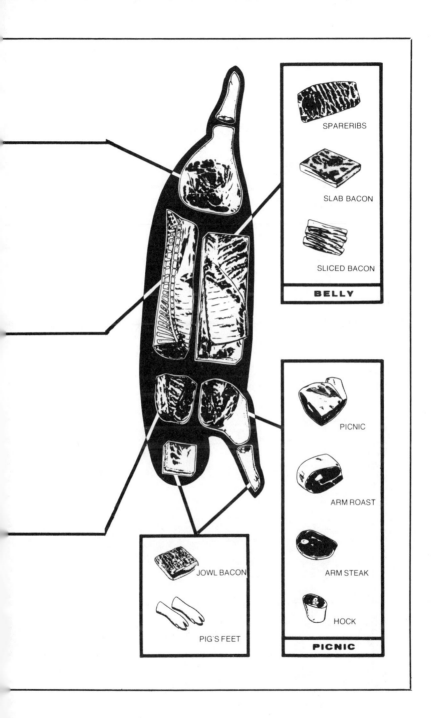

SPARERIBS

SLAB BACON

SLICED BACON

BELLY

PICNIC

ARM ROAST

ARM STEAK

HOCK

JOWL BACON

PIG'S FEET

PICNIC

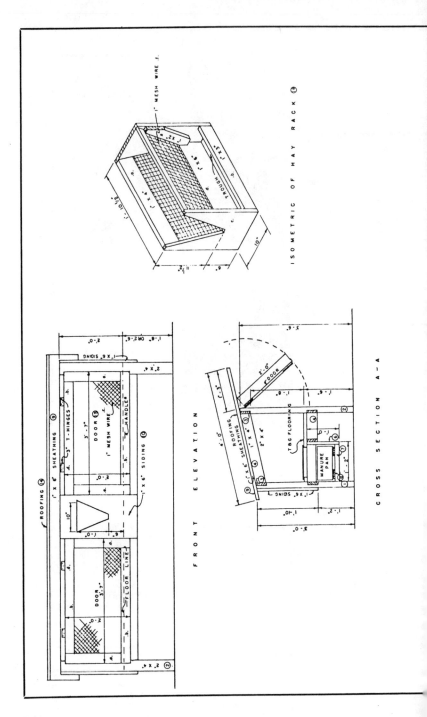

ISOMETRIC OF HAY RACK

FRONT ELEVATION

CROSS SECTION A-A

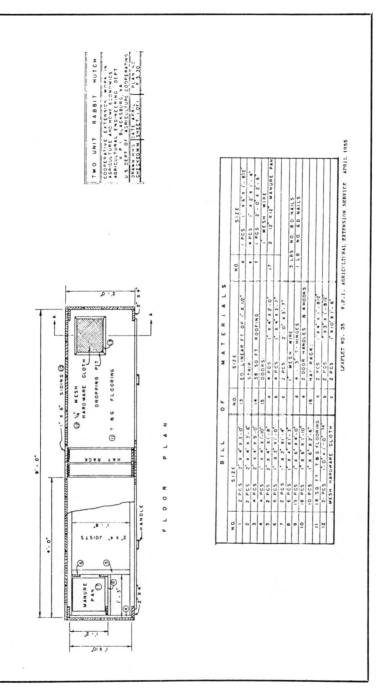

Fig. 9-4. Details for a two unit rabbit hutch and hay rack

ready for breeding until they are about five or six months old. You will want to select a medium or heavy breed, among which the most popular are *New Zealand, American, Bevern, Chinchilla* and *Flemish Giants*. Get the stock from a reliable breeder, and get a guarantee of the stock's health and productivity.

Productivity should be high, as rabbits have a short 31 day gestation period. The doe can be bred again when the young are five or six weeks old. This allows each doe to produce four or five litters a year. Young rabbits of medium breeds are ready to market or eat when they are weaned at two months of age and weigh about 4 pounds, so each doe can easily produce about 100 pounds of meat a year.

When the doe is nursing her young, protein should make up 20 percent of her ration, grain about 39.5 percent, roughage 40 percent and salt ½ percent. Dry does, bucks and young rabbits will do well on an 8 percent protein supplement, with 31.5 percent of grain, 60 percent roughage and ½ percent of salt. You can buy rabbit feed already mixed, in pellet form. Mix your own from linseed meal, cottonseed meal and soybean meal for protein. Then add corn, barley, oats, wheat or milo for grain. Alfalfa or clover hay provides the roughage needed, and miniature salt blocks are available. Each doe, and her four litters, will need about 400 pounds of the mixture per year.

For a treat, you can add on occasion small amounts of green feed such as cabbage, lettuce, fresh cut grass, or other garden crops. Make sure none has been sprayed with insecticide.

HORSES

All sorts of arguments against and in favor of horses on a small farm can be raised. Much depends on what you plan, and my dream at one time was to raise horses as a means of making a living. That died as the price of land went up. Even my modest schemes for about 18 or 20 mares foundered on the financial rocks of the 20th century. A good horse is a definite pleasure, as well as an expense, and one that many people enjoy on just a few acres. I have one friend up in New York who is raising Arabians on just about 10 acres of land. I am sure of one thing, though. My friend is making little or no money raising his horses, what with having to buy all his feed and paying stud fees, taxes and high veterinarian fees. But he loves the horses.

Today, there is somewhat of a return to the use of draft animals on farms and even in some logging operations, instead of fuel guzzling tractors and skidders. I doubt we will ever see a full scale return to farming with horses for two reasons. First, it is slower than mechanized farming. Second, it is a lot more work. Draft animals must eat whether working or not, while just shutting off the switch cuts the feed off a tractor. Still, if you're not against taking a bit more time, working a bit harder, and growing your own feed, the idea may prove practical for you.

Light horses or *pleasure horses* are another matter entirely. I doubt there is any justification beyond simple pleasure for such animals on a small farm. Again, there is nothing wrong with pleasure that I can see. If one of your pleasures happens to be horses, then select one (Fig. 9-5).

Draft Horses

Draft or *work horses* were originally developed for warfare. The knights of the Middle Ages may have been small in

Fig. 9-5. Doug Meador puts a horse he has trained through some paces.

stature, but all that tinplate they wore would soon break the back of a Thoroughbred, Arabian or *Quarter Horse*. Light horses developed in many ways in various countries throughout the world, while draft horses primarily come from England and the Continent where feudal armies once battled.

Looking at the breeds of draft horses and light horses will point up some of the differences. We can later look at the similarities in such things as feed and care.

Percherons come from a small province in France or at least they originated and are still bred there, as well as in this country. Percherons first saw these shores in 1839, and by the 1880s were quite popular. By 1930, two-thirds of the registered draft horses in the United States were Percherons. The Percheron combines size with a great deal of spirit and action, which once endeared it to many farmers. Today, Percherons can be found in white and black, in about equal numbers, though the occasional *chestnut* and *bay* will occur. During the 1920s and 1930s, the *Belgian* began to overtake the Percheron in popularity and remains in first place today. Colors here are more varied than with the Percherons, and there are many Belgians with *sorrel* coats and white manes and tails. *Clydesdales* are the third most popular (though the most frequently seen) breed of draft horses in this country. They have a white face and white legs with a silk-fine feather on the legs which, combined with high leg action, makes the Clydesdale a real show stopper. Clydesdales come out of Scotland's valley of the river Clyde, and bay is the dominant color, though there are many blacks and some chestnuts.

Britain has produced two less well known breeds, the *Shire* and the *Suffolk*. The Shire is similar in appearance to the Clydesdale, but is somewhat more massively built. The Suffolk is the only breed originally developed for farm work rather than war. All are chestnuts, with very little in the way of white markings, and they are built something like a chunkier Belgian.

While not a breed, *chunks* may prove a good buy as working animals. A chunk is a light draft animal, usually bred with a draft breed stallion on a light breed mare. They cost less to buy then heavy draft animals and also cost less to feed. Obviously, they can't pull the loads a heavy drafter can, but they can still do a pretty good job of hauling and plowing on a small farm.

Mules

Mules, jacks, jennies, hinnies and animals of this nature are basically thriftier animals than horses of any breed. They have tremendous strength and durability in relation to their size and also seem to have more horse sense than do horses. Mules and jacks will not overeat and founder themselves. Founder is a separation of the laminae in the hoof caused by overeating and other problems. The mule is a sterile hybrid of a jack and a draft mare. It has great endurance and is tougher than a horse. The mule remains in good shape under adverse conditions better than a horse can.

Today, only two classes of mules mean much. Early in the century, breeders developed a type of jack known as the *Mammoth Jack*, with top grade specimens reaching up to 16 hands and weights up to 1200 pounds. Breeding a Mammoth Jack to a Percheron dam produces draft mules of quite good size, usually from 15 to 16 *hands* (a hand is 4 inches). The *cotton mule* is more likely to be found around here, though I've also seen a few draft mules. Cotton mules range in size from 14 to 15 hands and are lighter framed and more active than draft mules.

Light Horse Breeds

Light horse breeds are more varied, as their uses were more varied throughout history. Thoroughbreds are probably the most familiar horse to Americans, as they are what we see running the Kentucky Derby, the Belmont Stakes and other flat races, as well as steeplechases. Registered Thoroughbreds can be bought for reasonable prices. The greater the quality of the horse, the higher the price is going to be.

Morgans are harder to find. They are a relatively small breed as far as build goes, with most in the 800 to 900 pound range and almost never over 15 hands. The Morgan has a delicate head, tapering necks, short legs and short bodies.

The *Arabian* is probably my favorite breed and is one of two hot-blooded breeds (Thoroughbred is the other) with which most people are likely to be familiar. This may be the oldest breed, in terms of selective breeding, in the world. Selective breeding practices are said to have taken place as far back as 600 A.D. The head on an Arabian is small, with curved,pointed ears, a small muzzle and well set eyes. It is another relatively small horse, with sizes seldom going much over 15 hands and often dropping down near 14 hands. Arabians tend to be expensive, too, and sometimes nearly as much as Thoroughbreds. I doubt that a good Arabian mare today could be bought for less than $2,500, and it doesn't take much in the way of a bloodline to send that figure shooting over $10,000.

Quarter Horses are changing. The old, chunky style Quarter Horse is not bred so often these days, as owners try to get more speed. Activity in the breed is strong, though, and old style horses are still available, though not commanding the prices of the racier types. As a cold-blooded breed, the Quarter Horse is a good, steady mount, with plenty of speed.

For colorful horses, there is no way to beat the Appaloosa. This is one of the fastest growing breeds around for several reasons besides their colors and spots. First, they are still reasonable in price, while gaining in value as the breed gains popularity. Second, the breed carries many of the best points of other breeds and adds a few of its own. Appaloosas are noted for their stamina, courage and a calm or steady disposition. Right now, Aps are the third largest breed in the country, with Quarter Horses being first and Thoroughbreds second.

Appaloosas cannot be mistaken for other breeds, for they have the white showing around the eye. In other breeds this is a bad mark, showing signs of an uneven temper; in Aps it is a breed requirement. The skin is mottled and spotted in black and white (this is most easily seen around the muzzle). Hooves have a distinct vertical black and white stripping.

Spot patterns and colors vary widely, and no two are alike. The patterns of the spots tend to change from year to year.

Paint and *Pinto* horses also have distinctive markings. *Overo* patterned horses have white markings extending upwards from the belly, while *Tobiano* horses have the primary white markings extending down from the back.

There are other breeds of light horses to be found including *Buckskins, Tennessee Walking Horses, Racking Horse*, and *Missouri Fox Trotting*, as well as *American Saddle* Horses and *Paso Fino*. Each has its own characteristics. You may wish to check with the various breed associations for information on which might be most suitable to you, and where you can locate breeders.

While not a breed, a *grade horse* can be a good buy for casual use and riding. Too many people today seem to think that papers will make a horse. An umregistered horse, or grade horse, is often the cheapest way to go, allowing you to get a good horse at a price no breeder of registered horses can afford to set. Good overall quality is the thing to look for anytime you are thinking of buying a horse, whether it is a pleasure horse or a draft horse.

Selecting a Horse

Age is a prime consideration in buying a horse, but too many people tend to consider a horse as old long before it is. Depending on the breed, most horses finish growing at about five years and mature, or settle down, at eight or nine. From then on, much of the condition at a particular age is dependent on how the horse is used and cared for. I have seen 17-year-old Thoroughbreds run very well in a steeplechase upstate, and know of at least two Arabian stallions still standing at stud past 21 years old (Figs. 9-6 through 9-8).

Generally, for work and riding horses you will want a *gelding*. Stallions can be fractious and are not necessary unless you plan to breed horses, while mares do tend to get edgy when in heat. If you plan to ride and are a beginner at it, don't go for an expensively trained horse that can do a lot of tricks. By the time you catch up to the horse's level of skills, he will have forgotten most of what he knows. What you need as a beginner is a horse that will go easily and quietly.

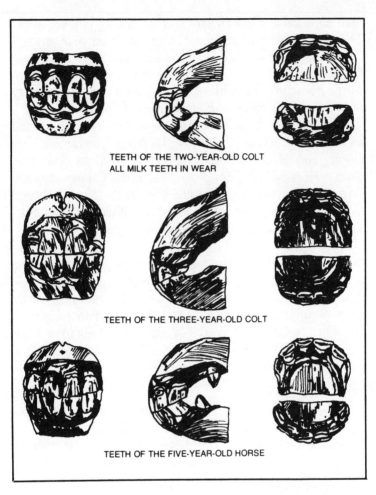

TEETH OF THE TWO-YEAR-OLD COLT
ALL MILK TEETH IN WEAR

TEETH OF THE THREE-YEAR-OLD COLT

TEETH OF THE FIVE-YEAR-OLD HORSE

Fig. 9-6. Teeth of two and three-year-old colts and the five-year-old horse.

Your own size will have some relation to the size of the horse you select for riding, while the size of the jobs to be done will have a relation to the size of draft animals. The oversized horse for the short rider can present problems of control and mounting. Even at my height, 6 feet 2 inches, I feel no real need for a huge horse to ride. I've ridden horses as small as 14 hands recently and found no problem, though I have also been on horses over 16 hands. On the latter, I feel as if I am on top of the Empire State Building (Figs. 9-9 and 9-10).

Checking a Horse's Manners

When checking a horse over, check his manners, too. Any horse, draft or pleasure, should be trained to give its hooves easily for inspection. This check, incidentally, is one too many riders overlook and one that should be performed both before and after any ride or, in the case of draft horses, any chore. How does the horse accept general handling? A well mannered horse will stand quietly while being groomed or treated. Ride the horse for a few minutes to check the gaits and to see if you are possibly buying a horse that is capable of running back to the barn the instant your attention lapses—known as *barn sour*.

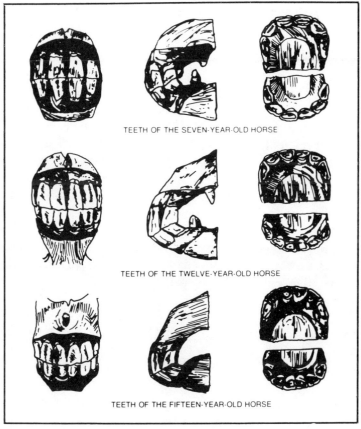

TEETH OF THE SEVEN-YEAR-OLD HORSE

TEETH OF THE TWELVE-YEAR-OLD HORSE

TEETH OF THE FIFTEEN-YEAR-OLD HORSE

Fig. 9-7. Teeth of seven, 12 and 15-year-old horses.

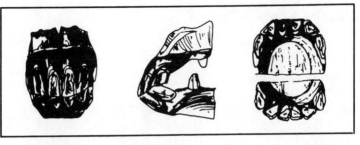

Fig. 9-8. Teeth of the 20-year-old horse.

Some horses also try to brush the rider off. Mount, dismount and remount. See how the horse stands for that, as well as for saddling. Now stall the horse and see if it tries to crowd you when you enter. A stall-trained horse should move its rump over when it realizes someone is entering the stall.

Looking At Conformation

Once the gaits, manners and handling are considered, you have arrived at the time to look at conformation. Check for blemishes and other such things. Breed variations must be considered when looking over any horse, but general rules of conformation should still apply. The head should be well shaped, with a clean line, good jaw breadth and muscles. Ears should be moderate or small in size and carried well—a horse's ears give much indication of its thoughts and feelings (if we can assume horses think in the same sense as humans do). Thus, they should move as you, or other people, move around the horse, following sounds alertly. In any breeds other than Appaloosas and Paints, there should be almost no white showing around the eye.

Check the horse's vision. The horse's visual range does not include the area around its mouth. Don't try to check the vision by patting the nose or stroking under the jaw (Fig. 9-11).

Move on to the chest, which should be deep and wide, with the legs set straight and square. Check the legs carefully, as here is the site of many problems with horses. Look for bowed tendons, which show up as swel-

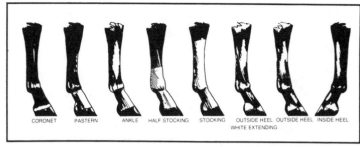

Fig. 9-9. Markings of legs in light horses.

lings of the tendons behind the cannon bones (check both front and hind legs). A *quittor* is a running sore found at the *coronet* (top of the hoof), and splints are bony growths on the insides of the front legs. Large splints can cause lameness. You will often see the marks of *pinfiring* on horses with large splints. Pinfiring kills the nerves in the area to cut pain; it does not cure splints (Figs. 9-12 and 9-13). Buck kneed horses have knees that bend forward, while the knees on calf kneed horses will bend backwards.

Some faults are more serious than others, but I would advise staying away from a horse with bowed tendons or splints. Bowed tendons will take a set, usually in about a year, and the horse can be used. But hard use will cause more problems. Splints, unless already pinfired, will possibly cause future lameness.

Checking for Hoof Problems

Lift a front hoof and check for problems. A hoof in good condition is easily notices, as there will be no sign of

Fig. 9-10. Face markings in light horses.

325

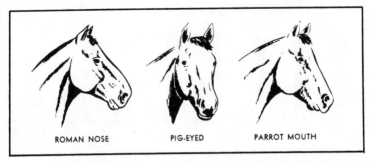

Fig. 9-11. Some undesirable characteristics for horses to have.

an acrid odor, which would indicate *thrush*, and no more than a few small cracks. The hoof will be reasonably wide and the heel won't be contracted or pulled in. Cracks in hooves don't grow back together, so different techniques may be used to immobilize the crack such that any new horn growing doesn't also crack (Fig. 9-14).

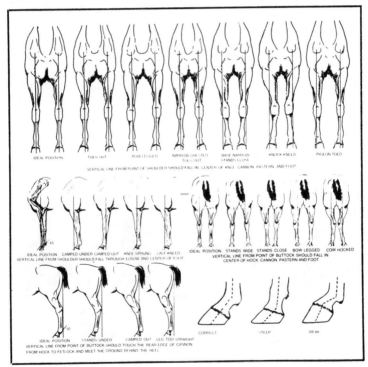

Fig. 9-12. Good and bad conformation characteristics.

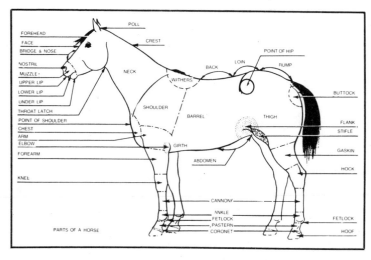

Fig. 9-13. Parts of a horse.

Founder, or laminitis, is a common cause of lameness in horses, though it shouldn't be. The sensitive laminae of the hoof become inflamed, causing the animal extreme pain. Check the gait of the horse. If it seems to be walking on its heels, avoid buying the animal. Founder causes most of the pain near the front of hoof, forcing the animal to walk on its heels (Fig. 9-15).

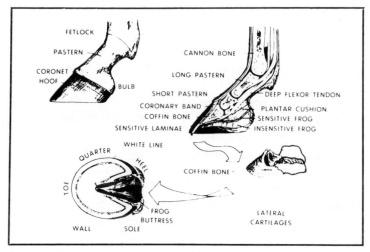

Fig. 9-14. Parts of the pastern and foot.

327

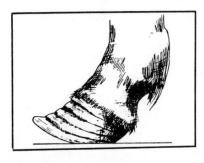

Fig. 9-15. Foundered hoof.

Examining Body Parts

Now move on to the side and check the general flow of one body part to another, and the overall look of fitting together. You should look for a slope of about 45 degrees at the shoulder, and a short, strong looking top of the back. The middle, or barrel, should be of good size and the ribs well spread. From the side, look for squarely set legs and pasterns sloping at 45 degrees.

The rear of the horse should appear wide and strong through the rump. Tail set should conform to breed type (some have tails set higher than others). Long flowing manes and tails go against breed type in Appaloosa, which are to have short manes and tails. A check for *stringhalt* means the horse will have to be put in motion. Stringhalt is an excessive flexing of the hind legs when the horse moves backward or forward. While the cause isn't known, surgery can help.

Other Considerations

Draft horses and mules will not be ridden often, if at all, so they should be made to do what you're buying them for, at least partially. They should be hitched and made to pull a good-sized load so that you can check for willingness to work, wind soundness, strength and any weaknesses that would show up during work. A particular check should be made to see if a draft horse is a kicker. Any horse that kicks a lot is a pain and can be dangerous. But the size of a drafter's hooves (some are nearly as big as dinner plates) makes a non-kicker even more desirable. Check the stall for hoof marks, and watch for capped elbows and scars on the hind legs. All may be an indication of a kicker.

If you're buying a team of draft horses, have them hitched as a team and work with a load to see if they pull well together. It's pretty much up to you as to whether or not your try to match colors in a draft team, I would surely try to match size so that the smaller member of the team won't be overworked.

Once the team is selected, or the pleasure horse chosen and brought home, you run into other equine considerations. Feeding and general care are extremely important in the life of a horse, and somewhat more delicate than with other livestock.

Feeding

While not extremely complex, feeding a horse takes more care in selection than does feeding a cow or goat. The same silage on which cattle thrive will kill a horse. The real complexity of feeding a horse is in the feed selection. Hay must be fresh and dry—the molds formed in hay that has been wet can also kill a horse. A horse's digestive system differs greatly from that of a cow. The horse has a single stomach of much smaller size, so that it can't bring back food to chew later. The horse must eat more often to keep the smaller stomach full.

With a grazing horse, on good pasture, there is little problem. But a stabled horse fed on concentrates can very easily overeat to the point of founder, and then have to be put down. Thus, the amounts of concentrated food the horse gets must be carefully controlled, and grain storage must be secure enough to prevent the horse from getting to it. Legume hays are in some ways a form of concentrate, so these should also be fed with care and stored carefully.

The nutritional needs of the horse and the values of the various feeds need consideration. *Alfalfa*, a legume hay, offers about 20 percent protein, while grass hays will often be as low as 7 percent and seldom over 8 percent. In most cases, this would make alfalfa the best feed, especially since in almost every area alfalfa will not sell for twice what, say, orchard grass does. However, it will provide close to three times the nutrient value. In most cases this is true. But a check should be kept on any horse as it is fed, so that any problems that might tend to creep into the stall can be overcome.

When you buy hay, do it in person. Don't simply order the stuff and have it delivered. Check to see the hay isn't damp or moldy and that dust is not excessive. Early-cut hay is best. Late-cut hay has fewer leaves and more stems; stems have little value nutritionally.

A good general diet for a horse will start with 12 or 13 percent protein (nursing mares need 21 percent), at least 2 ounces of salt, fed free choice, plus 70 grams of calcuim, 60 grams of phosphrous, 68 grams of potassium, 6.4 grams of magnesium, 640 milligrams (mg) of iron, 400 mg of zinc, 340 mg of manganese, 90 mg of copper, 2.6 mg or iodine and 1.5 mg of cobalt. As far as vitamins go, provide 50,000 International Units of A, 7,000 of D and 200 of E. Add in 400 mg of *choline*, 60 mg of *pantothenic acid*, 40 mg of *riboflavin*, 25 mg of *thiamin*, 8 mg of K, 2.5 mg of *folic acid* and 125 mg of vitamin B12.

The horse will need about 2 ½ pounds of feed per day, per hundred pounds of body weight. The mineral and vitamin needs just listed are for a 1,000 pound horse, and you will need to adapt them a bit to suit your animal.

Almost certainly you will feed locally grown hays, and these will vary with area. Alfalfa, the clovers and lespedeza are legume hays with a high protein content and a lot of calcium, but they are low enough in phosphorus to require a supplement. Legume hays are normally fed in combination with grass hays to that protein levels aren't too high. Any change to a richer food, such as legume hays, should be made slowly. Grass hays include *brome, timothy, bermuda, orchard grass* and some others. Generally, overall nutritional contents are a lot lower then those of legume hays.

Pasturing, if the land is available, is the cheapest way to feed a horse through much of the year. A good pasture requires care and upkeep, but it is still a lot cheaper than buying hay. A favorite pasture in this area is *Kentucky bluegrass*, which reaches a height of about 7 inches and has a root system type that is good at healing torn up areas. Fescue is also used, but horses don't seem to like it much for some reason. It may lack taste to them. Orchard grass can also make good pasture, especially if combined with one of the clovers or bluegrass. Use care in turning horses out on early spring pasture, as the new grass is lush and heavy with water and could cause founder. Limit any horse turned out on fresh pasture to about 15 minutes of feeding for the first two weeks.

Feed concentrates include the grains, such as oats and corn, but today it is also possible to buy pelletized alfalfa and other hays if you need to. Oats is generally the preferred concentrate in this country, since the price is usually reasonable and nutritional values suit horses well. Look for the heaviest oats possible when making your selection, and don't buy any weighing much less than 30 pounds per bushel.

Barley can also be fed to horses, but must be ground or rolled first. Nutritional content is about the same as oats.

Corn is good as a horse feed. It is a bit lower in crude protein than oats, as well as being a bit low on crude fiber.

All grains should be fed by weight, not volume, as the weight of a bushel of any grain can vary a great deal. As an example, a bushel of oats may vary in weight from as little as 23 pounds on up to 36 pounds, which is more than a 50 percent jump.

Bagged supplements also can be bought. Some are quite good, especially when you are trying to bring an older horse back or don't have time to figure and mix your own feeds. Check labels to see the contents of the premixed feeds.

Treatment Against Internal Parasites

Other than food and water, your horse will need treatment for internal parasites, usually on a 30 or 60 day basis. Internal parasites are a fact of life for horses. All horses have them, and some horses die from them. Treatment is not cheap—using feed administered wormers for a 900 pound horse will cost about $60 a year if needed monthly and half that if needed bi-monthly—but neither is losing a horse.

There are five internal parasites that provide the main problems with horses. *Bots*, or *gastrophilus*, are the eggs of the adult *botfly* and will be found from late summer through fall on the hair of the horse's legs, neck and head, and in some cases right on up the legs to the belly. The horse ingests the eggs, where the moist heat of the mouth starts them hatching into larvae that travel on through, emerging from spring fecal matter as adult botflies. Damage is done to the stomach lining by bots, and extreme infestations can cause stomach rupture. Interference with digestion is also a problem. Bots can usually be fooled into dropping off the horse with a warm water rinse, and special bot knives are also useful for reducing the number of eggs.

Pinworms, or *oxyuris*, are found as adult worms in the rear intestinal tract where the females move to the anus and deposit eggs around the opening. Eggs, after being dropped with fecal matter in stables and pastures, are eventually eaten by the horse and develop into larvae in the large intestine. The primary damage likely is the irritation the eggs cause, which may force the horse to become a tail rubber.

Bloodworms start as eggs on pasture, taking about seven days to develop to the infective state (there are two types. The female may lay as many as 5,000 eggs in a single day. The larvae are picked up as the horse feeds, and they go on to the intestinal tract to penetrate the wall of the intestine. Migration causes them to move up blood vessels, causing damage and irritation as the movement goes on. Damage occurs when blood movement is slowed, and can also include damage to the heart, liver and the lining of the abdominal cavity.

Roundworms, or *ascarids*, are damaged little by heat and cold. They also have a dormant span that may last for months. Adults in the upper intestine lay eggs and interfere with digestion, with one result being severe diarrhea. In severe cases the whole intestine may be blocked and ruptured.

It is impossible to totally rid a horse of all internal parasites for all time, so a continuing program of worming must be kept up to keep your animals healthy. There are now about nine substances on the market that do a good job on most worms. Some are more effective against one type than against others, while one, *Trichlorfon*, works well on all but bloodworms. It is necessary therefore to change wormers every other month or so. Follow the manufacturer's directions carefully. Use at least two different kinds of wormer, preferably three, and you should have good results. If your horse remains unthrifty and shows other signs of parasite infestation, call your veterinarian. The vet can tube worm your horse to get the material directly to the stomach. Horse care includes other things than worming, and keeping the horse clean and neat looking is part of it.

Grooming

Grooming can be expanded to get things to the point of getting a horse ready for a show, which can get a bit complex, from the basic washing to the braiding of the mane and tail for some classes of competition. In general, grooming is the day-to-day business of keeping the horse clean and as neat as possible, while making sure it hasn't any injuries. Pastured horses won't often need a lot of care until just before they are to be used, unless the pasture is a muddy mess in too many spots. Stabled horses and horses worked regularly must be groomed more often (Fig. 9-16).

A good grooming is one of the best ways of getting to know a horse better, and serves as a good time for checking the animal out for sores and injuries. It starts with a hoof check and cleaning. Use a hoof pick and lift the horse's hooves one at a time. For front hooves, stand at the shoulder and lift the hoof with one hand. The horse will, if properly trained, more or less give its hoof, but some require urging which can be done by using the thumb and forefinger to press in at the coronet, on opposite sides of the hoof. Move the hoof backwards—to the horse's rear, not yours—and tip the hoof so you can clean with the pick and check the cracks and bruises. You should have your inside shoulder touching the horse's shoulder as you lift the hoof, but don't allow the animal to put weight on you. You want to give it a feeling of security, but a lazy horse will often try to stand or-lean on anyone checking hooves.

Fig. 9-16. Some important grooming tools, including currycombs.

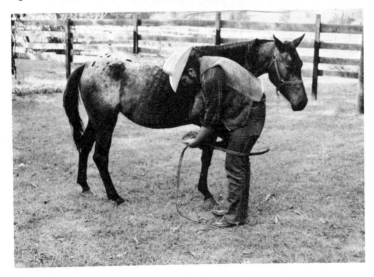

Fig. 9-17. Lift the horse's front hoof carefully.

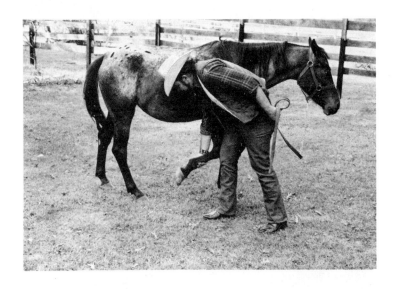

Fig. 9-18. Caring for a front hoof.

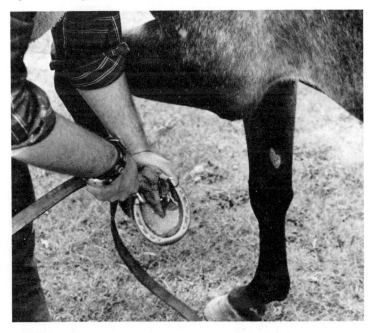

Fig. 9-19. Jim Shands patiently works on his mare's hoof

335

Fig. 9-20. Lift the hoof carefully.

Fig. 9-21. Inspecting a rear hoof.

336

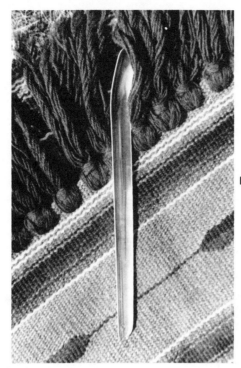

Fig. 9-22. A sweat scraper.

Fig. 9-23. Other grooming tools.

Rear hooves are checked in the same way, with you using your outside hand at the hip of the horse to get it to shift weight off the foot. You are again facing to the rear of the horse, and the inside hand is gently but firmly slipped down until it grips the hoof to be raised. Don't just reach and grab, as that will tend to make even the calmest horse jittery. (Figs. 9-17 through 9-21).

From the hoof check, move to the grooming tools. You will need a good rubber *currycomb*, a mane and tail comb (get a small one of heavy aluminum as I have yet to have a plastic one last beyond two or three uses) and a *sweat scraper*. You can also get a *grooming mitt*. Mine is of rubber with raised nipples all over its surface. A couple of grooming brushes, one soft and one fairly stiff, will also be handy (Figs. 9-22 and 9-32).

The rubber currycomb is used to rough out the coat to remove caked sweat, dirt and grit. It is used in a circular motion with a fair amount of strength. The hair is left roughed up. Never use a rubber or metal currycomb below the knees or hocks or on the horse's face. The bone is too close under the skin in those areas for that kind of pressure. The brushes, first the stiff and then the soft, are used to brush the hair back down. Use the mane and tail comb to get

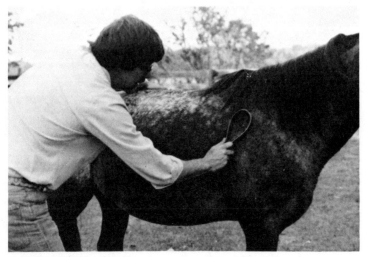

Fig. 9-24. Grooming a horse.

Fig. 9-25. The technique of using a grooming brush.

out any snarls in those areas, and you are done with the horse care. You will get the job done quickly, though a lot will depend on your horse's manners and the amount of dirt it has picked up. At a guess, a moderately used horse can be curried and brushed in 15 or 20 minutes by someone with a bit of experience(Figs. 9-24 and 9-25).

10

Soil

Soil types and soil care are inseparable for any form of farming. If you plan any scale farming of crops such as vegetables, grains or hay, then the importance will rapidly come clear to the first time a field fails because the pH is off or there is too little nitrogen. Much of the soil in this country has been mistreated in one way or another over the past few hundred years that we have farmed it. Some reclamation may be necessary even on a working farm and in areas where erosion has been a problem, or where the ground was just worn out before the farmer moved on. More effort and expense, will be needed, as will a longer time to see results. I've always said that no matter where I moved and planted a vegetable garden, the first year, with a single exception, has never been anywhere near as good as following years.

SOIL CLASSIFICATIONS AND QUALITIES

Soils are classified according to their makeup: *sandy, clayey, humus-laden* or *loamy* and almost any combination in between. The soil around here is most often a heavy red clay type, which is fine except for a couple of things. It is fine because it is heavy in most minerals, but not so fine in that the stuff is murderous to work. I've seen New Yorkers almost cry the first time they stick a spading fork into the ground here. It's quite easy to snap off a handle. Most people will either hire the plowing out or use a pick axe to break ground for the first time if they have any sense at all. Sand soils present an opposite example. They are very easy to work, but there is almost no plant food material and water runs on through without any effort. Plants will shrivel and die quickly from lack of ground water. Loams, with good workability and high humus content, are the most desirable for growing almost any kind of plants outside of cacti. Loams combine clays, sands and vegetable matter, so they have good food content for plants, hold water well and are easily worked.

Before even bothering with soil testing, you should check out the type of soil you have. If the soil is a clay type, no matter whether it's red, blue or yellow clay, you will want to add sand and humus to it. If it is a sandy soil, consider adding some clay. Actually, in both cases it is usually much easier to add vegetable matter than it is another type of soil in order to modify things. In really heavy clays and porous sands, a lot of vegetable matter may be needed, with some clays needing several tons of manures, sawdust compost for just 2500 square feet of land. Obviously, such modification is a lot more practical in a vegetable garden of good size than it is in a 50-acre hayfield. Wood ashes and other materials also help. In many areas a dressing of lime the winter before planting would be a good idea. Your county extension agent can test soil samples for you to see for sure whether or not you need the lime and other material.

Texture

Soil texture is extremely important in vegetable gardens, and most especially so in those where many root vegetables are to be grown. My first experience with Virginia clay and carrots doesn't really merit retelling, but I would guess those carrots were short enough to use more as Christmas tree light bulbs instead of as food. Coarse soils are known as quick because they dry rapidly, warm up quickly and allow you to sow seed early. Coarse soils also tend to require a lot of water and a fertilizer, since water runs through quickly and carries the fertilizing elements with it.

Medium sand loams don't allow such early sowing, but do a better job of holding water and nutrients for the plant once sowed. Fine sandy loams are a bit later even than the mediums. Late sown crops do best in a heavier, clayey soil that retains a lot of water and holds fertility well.

Humus

Humus is the decayed organic material, most often vegetable, contained in soils. It increases the water retaining qualities of the soil and makes soil easier to work, while adding to sun absorption and holding plant nutrients. Helpers such as earthworms are far more numerous in humus-heavy soils than in clay or sand but, unfortunately, so are little monsters such as grubs. Natural humus consists of tree leaves, grasses and animal manures of many kinds. Today there is not always enough to go around, so it may be necessary to make you own or use manures from your own or someone else's stables, sty, chicken coop or whatever. Compost piles should be started and kept going so that materials can also be added to the soil as needed.

Color

Color is not really an accurate indicator of soil quality, though there are some indications that may be taken from soil color. Dark-colored soils obviously are going to catch and hold more of the sun's heat. A brown color may well indicate soil acidity. When the brown turns to red, as it does around here, you can expect to have to lime your fields and gardens every few years to keep acidity down (a few vegetables, such as potatoes, grow best in acid soil, but most grow best in nearly neutral soils). White and light colored soils are generally lacking in organic matter and clay, with an excess of sand, so they cannot catch and hold water well enough to grow crops.

Tests

To discover what your land needs, I would carefully take soil samples from various spots in a plot. Either use one of the Sudbury testing kits or have the extension agent do soil tests. In this way you will know if you are coming up short on potash, nitrogen, lime or whatever. And you will know how much of each is needed to correct the condition. Adding too much fertilizer, whether organic or chemical, is a waste of money (and may actually burn plants in some cases), while too little fertilizer does not do the job.

MANURE APPLICATION

Applying manure of one kind or another is one way to add to humus content and soil fertility right away. Manure makes such a fine fertilizer for several reasons: the presence of microorganisms in the manure to help speed decay, the release of nitrogen and minerals as the manure decays, and the addition of humus to the soil. It is unfortunate that with the decline in use of horses in this century, manures have gotten harder and harder to come by. It is still possible for most people to find some manure, but it tends to cost money. I still know a few places where I can get it if I'm willing to clean out the stalls and cart the stuff off myself. You may be able to locate similar sources in your own area. In my area, looking for private horse owners and riding stables is the best idea, as the dairy farmers use the manure to fertilize their own fields. Dried and deodorized manures are available in garden stores.

Manure application depends on whether it is fresh or rotted (especially horse manure which will, if fresh, burn plants badly). In all cases it is applied before the ground is plowed if it is fresh, while rotted and powdered manures are applied after plowing. For a 2500 square foot garden, you could use 250 pounds of sheep manure, about 200 pounds of poultry droppings, about 350 to 400 pounds of horse manure, and about 400 to 500 pounds of cow manure. Apply fresh manure in the fall and work it into the soil.

FERTILIZERS

Commercial fertilizers are another matter. Though the fertilizers increase soil fertility, they do not add humus to soil, although they can be manufactured more closely to fit a particular soil's needs for other nutrient forms than is generally possible when using manures. Much of the commercial fertilizer available today is made from petroleum. Thus, the price has risen to a point where care needs to be used in testing the soil so that too much is never used.

Nitrogen in soil is highly soluble and leaches out over a period of time, so it must be replaced in some manner. It is the most often needed component of any fertilizer because of this leaching out quality. If your plants turn up puny, with yellowish growth instead of green, the nitrogen is lacking in the soil. If the greens are rich, then there is sufficient nitrogen. Nitrogen should be applied early in the season and doses kept rather small and frequent so that too much leaching doesn't happen during the growing season.

Potash feeds the fibers of the plant and may show up short in sandy soils and in soils used to grow many root vegetable crops. Wood ashes provide a good source of potash (with a content of about 4 percent, plus all the minerals of the plants burned to make them). Sifting dry ashes from your wood stove over the garden is a good idea. Potash can be applied at any time of the year, since it becomes fixed in the soil and doesn't leach out as nitrogen does.

Phosphorus contributes strongly to the ripening of fruit and vegetables. Phosphorus should never be mixed with lime, ground limestone or any materials heavy in lime during application or immediately afterwards. Superphosphate and double superphosphate are common compounds used to add the material to soil.

Complete fertilizers will contain all three nutrients and should be applied, if used, at the start of the growing season when the ground is first broken. After that, nitrogen should be applied at needed intervals to keep growth going well.

GREEN MANURES

For the organic gardener, some forms of *green manures* provide the best solution to adding humus and fertilizing a garden. Green manures are sometimes called cover crops, but in truth are not really crops. The plant used as green manure is turned under at the early spring before growth is heavy. You will find two classes of green manures. The first class is the nitrogen *gatherers*. Essentially, this group of plants gathers nitrogen from the air and returns it to the soil through bacterial action (the particular bacteria clump in the roots of the plants). Nitrogen *consumers* gather the nitrogen in the soil and are of less importance, since the idea of a green manure is to add nitrogen, and humus, to the soil and not to use what is already there.

The main nitrogen gathering plants are alfalfa, clovers, *vetches, peas* and *cowpeas*. The nitrogen consumers are mainly *buckwheat, rye, cowhorn* and *turnips*. The former group tends to be more expensive to plant and grow. Alfalfa must be cared for carefully if it is to be cut as hay, but needs a bit less care if it is used as green manure. Still, the seed is fairly expensive today. Often you can use a combination of the nitrogen gatherers and the consumers to get good fertility—much depends on how bad the land is to start. Really poor land may require just the nitrogen consumers, while better land may provide excellent crops after sowing with clover and rye, for example. This will save the nitrogen already present and provide a fair amount more. Nitrogen gatherers are usually sown during late spring or early summer, and can then be plowed under during late summer or early fall.

Green manures may require a fertilizer to get a decent beginning themselves, even though they are sown to improve the soil. Nitrogen is not usually a need, as correctly inoculated legumes will draw it from the air. A bit of potash may well be needed to get things going well, along with a dose of phosphorus. The potash is likely to be most needed if the soil is sandy.

LIME

Lime is what is known as an indirect fertilizer. It is an *alkali* and is used to maintain, or to attain, a neutral pH in the soil. Fertilizers, particularly commercial fertilizers, tend to finally form acids in the soil. The lime is needed to prevent plant damage.

Limestone, ground finely, is spread as your soil tests indicate the need. Generally, the leaching out process, along with the acidity combination, takes some time. Applications are seldom needed at anything closer than three year intervals (keep a check annually, though, just in case). Lime, like wood ash, should not be brought in contact with manure, as this forces the nitrogen carrying ammonia from the manure. Hydrated lime is best and is applied after plowing and disking the field.

COMPOST

Compost is a fantastic and important substance for small or large gardens. It is especially good for use in sandy and heavy clay soils.

A compost pile can be made by placing 8-inch wide boards, at least an inch thick, on the ground to form a rectangle 6 feet by 8 feet. I use concrete blocks to hold the boards in place, but large rocks also do well. Fill the compost bin with a layer of dead leaves, grass clippings or other such material, and soak it down good. Next, you can use a 3 or 4-inch layer of manure and another layer of green material. As the layers rise, they should be tapered in so that your pile finally forms something of an "A" shape. When the pile is completed, it can be covered with a sheet of heavy black polyethylene. Make a couple of slits in the peak of the plastic and force it down to a hollow as long as the top of the pile, and at least 6 inches deep. The long hollow is kept filled with water during dry weather.

Materials used in addition to manure, leaves and grass clippings can include kitchen scraps, both meat and vegetable, egg shells, crop trimmings and thinnings. Do not use fat from the meats, solid bone or grease as they retard the decay process. If you make a compost pile in the fall, it is left to sit until late the following summer. At that time, you should slice it open and move the inner parts outside and the outer in. Let it stand to ripen until the next spring.

Compost is sliced and sifted through a ½-inch mesh of hardware cloth before use. This breaks up clods and removes any stones that may have been included. If the compost is allowed to stand for a full two years, it will be much finer than one-year compost. It is probably best to keep at least two compost piles working when making two-year compost.

11

Vegetables and Herbs

With the recent proliferation of farmers' markets, growing vegetables offers the rural dweller a good way to make a fair amount of money. Even city denizens appreciate the taste of truly fresh vegetables over the plastic taste and texture of, for example, tomatoes shipped green and gas ripened on the way to market. I've never been able to determine what "vine ripened" on those little tomato cartons really means. I think they must put in one early vine and let one tomato ripen on it, and then gas the rest.

SELECTING VEGETABLES

If profit and not pleasure is your motive in growing vegetables, then it is best to make a careful selection of types. Some crops are hard to raise and are a gamble for even the highly experienced truck farmer. Still, on occasion the gamble may pay off. We have one mushroom farm in the area that started several years ago. At that time, the banks wanted no part of the deal. Now, six years later, it is successful. Cauliflower is another crop that can be hard to grow since it needs cool weather, plenty of water and shade for each head as it develops. It is, really, a fussbudget's crop. Watermelons, cantaloupes and cucumbers can be hard to grow in some areas of the country because of a wilt disease, though many new and resistant strains are available.

Selection, at least to start, should begin among the vegetables known to be relatively easy to grow, such as corn, tomatoes, green beans and various kinds of squash. Onions and potatoes also do well, but most kinds of potatoes are a fairly long season crop, though onions can be put as sets and picked as scallions for sale. Radishes are good as a really quick crop, but sell pretty cheaply year round. They may not bring in much per batch. Still, with even a short growing season of 110 days or so, you should be able to get four crops of the speedier varieties. Peppers do well from transplants and are simple to raise, while still bringing a decent price.

Succession cropping is also an excellent idea, whether your garden produces vegetables for the home or market. Beets can be sown after green beans are picked, or after lettuce starts to bolt from the heat. Carrots do well as a late ripening crop, but make sure the soil is soft and loamy if you want decent size. Let's look at some of the vegetables you may plant and from which you may reap nutrition or profits.

ASPARAGUS

Asparagus is a perrenial and needs a rich, deep loam soil as free of stones as possible. It is planted in a bed that should be off to one side of the garden, so it won't upset tilling routines in the rest of the garden. Asparagus demands a lot of lime to keep the soil neutral. Plants are placed in a dug trench about 14 inches wide by 14 inches deep. At the bottom, place an inch of finely ground limestone and dig that into the subsoil. Compost can be used to fill the rest of the ditch, up to about 8 or 10 inches of the surface. The roots are set about 18 inches apart and watered well. Planting should be done in April or May in most areas of the country. Most asparagus types will not provide a crop until the second season. When the shoots begin to come from the roots, hill them with compost. Harvesting is done in the spring and should keep on for no more than two weeks or so. Any plants coming after that are allowed to bolt and go to seed. Mulch for the winter. Look for about 30 pounds of asparagus from every 100 feet of row.

BEETS AND BROCCOLI

Beets are an easy crop to grow but do best in a light, loose soil, on an open well drained spot, in the sun. The ground should be well dug and fertilized deeply as surface feedings will do little for a plant with a taproot, in some varieties, that may extend down as much as 4 feet. The soil must be neutral for best growth. Early beet seeds are sown an inch deep, with late beets going in 2 inches deep. Beet seed will germinate far better if soaked at least 24 hours in water before planting. Early beets are planted in March or April, while the late beets go in during April, May or June. Early beets can be followed with succession plantings of cabbage or other plants. Early beets are picked and used, or sold, just before or at maturity (depending on type, this may be from 53 to 60 days), while late beets are best left in the ground until the first frost. You should be able to get about 2 bushels of beets for every 100 feet of row.

Broccoli needs a rich, damp, easily worked loam that is cool, well drained and very sunny. Calcium needs are heavy, and hydrated lime should be liberally applied as well. Broccoli seeds are planted at a ½-inch depth, while transplants go in about 3 inches in rows at least 18 inches apart. Late plantings should go in 2 to 3 feet apart, and rows to be tilled with mechanical devices should go in at least 30 inches apart. Thin plants go about 18 to 36 inches apart in the rows. Broccoli requires good amounts of water for best growth, and is helped by mulching when the weather is hot.

Plant early broccoli in March or April and late broccoli in April or May after peas have been harvested. Early broccoli will take about 80 days to mature, with the late taking about 85 days. If you take the central and small side heads from a broccoli plant, do not uproot it. After the first harvest, the plant will grow more small heads for later use. You can look for about 45 medium-sized heads from 100 feet of row (Fig. 11-1).

CABBAGE AND CANTALOUPES

Cabbage requires a rich, moist loam, easily worked and well-drained. Heading is best if the weather is cool, and a lot

Fig. 11-1. Premium crop hybrid broccoli.

of calcium is needed for good growth. The soil should be as close to neutral as possible. Seed are planted to a depth of ½-inch and plants to 3 inches, just as with broccoli. Keep plants 18 inches apart in the row for early cabbage and 2 feet apart for late, with 30 inches between rows. Cabbage requires a lot of moisture during dry spells. Early varieties are planted before May 15th, while late cabbage goes in from about mid-June to mid- or end-July. Early cabbages take about 65 days to mature, while late cabbages can take as long as 105 days. Early cabbage is picked as needed, while the late is left on the plant until first frost. Look for about 100 pounds of cabbage to 100 feet of row from early varieties, and about 75 pounds more per row from the late (Fig. 11-2).

Cantaloupes need a light, well-fertilized warm soil in a sunny, well-drained area. Soil is best if it is humus mixed with sandy soil. As I said earlier, a cantaloupe is not the easiest plant to grow, but it will do nothing in a heavy or acidic soil. Plant ½-inch deep and keep hills 5 feet apart, using three seeds in each hill. If planting in rows, keep the seeds at least a foot apart and rows 5 feet apart. Cantaloupes require a great deal of moisture. Seeds should never be sown until the ground is thoroughly warmed, usually no earlier than the middle of May and often a lot later. Some mature at 85 days while others take as long as 100 days. Determine ripeness by placing your thumb on the stem at the junction with the fruit (for our purposes, cantaloupes are being considered as vegetables).Press lightly. If the stem parts easily, you have picked the fruit. If a lot of pressure is needed, back

Fig. 11-2. Tasty Hybrid cabbage.

off for a few days. Yield is not all that great with cantaloupe, as a 100-foot row will usually only bring about 60 cantaloupes to the table or market.

CARROTS AND CAULIFLOWER

Carrots need a fertile loam, with preference going to a sandy, fertile loam for best growth and uniformity in shape and size. The site should be open, sunny and well drained. Carrots will do well in most any decent garden soil, though it should be well worked and as free of stones as possible. Carrots are planted to a depth of only ¼ inch. Because the seed is so small, I like to mix it with dry sand before planting. Carrots should be thinned to 4 inches apart in the row, and rows should be kept at least 14 inches apart. Early carrots can be planted in most areas in March and April, with late ones going in during April and May. An average maturing date is about 70 days after the seed goes in. Carrots should be dug in the fall, just after the first frost, and will provide about 100 pounds of roots to 100 feet of row.

Cauliflower needs a well-fertilized, moist loamy soil in an open area that is well drained and sunny. Heavy calcium doses are needed, and a neutral soil should be maintained. Seeds go in to ¼ inch, and plants are put out to a depth just slightly deeper than they were in the seed bed. Keep the plants 20 inches apart in the row, and the rows at least 30 inches apart. As was mentioned earlier, this is one of the more difficult vegetables to grow. Seed should be sown only very early in the spring. This will usually mean at least five weeks indoors in flats before the plants are moved to the garden. Cauliflower, once started, grows quickly but needs a lot of fertilizer and water. Any lack of water will ruin the plant right on through its life stages. Shade individual heads as they begin to mature. Most will take 85 to 90 days to mature from plants. When getting near harvest time, you will be easily able to tell when the head is developed. You can shade the small heads by loosely tying the plant leaves over them at the time they first start to form. You will get about 50 cauliflower heads from 100 feet of row.

CELERY

Celery is a vegetable with requires very fertile soil and a great deal of moisture and sun to do well. It also needs a neutral soil. Celery is sometimes a bother to grow as it must be blanched or bleached, which means that about 10 days before harvest the larger outer leaves are tied up around the plant, or large boards are tied around to do the job.

Celery seed is covered only with a thin sprinkling of clean sand. Rows should be 28 or 30 inches apart, with plants 6 inches apart in the rows. When blanching the heads, the boards should cover all but the top 6 inches of the plant. Plant the seeds in March or April, and expect to wait from 115 days to 130 days (from seedlings). Once plants reach about two-thirds of their final growth, they are reaped as needed. You should get about 200 heads from 100 feet of row.

CHINESE CABBAGE AND CUCUMBERS

Chinese cabbage needs a rich, moist loam soil, with a tendency towards coolness such as you might find on a north facing slope. Well-fertilized soil with a lot of moisture is needed for Chinese cabbage. The soil should be no more than very slightly acidic, with neutral preferred. Plant at half an inch, with 30 inches between rows and 16 inches between plants. Since Chinese cabbage is a cool weather crop, plant-ings should be made in late summer to early fall, depending on your location. Most varieties take from 73 to 78 days to mature, so check the average last frost free date for your locale and determine when the cabbage seed should go in the ground. Expect to get about 70 heads from 100 feet of row.

Cucumbers need warm, well-fertilized sandy soil. They will do well in a cool, moist shaded location. Right now, I'm having pretty good luck with a couple of varieties in the direct sun and in a heavy clay soil, even after several weeks of no rain. Twice weekly watering seems enough. A moderate acidity in the soil will aid growth, but strongly acidic soils will cause failures. Cover seed with a ½ inch of soil and keep rows 4 feet apart, with the same distance between plants. Supply plenty of fertilizer and keep the cucumbers well dampened. Mulching is a great aid in dry spells. Plant after the date of last frost in your area is well past. Cucumbers will take from 55 to 70 days to mature, depending on variety and final size wanted. Pick cucumbers before they start to turn a yellowish green. With a bit of luck, you can look for 1½ to 2 bushels of cucumbers from every 100-foot row (Fig. 11-3).

EGGPLANT AND ENDIVE

Eggplant requires a well-fertilized loamy to light clay soil in a well drained and sunny locale. These plants must have a lot of nutrients and moisture to produce well. Soil should be just slightly to the acid side, and seeds are planted about ½ inch deep or a bit less. Transplants should be set out just slightly deeper than they were in the flat. Eggplant goes in after the last expected frost date and are thinned to 48 inches apart in the row, with rows also 48 inches apart. Maturity will take from 60 to 80 days, depending on the variety, and the plants are gathered when the surface is very glossy. Overripe plants will have a dull finish. A hundred feet of row should produce in excess of 100 eggplants.

Endive also requires a good, fertile loam. Keep the field open and make sure it is well-drained. The plant is mostly water, so it needs a lot of water to grow well. Place the seed in some dry sand and sow (it's small) about ¼-inch deep, keeping the plants thinned, finally, to a foot apart, with rows 18 inches apart. Endive is a fall crop, so it is sown between June and July in most areas, with warmer southern climates calling for an August sowing. Maturity, as always, depends on variety and will range from 60 to 90 days. You do not have to worry too much about frost with endive, as it will withstand pretty much anything but a hard freeze. Heads are usually harvested when they are about 15 inches high. The outer leaves are removed leaving the crisp, creamy white inner leaves. Endive should be blanched or it will develop a bitter taste. When plants are at about 10 inches, gather the outer leaves in a bunch at the top of the plant and tie them with string. Don't wait more than 10 to 14 days to harvest the heads or they may rot.

Fig. 11-3. Bush Champion cucumber.

KALE AND KOHLRABI

Kale needs a fertile loam soil very close to neutral, which is sunny and well-drained. It is best that the location be one where no cabbage family crops were grown the previous year. Plant to a depth of ½ inch, and thin to 15 inches apart for the plant, keeping rows 20 inches apart. Plant in August in most areas, and expect to see mature plants in from 55 to 60 days. If you plant 100 feet of row, you should gather in about 2 bushels of kale. Kale is almost winter hardy and will keep producing in very cold weather, after frost, though mulching will help keep roots from freezing.

Kohlrabi needs a well-fertilized, moist soil that is easily worked and well drained, but not in complete sun all day long. Until last year, I had never tasted this vegetable, which is one of the oddest looking around. It's worth trying. You will need a good soil of calcium content. Plant to a depth of ½ inch. Keep plants 4 inches apart and leave 15 inches apart. Plenty of water will be needed for this member of the cabbage family (it tastes to me like a cross between a potato and a cucumber, not like cabbage at all). Planting for a spring crop should take place in March or April, while a fall crop can be put in during August. Maturity requires 55 to 60 days.

LEEKS AND LETTUCE

Leeks need a fertile, deep loam soil and will do well in a moderately acidic soil if the soil is nitrogen heavy. Seeds go in at a ½ inch depth, while plants or sets do the same. Thin to 6 inches apart (plant sets 6 inches apart). Keep 1½ feet between rows. Plant seeds in March or April, and put out transplants in April or May. Maturity time is from 125 to 130 days, and a 100-foot row should provide about 200 plants.

Lettuce needs a loose and fertile loam soil, though the soil does not need to be deep for this shallow rooted salad material. Soil type is relatively unimportant, as long as the weather is cool and temperate (hot weather makes most varieties of lettuce bolt). Partial shade is fine. Plant at ¼-inch and thin to package instructions, while keeping at least a foot between rows. Early crops can go in during March and April, while a fall crop would go in during August or September. Sowings two weeks apart up to the end of May will help keep you in fresh lettuce. Maturity varies widely, with almost all coming in well inside 85 days. Yields are impossible to predict as there are so many varieties (Figs. 11-4 and 11-5).

Fig. 11-4. Royal Oak Leaf lettuce.

Fig. 11-5. Green Ice Lettuce.

LIMA BEANS AND ONIONS

Lima beans need a good loam with plenty of humus in an open, sunny area free from any shade. Almost any soil will do, though a slightly acidic soil will usually give best production. The beans are planted to a depth of 1 inch, and plants kept 8 inches apart in rows 30 inches apart. Planting time is late, after the soil has warmed thoroughly, and no earlier than late May in most spots. Maturity will vary as to variety, with pole types taking as much as 90 days to mature and bush types as little as 68 days. Open a pod to check maturity and harvest immediately. Yields will vary, with the bush types maturing earlier but producing less and the pole types coming in later with more, but the average for a 100-foot row should be about 2 bushels.

Onions do well in a fertile and moist loam soil. They do best if there is a subsoil of clay, but the area must be well drained and moderately acidic for good results. Sow seed ½ inch deep, or place sets at least an inch apart (I prefer two inches, though some say it cuts yield). Plants are placed a bit deeper than they came from the flat. Maturity varies from about 100 to 115 days, depending on variety and size desired. Harvesting is done after the plant tops have dropped and been broken back to the ground to let the bulbs mature. When the bulbs are mature, they are taken from the ground and dried for two days before storage or shipment. You should get about 1½ bushels from 100 feet of row. Scallions don't form bulbs as do onions, and take about 95 days to mature. They are perennial, as long as some of the plant is left in the ground (Fig. 11-6).

PARSNIPS AND PEAS

Parsnips require soil worked well to a depth of at least 2 feet in an open and sunny area. Soil should be neutral or nearly so, and of good quality and well-fertilized. Parsnips need large amounts of water only at the start, and will survive almost anything after they are well-started. Seed is planted to a depth of ½ inch, and plants are thinned to 3 inches apart in rows 1½ feet apart. Planting is done in March

Fig. 11-6. White sweet Spanish onion.

or April, and maturity dates range from 85 to about 105 days. Normally, parsnips are left in the ground until after the freeze hits and may be dug in early spring, or they can be dug before the ground freezes solid. Each row will provide about 2 bushels per 100 feet.

Peas like a fertile, sandy soil and do best in partial shade in hot areas. Acidity of a moderate amount is fine, but too much nitrogen should be avoided. The plants must be kept well-watered. Plant peas as early as the ground can be worked, and make successive sowings about every two weeks up through the beginning or middle of May. Plants should be 2 to 4 inches apart in the row, and you will need about three feet between rows. Bush varieties need no support, but using some sort of support is essential to higher growing types. I tend to like 2-inch chicken wire strung between a couple of poles for this job. Maturity dates vary but are mostly in the 55 to 65 day range. Peas are harvested each day as they become ready (they are ready when the peas show well-formed in the pods). There are so many varieties to be found that it is nearly impossible to say what the yield might be, but do not expect much more than a bushel of green peas per 100 feet of row and 2 bushels of edible podded types (Fig. 11-7).

PEPPERS AND POTATOES

Peppers need a mellow soil, loamy but not overly fertile. The location should be sunny and well-drained. Too much nitrogen in the soil favors leaf growth instead of fruit growth. Soil should be neutral. Plants go in just a bit deeper than they do in the flats, and seeds are planted ½ inch deep. Plants should be 2 feet apart in the row, and rows 30 inches apart. Keep the plants well watered in the first growth stages, though later, unless a drought strikes, you probably can dispense with watering. Plant them in May or June, well after frost damage and after the ground has warmed up. Expect maturity dates to range from about 65 to 75 days. Harvest the peppers when they are ripe. You can look for about 4 bushels of peppers from every 100 feet of row (Fig. 11-8).

Fig. 11-7. Sweetpod Snow peas.

Potatoes need a fertile, sandy loam for best growth, and the soil can be more than slightly acidic. Alkaline soil, when too much lime is used, can cause a disease called *scab*. Seed potatoes are cut into sections, making sure that each section has an eye. These are planted at a depth of 3 inches about a footprint apart. Moisture is needed and potatoes are planted, for early plantings, in March and April, and for late plantings in late May and early June. Potatoes will take from 80 to 140 days to mature, and the early or "new" potatoes are dug during the summer. Late potatoes are harvested after the vine dies and lies on the ground. Do not allow them to stay in the ground after frost. A hundred feet of row will yield about 3 bushels. If your family is about average, you can expect to consume some 15 or so bushels a year. But it would be wise to grow enough to allow for spoilage of possibly 20 percent. Often partially spoiled potatoes will make good seed potatoes for the following year.

Fig. 11-8. Tasty Hybrid pepper.

RADISHES AND RHUBARB

Radishes need a light and sandy loam that is well-drained and not overly hot. Almost any good garden soil will produce a good crop for you. Plant ½ inch deep, with about 15 or 16 seeds per foot of row, and keep rows a foot part. Planting can take place as soon as the ground can be worked for most varieties. Heavy watering is needed if a woody texture is to be kept away. Varieties that mature in as little as 23 days are available, while some may take 55 days.

Rhubarb needs deep rich loam and should be, like asparagus, well to one side of the garden since it is also perennial. Moderately acidic soil is fine, but there should be plenty of moisture. Lots of humus and fertilizer are needed. Plants go in to a depth of 2 ½ inches, and rows are kept 4 feet apart as are the plants. Over time the plants will thicken in the rows. About every five or six years you should dig out about a quarter of the row, separate the roots and replant. First planting takes place in April or May, and separation should take place in the fall. Harvest mature leaves in the spring, pulling them from the plant. Expect to get about 200 leaves or stalks from 100 feet of row.

SNAP BEANS AND SPINACH

Snap beans do best in a sandy loam soil and do not need a lot of fertilizer to do well. Watering may be needed in dry weather spells. Beans are planted an inch deep and should be covered with that much sifted soil. Bush beans are kept to 3 inches apart in rows 18 inches apart, while pole beans are set with 6 or 8 seeds per pole and the poles spaced 4 feet apart. Use poles about 10 feet long and make a tepee of every four of them, tying the tops together with heavy twine. That way you don't have to sink the poles into the ground. Plant after the beginning of May when the ground has warmed up well. Beans are picked just as they mature and should not be left on the vines longer, as that retards the growth of new beans. Working among bean plants when wet spreads a rust disease, so this should not be done. Maturity dates will vary from 49 to 80 days, with pole beans taking longer to come in. Look for an average of about 2 bushels per 100 feet of row.

Spinach requires a good soil with a lot of nitrogen available. Again, a north facing slope is best as this is a cool weather vegetable. Fertile garden soil of any type will do fine. A neutral soil is best but not essential. Seeds can be scattered or sown to be 3 inches apart in rows (mix with dry sand as the seed is quite small and hard to handle). Rows need a foot between them. Plant in March or April for early crops and, for late crops, in August and September. Succession planting of spinach planted early is a good idea. Spinach itself can be planted at two-week intervals into early summer to keep the fresh vegetables coming. Maturity requires 49 to 50 days for most varieties. You harvest outer leaves, letting the inner leaves mature for later picking. Expect to get about 3 bushels from a 100-foot row.

SQUASH

Squash does best in a fertile sandy loam, with plenty of humus, in locations that warm quickly. The soil should be slightly acidic. Summer squash is planted at a depth of ½ inch to an inch, with winter squash going down 1 inch. Summer squash of most varieties does fine at 3 feet apart in rows, with rows 3 feet apart, while winter squash often needs twice that distance. Check the seed package, as there are so many different varieties it is impossible to be more explicit. Summer squash is planted in April or May and winter squash in May or June in most areas. Do the heaviest planting in winter squash since that keeps well, while summer squash does not. Most summer squash such as the *yellow crookneck* and the *zucchini* are abundant producers and may overwhelm you with vegetables. I have gotten heartily sick of both kinds at one time or another even though we seldom plant more than four to six hills (four seeds to a hill). Pick summer squash before it reaches maturity, as it tends to be more tender and tasty then. The older it gets, the larger and the tougher it becomes. Winter squash is picked just before the first frost is expected. Not even an estimate of yield can be given as there are so many types.

SWEET CORN AND SWEET POTATOES

Sweet corn needs a fertile medium soil without an overabundance of nitrogen. Corn can be planted in pretty rough soil as long as there is enough humus in it. Neutral soil is best, and the seeds go down ½ inch to an inch. The experts recommend greater spacing in some spots, but I keep plants to about 10 inches and get good results. The planting is done after all danger of frost is over, say in May or early June. Late plantings can be made in June and July if your growing season is long enough. If you plant one row a week during the spring, though, you should have sweet corn to carry you through. Maturity can range from about 75 days to as long as 95 days. Corn is picked at the milk stage—the point where a squeezed kernel gives off a milky fluid. I like to pick it and bring it into the house to a pot of already boiling water, with a bit of lemon juice in the water. Then I shuck it directly into the water. Depending on variety, you can look for from 45 to 55 ears per 100 feet of row (Fig. 11-9).

Sweet potatoes need a warm and sandy soil in a warm, if not sunny, location. Plant 4 to 6 inches deep in a soil that is slightly acidic and not overly rich with nutrients. The plants are kept a foot apart in the row and about 3½ feet apart from other rows. Most sweet potato planting is in May, after the ground has warmed up. Keep a check on the potatoes after a couple of months, and remove the roots when they are of the size you want. Cure the dug potatoes for about 10 days at 85 degrees, if possible, and in high humidity. You will get as much as 2 bushels per 100-foot row.

TOMATOES

Tomatoes are just about every person's favorite vegetable to grow. They will do best in a light soil that is well-drained. Mine are in heavy clay but are still producing 1½ and 2 pound tomatoes, which shows how easy they are to grow. Oddly enough, a very acidic soil will retard growth, even though the tomatoes themselves are very acidic compared to other vegetables (which makes them safer for low pressure canning). Near neutral soil is best.

Set the plants in ½ inch deeper than the original setting. I have seen some people run most of the plant underground into a short, shallow ditch, leaving only an inch or two of leafy part about the ground. This seems to work well. Use sec-

Fig. 11-9. Sugar Sweet Hybrid corn.

tions cut from a milk container around the plant and slightly below ground level to prevent cutworms from snipping the roots off. Set plants at least 3 feet apart and make sure they are well supported after major growth begins. Tomato cages are good but expensive. Some people set up posts at the end of rows and run heavy twine down the rows. Then they tie the tomato plants to the twine. Watering should only be needed in extended dry spells.

The plants go in after all danger of frost is past. Plant both late and early varieties to make sure of a continuing supply through the growing season. Maturity dates vary from about 58 days to 82 or 83 days, and tomatoes are obviously ripe when mature. Different varieties provide different yields, with slightly different flavors. An estimate of yield is again impossible, except to say you will enjoy it. All of the crop must be harvested by frost. Large green tomatoes can be wrapped in newspaper or brown paper and stored in a cool, dark spot where they will continue to ripen, supplying tomatoes for use into the winter. For the next year, move your tomato patch to another area of the garden, as some types of disease may remain in the ground over the winter and into the spring (Fig. 11-10).

TURNIPS

Turnips need a soil that is light and not too heavy in nitrogen. A turnip is a cool weather plant that does well in soils that are not overly rich in nutrients. Moderate acidity is tolerated, and watering is only needed until the long taproot has time to grow. Early turnips are planted ¼ inch deep and late ones half an inch, in rows 15 inches apart, with the plants thinned to 6 inches apart. Maturity comes in 48 to 57 days, after which the turnips can be left in the ground until frost without harm. You will get about 2 bushels of turnips from 100 feet of row.

SELLING VEGETABLES

From the preceding vegetables, you can select those you might want to sell or use yourself. I might suggest that vegetables grown for sale, such as tomatoes, be carefully

Fig. 11-10. The Big Girl Hybrid VF tomato is a real favorite.

selected as to maturing dates. Fresh tomatoes first on the scene will bring good, premium prices, but later ripening varieties tend to go for something like 5 pounds for a dollar in my area of Virginia. Even though a good plant will provide as many as 15 pounds of tomatoes, that still does not leave much profit margin when all is considered. Summer squash can be even worse money makers. Potatoes can also get you in trouble financially, as potato prices tend to drop as local competition bounces off the big producers. Still, with no middle man and a busy farmers' market in your area, you might do extremely well with even these vegetables.

Potatoes offer one more fascinating variation in growth methods. Some of my friends simply laid seed potatoes on the ground, under a foot of straw. The yield was incredible and the work minimal.

TYPES OF HERBS

Placing herbs in your garden can have a multitude of benefits, for some are fragrant and all are tasty. Many are quite beautiful. Uses can range from simple taste additions to keeping insects from other garden plants or, in some cases, storing items that might be spoiled by little critters.

☐ **Sweet Flag**. This is a perennial and can be laid among furs to protect them from moths. The root is the portion used. The essential oil of the bark was one time, and may still be, used in perfumes. Try a bit of the leaf in custard pudding. Its natural habitat is moist areas, but cultivated sweet flag does well in fairly dry soils and seems to prefer sunny areas. The roots are harvested in the fall, and propagation is by root division.

☐ **Chives**. These plants are familiar to many of you because they are used, finely chopped, in salads. They also go well in some omelets and with cheeses. A perennial, chives are propagated by dividing the clumps and planting the small bulbs found. Cutting may weaken them enough to require fertilizing if you use a lot.

☐ **Dill**. This is an annual native to Asia Minor and Europe. It is grown from seed and takes about 75 days from sowing to harvest. Dill is used to produce such things as the dill pickle, and the young tops and leaves may be used to add to vinegars. It is also useful in some fish sauces. Pick the fresh leaves when the flowers are just beginning to open.

☐ **Chamomile**. This herb is another perennial. It is used as a tea when boiling water is poured over the tiny yellow flowers and steeped for a bit. The tea is supposed to be good for a weak stomach and as a hair rinse. It prefers a sunny, dry location and is grown from seed, indoors, and then transplanted outdoors.

☐ **Chervil**. This is an annual and seems to prefer a somewhat shady location. It is fine in salads, most particularly potato salads, and is also good in soups.

☐ **Horseradish**. This is a perennial—to the point of being a pain at times—because growth can be rampant. Pieces of the root are planted 2 feet deep and 3 feet apart in good, fertile, loamy soil. Dig the roots in the fall and store them in sand to keep them from withering. Horseradish is said to stimulate the appetite, but to most of you it will be familiar as a condiment used hot or cold on meats. It has a very sharp taste.

☐ **Tarragon**. This plant is a widespread perennial (it comes from eastern Europe, Siberia, Tartary and Chinese Mongolia) that grows to a wide and shrublike 2 feet. True tarragon must be propogated from root cuttings, and it is best first set out in spring. Mulching is often needed to get the plant through the winter. It is used as a flavoring in a salad, and the leaves may also be added to vinegar to give it a distinctive flavor.

☐ **Black Mustard And White Mustard**. These are hard to tell apart, but both are annuals that have a strong tendency to spread like weeds. The young leaves add a good, peppery tang to salads, and the mustard seed can be bruised for use as a condiment.

☐ **Peppers**. These include the red pepper, chili pepper, cayenne pepper and others. Fruit is picked when ripe and the plants are annuals, doing best on moderately good, not overly fertile soil. As a medicine, some peppers are believed to be good for digestion and as a cure for sore throat. As foods, the hot peppers make fine flavoring for many dishes, from chili to spaghetti sauce.

☐ **Caraway**. This is a biennial that grows best in a sunny, dry area and may need a bit of protection over the winter in cold areas. Caraway is medicinally said to be useful in digestive problems and is also used to mask the flavor of bitter tasting medicines. As a food, it is used to add flavor to breads, cakes and cheeses.

☐ **Coriander**. This is an annual preferring a warm, light garden soil with fruit that ripens in about two months. Seeds are picked just as they are ready to drop off the plant. Used in making curry powder and other mixed spices, the seeds can also have the oil distilled and used in breads and cakes.

☐ **Saffron Crocus**. This is a perennial fall-flowering crocus (most others flow in Spring) that needs sun and shelter. The bulbs must also be separated every three years or no flowers will be produced. The flowers are picked as soon as they open, and the stigmas snipped off with small scissors. The saffron is then dried in the air. Commercial raising of saffron is not practical, as it takes half a million flowers to make a pound and the snipping is very tedious. The dried saffron has an astringent taste, but it provides a brilliant yellow color to food and blends well with other spices and herbs.

☐ **Cumin**. This is an annual whose seeds are used to flavor liqueurs, breads and sauerkraut. It is also used as an ingredient in curry powder. Plant it at the end of May, and in two months the seeds are ready to be picked and dried.

☐ **Florence Fennel**. This is sown in spring, thinned to 8 inches apart, which needs good, loamy, fertile soil. It can be used as a vegetable—the stems, usually.

☐ **Sweet Fennel**. Another annual which is eaten raw as an appetizer or snack. The leaves can be used to flavor sauces.

☐ **Bitter Fennel**. A perennial but not hardy much above southern Maryland. It is grown from seed and needs a light, well-drained soil. Thin to a foot apart. Seeds are gathered just before full ripening, and are used to flavor liqueurs, soups and bread.

☐ **Wintergreen**. A perennial grown in shady areas in light, loose soil. Thin to 6 inches apart. Oil of wintergreen is used as a rub, or at least it was 21 years ago, and the dried leaves can be made into a tea.

☐ **True Lavender.** A shrub that likes a light, well-limed soil with an overlay of loam. Too much moisture will kill the shrub. Cut stems and branches in sunny weather, and make the cuts as close to the woody stock as possible. Cut when the whole branch is in flower and the longest of blossoms has begun to turn dark. Lavender is used as a perfume, and dried flowers are laid in with linens to given them a scent.

☐ **Peppermint**. This is a perennial that prefers moist soil with a good amount of humus. It is propagated by using snips of the runners set into moist sand. Only the leaves are used for flavoring, since the stems are bitter. A tea can also be made of the dried leaves.

☐ **Spearmint**. This has about the same requirements as peppermint for growth. It is somewhat more popular in many areas as a flavoring being crushed into sugar to mix with drinks, and scattered over glazed carrots. It makes a milder tea than does peppermint.

☐ **Sweet Basil**. This is an annual and is joined with *bush basil* and several others to form a family of popular seasoning herbs. Most are easily grown from seed when all danger of frost is gone, if placed in a sunny, well-drained locale. It is used in soups and stews of many kinds, as well as other dishes.

☐ **Sweet Marjoram**. This is a non-hardy perennial, which means it will have to be planted each year in areas that freeze hard. Seeds are started in a cold frame and transplanted after the last expected frost. They need a sunny, dry area. Leaves are stripped off the plants just as the flowers come on. Sweet marjoram is used to flavor sausages and roast chicken, as well as a garnish and a flavoring for salad.

☐ **Parsley**. This is a biennial. We are probably all familiar with the fern-leaved variety that is a favorite for garnish in this country. It needs a moist soil that is reasonably humus-laden and fertile. Cut the leaves as needed and collect seeds when ripe for replanting. Parsley is used as a garnish, sometimes whole, often minced over potatoes, carrots and other vegetables.

☐ **Rosemary**. This is a shrub that is hardy from about southern Maryland on down, and should be started early in a cold frame or indoors. Fertile soil is needed if cutting is heavy. A good garden soil that is sunny and well drained also helps. Leaves are picked as the plants flower if they are to be dried. Otherwise, pick and use as needed. The leaf tips are distilled to give oil of rosemary which can be used to perfume soaps.

☐ **Sage**. This is a perennial and the small plants can be bought from nurseries. They need a good, well-dried garden loam. Overcutting late in the season and the first season is to be avoided. Dry the leaves in the shade to keep them from turning black. Sage is used to flavor pork, and the stuffing in some poultry, as well as in sausages and cheeses. It also makes a tea, sometimes used as an astringent for sore throats.

☐ **Sesame**. This is an annual that comes up from seed, and which should be planted after frost danger has passed in a sunny, well-drained area. Pick the seeds when they are ripe; then bruise the seeds and stick them in hot water. Skim off the oil that rises and use it instead of cooking oil, or in recipes calling for fat. The seeds can also be sprinkled on cookies after they are dried.

☐ **Thyme**. This is a small shrub that gets about 6 inches high. It tends to grow well on rocky, sunny hillsides and in sunny, well-drained locations. Plants are cut in full flower and then dried in the shade. It is a seasoning used for many foods, including some cheeses.

GARDENING

Herb gardening is little different than any other kind. Because of the diversity of plants, though, your plot may need several different kinds of soil. Years ago, when we first tried going to fresh herbs and started some chives, we worried far too much about its habitat. That stuff seems to grow well anywhere the soil is even halfway decent.

If you grow several herbs requiring different kinds of soil, it is simple enough to scatter them through areas on your land where such soils are available, or can be made available, without disrupting other gardening plans. An herb garden can be wondrous thing in adding fresh flavor to meals and stored foods without spending the ridiculous prices asked for condiments and herbs today.

12

Raising Fruit Trees

There is nothing quite like being able to pluck a few cherries, apples or pears from your own tree almost any time you wish after they start to ripen. Canned, frozen or dried fruits, from your own small orchard can be a real delight during the middle of a nasty winter season (Fig. 12-1).

PLANNING AN ORCHARD

Planning a home orchard is of greater importance now than ever before. There are so many varieties of fruit trees from which to choose, and careful planning will make the overall job of caring for and harvesting from the trees a great deal easier over the years. You need to give attention to insect and disease control in the trees, placement of the orchard in relation to your home, pruning, fertilization and basic soil management. Obviously, there is little point in trying to grow the wrong varieties of fruit trees for an area. Upstate New York is not the place for the peach grower. Yet, many other fruits will do exceptionally well there. It is my opinion that apples grown in the north are better than those grown in warmer climates. The bite of frost seems to aid flavor. Frost kills peaches, though, if it goes deeply.

Site Selection

For the home orchard, try to locate things as close as possible to your home. Less traveling to work on or around

Fig. 12-1. This dwarf apple tree is bearing full-size fruit.

the trees can mean more of the work gets done with less fuss. For those with little space near the home, semi-dwarf and dwarf varieties can often be used as ornamental plantings (assuming you take into consideration the mature size of the trees). Dwarfs seldom grow more than 8 or 10 feet a tall, but semi-dwarfs can range to 15 feet or so. A standard apple tree may reach 25 feet. Dwarf fruit trees produce less per tree than standard or semi-dwarf ones. The average for a dwarf is a bushel per tree, with the standard going as high as eight. The semi-dwarf yields about four. Bearing begins much earlier, at about two to three years instead of four to six for the semi-dwarf and six to 10 for the standard. Dwarf life expectancy is a lot shorter at 15 to 20 years than either the 20 to 25 years of the semi-dwarf or the 35 to 45 years of the standard. Still, despite lower yields and shorter life, the dwarf will often be the choice where space is limited, and where you do not wish to do a lot of climbing to pick and prune.

The size of the planting depends pretty much on your intent and desires. If commercial growing is the idea, then the orchard will be a lot larger. For family use there will be no need for 50 standard apple trees. Check Table 12-1 for an indication of how some popular fruits average out as to bearing amounts. Plant a range of trees covering the range of preferred fruits in your family, too. Table 12-1 also gives the minimum desirable distances between trees for my area. A check with your local extension department's county agent will provide you with the needed distances for your own locale.

After the basic location is settled, some other thought should be given to site selection. You should take into consideration not only soil conditions, but also air drainage. Cold air flows downhill, meaning you should avoid setting plants in low spots where possible. The cold air flow may kill the trees, or the fruit may be ruined. Low wet spots are to be especially avoided, as are areas with frost pockets and strong prevailing winds. If the soil is not a deep well-drained sandy loam or sandy clay, it will be needing preparation to change it to that type and probably work to keep it that way. Fertile soil is needed, but fertility can be easily improved. It is

Table 12-1. Statistics on Various Fruits.

FRUIT	MINIMUM DISTANCE BETWEEN PLANTS	APPROXIMATE YIELD PER PLANT	BEARING AGE	LIFE EXPECT- ANCY
	feet	bushels	years	years
Apple-standard ------------------------30		8	6-10	35-45
Apple-semidwarf -----------------------20		4	4-6	20-25
Apple-dwarf-----------------------------12		1	2-3	15-20
Pear-standard--------------------------25		3	5-8	35-45
Pear-dwarf------------------------------12		½	3-4	15-20
Peach-----------------------------------20		4	3-4	15-20
Plum-------------------------------------20		2	4-5	15-20
Quince-----------------------------------15		1	5-6	30-40
Cheery-sour----------------------------25		60 qt.	4-5	15-20
Cherry-sweet--------------------------25		75 qt.	5-7	20-30

difficult and sometimes expensive to improve internal soil drainage.

Adaptation of Fruit Varieties

Adapt varieties to local soil and climate. Try to select varieties resistant to insects and diseases. Table 12-2 lists some varieties suitable for the middle Atlantic regions of the country. Again, your county agent will be able to tell you what will do well at the spot where you live. You might wish to set several varieties ripening at different times to ensure a long season of fresh fruit. Some varieties do better frozen or canned than do others.

Some varieties of fruit require *cross pollination*, including apples. For proper cross pollination, you will need three varieties of apple. They cannot be limited to *Summer Rambo*, *Winesap* and *Stayman* which will not cross pollinate. *Golden Delicious* is used by many growers as a good, general cross pollinator of other varieties. Pear, plum and sweet cherry trees require at least two varieties for successful cross pollination, while sour cherry, peach and nectarine are generally self-fruitful. Make sure also that any cross pollinating varieties overlap in bloom or the cross won't work. In other words, the trees have to be in flower at the same time for the bees to do their work.

Price is always a consideration, and good nursery stock is not cheap. You can expect to spend something on the order of $15 for dwarf varieties of many fruit trees and as much as $18 for some semi-dwarfs. Standard size trees are usually a bit cheaper, but it takes a lot longer for them to begin to bear. Try to select one-year-old trees. Buying ready-to-bear or older stock from the nursery is almost always a mistake, as the shock of transplant sets them back far enough in fruiting that year-old stock bears almost as soon at much lower cost. There is less chance of loss with younger trees, too.

For *peaches, nectarines* and *apricots*, look for ½-inch thick three about 4 feet high. One-year-old whips about ¾ inch in diameter and 4 to 7 feet tall are best for apples. *Pears, quince, plums* and *cherries* may be planted as one or two-year-old trees. When you buy apple trees on dwarfing

Table 12-1. Varieties Suitable for Middle Atlantic Region.

APPLES
Lodi c
Jerseymac c,d
Paulared c,d
Summer Rambo c,d
Grimes Golden c,d
**Jonathan (red strain) c,d
Golden Delicious c,d
**Delicious (red strain) c,d
**Winesap c,d
*Stayman (red strain) c,d
**Rome Beauty (red strain)
  c,d

CHERRIES (sour)
Montmorency c,f

****CHERRIES** (sweet)

Napoleon (Royal Anne)
  c,d
Vernon c,d
Ulster c,d
Hedelfingen c,d
Windsor c,d
Hudson c,d

PEARS
Moonglow c,d
Magness c,d
Maxine c,d
Seckel c,d
Orient c
Kieffer c,d

PLUMS (JAPANESE)
Early Golden c,d
Methley c,d
Shiro c,d

PLUMS (European and
  Prunes)

Mohawk c,d
Richards Early Italian
  Prune c,d
Iroquois c,d
Stanley c,d
Shronshire (Damson) c
Oneida c,d

NECTARINES
Pocahontas d
Cherokee d
Cavalier d
Lafayette d

PEACHES

Earlired c,d
Sunhaven c,d,f
Redhaven c,d,f
Triogem c,d,f
Washington c,d,f
Glohaven c,d,f
**Sunhigh c,d,f
Cresthaven c,d,f
Georgia Belle (white) c,d
White Hale (white) c,d
Redskin c,d,f
Tyler c,d,f

****QUINCE**
Orange c

* Principal uses: c—cooking; d—desert; f—freezing.

** In Eastern Virginia where mildew, blight, brown rot, bacteriosis,
fruit cracking, and poor color can be serious due to climatic conditions, these varieties are difficult to grow.

rootstock, find out which kind of rootstock you are getting. In
this area, three are suggested with *EMX-1* listed as very
dwarfing but with a rather weak root system. Trees on
EM-VII and *MM-106* grow to a size about two-thirds of the

same variety on seedling rootstock. The real work comes once the planning is done and the trees are bought.

PLANTING TIME

Planting time is important to nursery stock, but in most areas of the country either spring or fall planting times can be used. In spring plantings, go for at least 30 days before the last killing frost is expected; in fall, about 30 days after the first killing frost is recommended for the Middle Atlantic states. Check your own out, for colder or warmer climates can make a solid difference in planting time. Planting when you have to use dynamite to get the root system of the dormant tree below the surface is not a good idea.

Root holes must be dug deeply enough to accept the entire root ball and must be wide enough so that no root crowding exists (Fig. 12-2). Spade the ground well for sev-

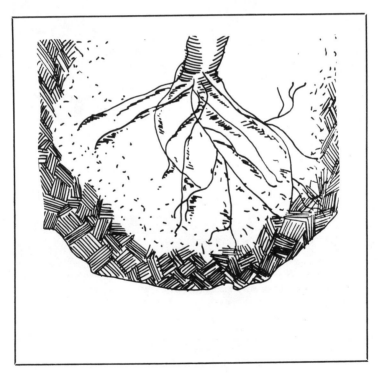

Fig. 12-2. Allow plenty of room for roots to spread.

eral square feet around where the tree will be standing. Prepare as you would any good garden soil, and include the soil under the roots and that soil to be returned to the hole.

Do not allow the roots of the nursery stock to freeze or dry out. When the order arrives, unpack the bundles and check the trees. Roots and packing material should be moist, and the bark should not be withered. If the bark is withered, the trees were allowed to dry out in transit and probably will not take. If you can't plant immediately, the plants can be held as long as two weeks in refrigerated storage—not in a freezer. If no refrigeration is to be had, heel the plants into a shallow trench and keep the trench moist.

A couple of days before planting, place the root system in a container of water. Prune roots of young trees only to remove broken or damaged pieces, or to head back some extremely long ones. If a tree is so badly scarred, or its root system so badly damaged that you doubt it will make it, save some effort and discard it (if the damage was in shipping, save it for claims). Dig the hole wider and deeper than the root system and leave loose soil in the hole; then set the tree in at just about the same depth it was set at the nursery. I like to add a bit of alfalfa hay under the tree, and it seems to work well in giving an added boost to growth for a month or two. On trees grafted to dwarf rootstock, do not set the graft of *scion* to rootstock below the ground under any circumstances.

When filling holes, pulverize the soil going in and shake the tree gently as the hole is filled. This shaking filters the soil among the roots. Use your foot to tamp the soil down firmly as you cover the roots. Use your foot to tamp the soil down firmly as you cover the roots. Add water when the hole is about three-fourths full. This aids in packing the soil and provides a better margin for the tree's survival. After the water has thoroughly soaked in, finish filling the hole, leaving the dirt on top loose. Again, I like to mulch around the tree—keeping the mulch at least 2 to 3 inches from the trunk—with hay before leaving it to grow.

CULTIVATION

Young fruit trees should be mulched and, if need be, cultivated until they begin to bear. Weeds need to be kept down so they do not rob the trees of moisture and oil nutrients. Keep cultivation shallow so that near surface roots are not injured. Keep the mulch area a couple of inches away from the trunk, and continue it on out a little past the spread of the branches. If no mulch is used, cultivate in the same way. Using mulch is generally better than using cultivation since it keeps down weeds, conserves moisture in the soil, and can also serve to keep the soil cool during hot months.

The mulch can be of many materials such as other kinds of hay besides alfalfa, pine needles, peat moss, grass clippings, sawdust and wood shavings. Sawdust about 3 inches thick will probably do fine, but for bulkier materials you will need sawdust at 6 inches and probably a foot thick. Black plastic can also be used, but it does nothing to add to the humus content or overall fertility of the soil. If the mulch material you use is low in nitrogen, it may draw some from the ground, causing a temporary soil deficiency. About ¼ pound of ammonium nitrate or ½ pound of nitrate of soda to each hundred square feet of mulched area will overcome the problem, as will the addition of a couple of wheelbarrow loads of well-rotted manure.

If you plant your fruit trees in rows, you can use the rows in one of two ways. What is ably called sod culture is nothing more than letting it grow as grass and keeping it closely cut. The area can also be used for low growing vegetables or other fruits such as strawberries. In both cases, fertility and moisture levels must be kept high enough so that the trees are not deprived of nutrients.

Young trees when first planted should be dormant and not need fertilizer (unless a mulch such as straw is used, as such mulches take nitrogen from the soil). Once your young trees are established and showing growth, start using a 16 or 20 percent nitrogen fertilizer, about ½ pound at a time, spread 8 to 10 inches out for the trunk. Do this starting the month before total thaw, and continue for three months. The fertilizing is kept up for the first two years. Usually only nitrogen is needed since the tree can take the rest of its nutrients from the soil, but sometimes light, sandy soils will require a complete fertilizer. In any case, if a good mulch is used, the fertilizing should not be needed. It is a good idea to not overfertilize, as this may bring on too great leafy growth, late fruiting and leave the tree open to winter damage.

If later fertilizing seems needed, test the soil or have it tested. Apply the fertilizer recommended after the leaves have fallen or in early spring before any active growth begins. For older trees, start about 2 inches from the trunk and spread of the branches.

Keep an eye on growth for an indication of fertilizer needs. If growth was slow one year, increase fertilizer. If growth was too rapid, cut back on the fertilizer. Both pear and quince trees are highly susceptible to fire blight disease, and too fast growth increases the chances of the trees contracting the disease.

Mature and bearing peach, nectarine and sweet cherry trees should average from 10 to 15 inches of new growth each year, with young, nonbearing trees growing about twice that much. Mature apple, pear, quince, plum and sour cherry trees will average about 8 to 10 inches of new growth per year while, again, twice that amount is expected on nonbearing young trees.

PRUNING

Correct pruning is very important to fruit tree productivity. It is done to regulate overall growth, increase production, improve fruit size and cost, and to reduce production costs. Essentially, pruning is a method of developing a strong framework and a maximum yield of high quality fruit. Most pruning is done during the dormant season, preferably just before active spring growth starts. This is so because the wounds heal more rapidly and flower buds are more easily recognized, while preventing injury from low winter temperatures. Summer pruning can be done to help train young trees to the correct shape, to remove watersprouts and other unnecessary growth, and to keep unnecessary growth to a minimum. You should be alerted to the fact, though, that all pruning has a dwarfing effect. For maximum yield, it is best to prune only as needed to develop a strong framework capable of holding up maximum crop yields, and to keep the tree open to sunlight, air and spray material, allowing for good fruit development and pest control.

Pruning procedures vary according to the type, age and variety of fruit trees. All newly planted fruit trees should be pruned in the spring before growth begins. This brings the top into balance with the root system, some of which was probably lost during transplanting. It also stimulates lateral bud development from which you get good scaffold limbs.

Apple Trees

Apple trees are most often trained to the *modified leader* system. This basically means the leader, or main trunk, is allowed to develop without checking its height until the scaffold limbs have developed reasonably well, usually, in standard trees, by the end of the third. At that time, you may find it necessary to cut back the leader.

If you plant one-year-old unbranched whips, pruning is held to heading at the desired height, which is about 30 to 35 inches for spur-type and semi-dwarf trees. If young trees are branched when they arrive from the nursery, the normal practice is to head the leader to the desired height, cut back half the terminal growth of any wide angle side branches suitable for development into scaffold limbs, and to prune off the rest. When the topmost buds on the leader grow out to 4 or 5 inches, cut off all except the terminal shoot. This encourages buds to grow in the lower portion of the tree, giving a greater number of shoots from which you can select scaffold limbs. This pruning can be done during the first summer or left until the dormant season.

A well-trained apple tree will usually have from six to 10 scaffold limbs, each about 8 inches from the next vertically. They should be evenly distributed up and around the leader, with the lowest scaffold branch no more than 16 inches from the ground. No scaffold branch should be directly above another. Each scaffold, for greatest strength, should form an angle of about 65 degrees with the leader.

Limb spreaders are often used to form the correct angle, as shown in Fig. 12-3. They also tend to encourage earlier production and are useful in training varieties that have

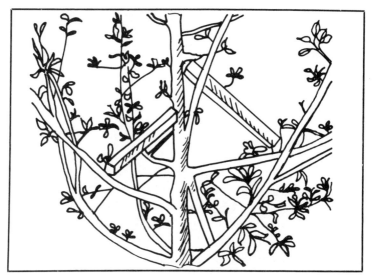

Fig. 12-3. Limb spreaders in place.

narrow angles, such as Red Delicious. Steel wire of about ⅛-inch diameter, or wooden strips with finishing nails in each end, are inserted between the chosen scaffold limbs and the main stem of the tree, thereby spreading the limb out to form the desired crotch angle. Do this early, though, for as the tree grows it becomes increasingly harder to spread the limbs.

Once the scaffolding pattern is set up, heavy pruning is to be avoided. Cut off watersprouts and branches competing with desirable scaffolds, and leave things be until the tree starts to bear. Pruning of a bearing tree consists of the removal of watersprouts; removal of diseased, dead or broken limbs; thinning of weak, low-growing and shaded branches; and the opening up of the top by careful removal of higher branches so that sunlight gets through to the center of the tree. Maintenance of the tree under a height of 18 feet can also be done be heading the top limbs to strong, outgrowing lateral limbs.

Pear Trees

Pear trees are trained along the same basic lines as those used for apple trees. The average young pear tree, though, tends to grow tall and leggy. Tipping or heading back the long shoots just slightly will encourage development of side branches. Heading back after the framework has developed is not a good idea because pear trees have a tendency to grow soft terminal shoots very susceptible to fire blight. Limit pruning to thinning out cuts.

Cherry Trees

Sweet cherry trees are also trained to the modified leader system, as are apple and pear trees. You must pay special attention when selecting scaffolding limbs, since sweet cherry is subject to winter injury and splitting at the point where the limbs with as wide crotch angles as possible to make sure your framework is strong. Head newly planted sweet cherry trees to a height of 40 inches. If any wide-angled later branches are on the trees when they are set, select the ones suitable for scaffold and head them back slightly, leaving the leader several inches longer. Four is a minimum and six is a maximum, 8 inches apart, for scaffold limbs, evenly distributed around the leader. Keep the lowest scaffold limb at least 16 inches off the ground.

Once the first year is past, avoid heading back if you can. You may have to cut back the leader and any upright growing scaffold limbs to keep the tree low enough to be convenient when spraying and picking. Mature sweet cherry trees are pruned usually only when you must take off dead or blighted limbs and broken limbs.

Sour cherry trees with no strong side branches running laterally should be headed back to 2 feet above the ground. Select laterals for scaffolding at the start of the second year's growth. If the tree has some good laterals when it is planted, remove any lower than 16 inches from the ground. Choose about three permanent lateral or scaffold branches along the leader, making sure they are 4 to 6 inches apart and not directly over one another. Do not head them back. In following years, select side branches from the leader until you have a total of five or six scaffold limbs well distributed above the lowest branch and running 2 to 4 feet up the main stem, or leader. Modify the leader by cutting to an outward growing leader. Once fruiting starts, pruning will be needed mainly to thin out excessive and crowded growth each year, allowing sunlight to get to the tree.

Plum and Peach Trees

The *plum* tree may also be trimmed in a manner similar to the apple tree. European and prune types generally develop into well-shaped trees, even if little pruning is done. You will probably only need to thin out excessive growth after heading the tree back to 3 feet at the time of planting. Japanese varieties are often more vigorous and may need heading back as well as thinning after they start bearing.

Peach trees are most often pruned in the open center system. Newly planted trees are headed to 30 inches, just above a lateral branch or bud. If the tree is branched when it arrives from the nursery, select three or four laterals well spaced up and around the trunk for permanent scaffold limbs. Keep the lowest limb about 15 inches off the ground and the highest no more than 30 inches above ground. Cut the laterals back to two buds, and remove all others. If no useful laterals are in place, head the tree and cut out all side branches to a single bud. This will allow a number of shoots to develop during the season, and you may select your scaffold limbs. Selection can be made during summer, or it can be delayed until just before second season growth begins.

Once the scaffold system is well along, prune the tree as little as possible. Remove all strong upright shoots going from the center of the tree, and lightly head back terminal growth on scaffold limbs cutting back to outward growing laterals. This will aid the development of an open center tree.

With peach trees, fruit is borne on wood of the previous year's growth. It is essential that the tree be pruned annually to stimulate new growth and maintain production close to the body of the tree. Pruning of the mature peach tree consists of moderate thinning and heading back to outward growing laterals to maintain a low and spread tree. Height should be held to 8 or 9 feet. Nectarine and apricot trees are pruned just as are peach trees.

The *quince* can be trained to the open center system like the peach, or cut to 10 to 12 inches above the ground and forced to form a bush-like tree. Quinces characteristically grow crookedly and slowly. They need little pruning. When fruit buds develop on the ends of the current season's growth, the main limbs are often cut back to stimulate shoot growth. Generally, all the pruning needed will be the removal of dead branches and limbs interfering with one another.

SPECIAL TRAINING

While the above methods of pruning will provide maximum yields of high quality fruit, you may wish to decorate your home or garden with fruit trees. There are many ways to train fruit trees to grow decoratively, based on the art of *espalier* developed about 400 years ago in France and Italy.

The simplest espalier method is the horizontal *cordan*, which adapts well to apple, pears and plums. Trees are usually supported by a wall, a fence or a wire trellis, and training to the four-wire trellis is reasonably easy. Such a system can serve for decorative purposes, or it can be used to separate one yard area from another. It can also be a way to provide a method of producing a high volume of fruit in a limited area (Fig. 12-4).

Use dwarfing rootstock for espalier-trained trees, and utilize the spur forms. Standard and semi-dwarf trees tend to grow too large and become very difficult to hold within bounds.

Set 8-foot posts 2 feet into the ground and space them a dozen feet apart. Run wires *through* the posts at heights of 18, 36, 54 and 72 inches. Plant two unbranched whips of the desired variety 6 feet apart between each two posts. Before growth starts in the spring, cut off the whips just above the first bud below the point where the whip crosses the lowest wire on the trellis. Usually, you will see three or even more shoots develop close to the point of the cut. Retain the top shoot and develop it as your leader. Move the other two shoots onto the wire as main scaffold branches, one on each side of the central stem. All other shoots are removed.

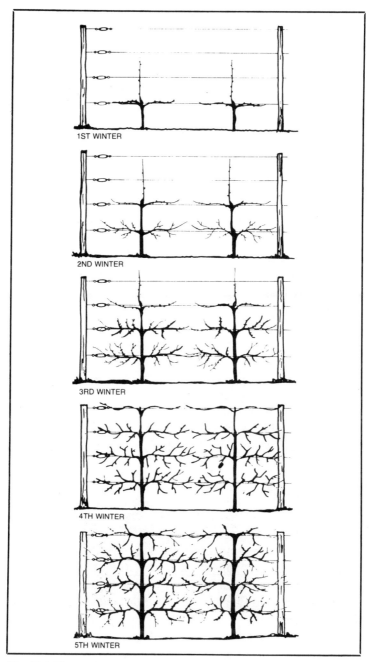

1ST WINTER

2ND WINTER

3RD WINTER

4TH WINTER

5TH WINTER

Fig. 12-4. Training fruit trees to the four-wire trellis system.

Tie the shoots selected for the scaffold limbs to the wire as soon as they are 10 or 12 inches long. Tie them loosely and with twine, making sure they are close to horizontal. If the shoots are tied below the horizontal, new growth at the end will stop and strong shoots will start along the upper side. By the end of the first season, the laterals should be well established and the main trunk should be above the second wire.

During dormant season pruning at the end of the first winter, cut the center leader off a bud below the second wire. Repeat the previous spring's process of developing a leader and scaffold branches along the wire. Repeat the process the next two seasons and you should have a total of eight scaffold branches, four on each side of the tree. The leader is bent to form one of the scaffolds along the top wire instead of being pruned off. By the time the fourth season is over, the trees should be producing heavily. Do all pruning during spring and summer months. Once new growth reaches 2 inches long in the spring, it is cut off, while you also remove about one fourth of the previous season's growth.

Once new growth reaches about a foot, cut it back to two or three buds. Repeat the process a month later, if needed. This encourages fruit bud formation and keeps growth in bounds.

The system may seem a bit complicated at first, but it really isn't. Yields are heavier than for conventionally trained trees with the same bearing surface.

THINNING

It is not at all unusual for peach and apple trees to set more fruit than can mature to a reasonable size. Thinning of excess fruit becomes necessary in such cases. Thinning not only allows the remaining fruit to increase in size, but also improves fruit color and taste. It will also cut down on limb breakage, promote general tree health, and induce regular annual bearing, in certain varieties, such as Golden Delicious, *Yellow Transparent* and *York Imperial*. If not thinned, these varieties have a tendency to bear heavy crops only every other year.

Peach thinning is a standard practice in commercial orchard operations. Experiments have proved that thinning as soon after blooming as possible makes for earlier ripening and larger fruit. Once the pits start to harden, there is little benefit. Peaches should be thinned so that they are spaced 6 to 8 inches apart.

Apples are thinned as soon as possible after the fruit has set. Thinning should be finished within 20 to 25 days after full bloom for greatest benefits. Thin apples to a distance of 6 to 10 inches between fruits. Delicious varieties need the largest spacing. In most cases, the center apple of a cluster is the largest and, thus, the best to leave in place.

Plums needing thinning will usually be of the more vigorous Japanese varieties. They are thinned to space the fruits at 4-inch intervals.

RODENT CONTROL

Rodents can be a mild to serious problem in orchards, so some forms of control are needed. Mice chew off bark at and sometimes below ground level and at times may completely girdle a tree, causing it to die. Most of the damage will take place during the winter. Keep mulch pulled back from the tree's base and check often for any gnawing marks. Trapping and poisoning can both be effectively used to control mice in an orchard, but always follow the poison manufacturer's directions to the letter.

Rabbits can also girdle and kill young fruit trees. Here a *mechanical guard* is the most effective means of controlling damage. Galvanized screen, or hardware cloth, with ¼-inch mesh is the best material for making up such a guard. Buy it in 3-foot wide rolls, and cut the roll into 18-inch wide strips. Cut the strips into 14-inch long pieces. Roll or bend the strips around the tree so the long side is up and down the trunk and the edges overlap. Twist a small wire loosely around the overlap to keep things raveled, and push the strip down into the ground as far as possible. Such guards will last a long time and can be left on the trees year round (Fig. 12-5).

The Department of Agriculture worked up a repellent often used by commercial growers. Mix up equal parts of fish

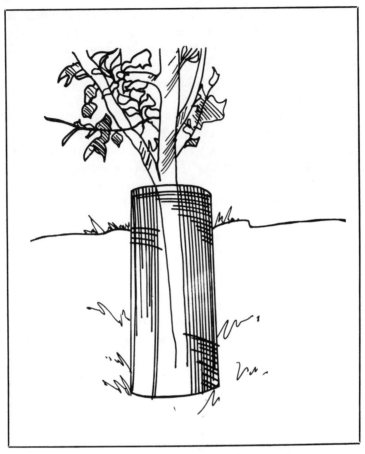

Fig. 12-5. Galvanized mesh used to protect trees from rodents.

oil, concentrated lime sulfur and water. Apply from the
ground up to the scaffold limbs with a paint brush.

SPRAYING AND SANITATION

The home fruit gardener is unlikely to want to or be able
to follow the same schedules as commercial growers, because the timed intervals involve different materials applied
at critical times. Several all-purpose fruit *sprays* are readily
available and will help to control most insects and diseases.
Careful following of directions is always necessary for good
and safe results.

Proper orchard *sanitation* keeps down places for destructive insects to breed and helps cut down on the spread of diseases. Without proper sanitation, even very frequent and heavy spraying may not do the job of controlling such problems.

Collect and burn all debris that is burnable. Remove and destroy all dropped fruit. Rake and burn apple and cherry leaves, and scrape the loose bark from trunk crotches and main limbs of all apple trees. Finally, prune out and destroy all dead and diseased limbs, branches and trees. With a bit of luck as to weather, you should have all the home-grown fruit you ever want through a large part of the year.

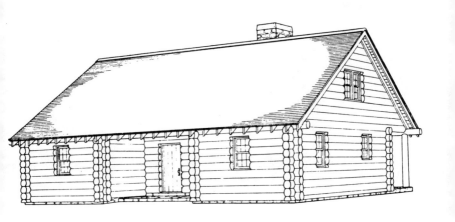

13

Growing Small Fruits

Fruits such as *strawberries*, *blueberries* and *raspberries* can add to the enjoyment of the growing season, while taking little or no space in even a small garden. Consider inserting some strawberries in the flower garden instead of some perennial shrub. The plants are attractive, and that would take no room at all from the vegetable garden. Pest control is generally easier than with tree-borne fruits, and bearing is almost always within two years of planting, if not earlier.

Soil preparation generally follows good garden soil preparation methods for all plants, with sandy loam soil high in humus the best for them. Select varieties with the greatest resistance to disease and insects, and get the best nursery stock you can. Figure your spacing rather carefully (Table 13-1) if you are not using the decorative garden for these fruits. Remember, though, that strawberries make good flower bed borders. Grapes and raspberries can be planted parallel to the garden of a trellis or on a fence along your property line. Blueberries can be planted to form a dense hedge or used as foundation plantings around your home.

Table 13-2 gives some varieties suitable for planting around the Middle Atlantic states. Your county agent can supply you with lists if your climate differs markedly from that area.

Table 13-1. Statistics on Various Types of Small Fruits.

| FRUIT | MINIMUM DISTANCE | | AVERAGE ANNUAL YIELD PER PLANT | BEAR-ING AGE | LIFE EX-PECT-ANCY |
	BE-TWEEN ROWS	BE-TWEEN PLANTS			
	feet	feet	quarts	years	years
Blueberry	6	4	4	3	20-30
Blackberry (erect)	8	3	1½	1	5-12
Blackberry (trailing)	8	6	1½	1	5-12
Raspberry (red)	8	3	1½	1	5-12
Raspberry (black)	8	4	1½	1	5-12
Raspberry (purple)	8	3	1½	1	5-12
Grape (Amer.) (Fr. Amer.)	10	8	15 lb.	3	20-30
Grape (muscadine)	10	10	25 lb.	3	20-30
Strawberry (regular)	3	1	½	1	3
Strawberry (ever-bearer)	3	1	½	⅓	2
Currant	8	4	5	3	10-20
Gooseberry	8	4	5	3	10-20

STRAWBERRIES

Strawberries are probably the most widely grown small fruit in the United States. The uses range from strawberry jam to pie filling and fresh eating, with or without cream, which may or may not be whipped. Strawberries are available in enough varieties to adapt to a great many climatic conditions, and are reasonably easy to grow.

Varieties

Those varieties listed here are readily adaptable to the Middle Atlantic states and places where similar soil and climate conditions prevail. If your requirements are different, check with your county agent for locally adaptable varieties. There will probably be plenty.

☐ **Earlidawn.** A very early variety, with blossoms somewhat tolerant to cold. Fruits are large, firm and bright red. They freeze well.

☐ **Earlibelle.** Produces heavy crops of bright colored, large, firm berries even in crowded beds.

Table 13-2. Varieties of Small Fruits
Suitable for Planting in the Middle Atlantic States.

BLUEBERRIES
- [1] Earliblue
- [1] Ivanhoe
- Blueray
- Bluecrop
- Jersey
- [2] Berkeley
- Herbert
- Coville

BLACKBERRIES (erect)
- Darrow
- Black Satin (thornless)
- Dirksen (thornless)

BLACKBERRIES (trailing)
- Lucretia
- [1] Boysenberry
- Lavaca

RASPBERRIES (red)
- Sunrise
- Latham
- Pocahontas
- Cherokee (everbearing)
- Heritage (everbearing)

[2] **RASPBERRIES** (black)
- New Logan
- Bristol
- Cumberland

[2] **RASPBERRIES** (purple)
- Sodus

[2] **CURRANTS**
- Wilder
- Red Lake

[2] **GOOSEBERRIES**
- Pixwell
- Red Jacket

STRAWBERRIES (regular)
- Earlidawn
- Earlibelle
- Earliglow

- Catskill
- Pocahontas
- Surecrop
- Atlas
- Redchief
- Guardian
- Marlate

[2] **STRAWBERRIES** (ever-bearing)
- Superfection (Gem, Brilliant)
- Streamliner
- Ozark Beauty

GRAPES (American Bunch)
- Price
- Seneca
- Himrod
- Fredonia
- Monticello
- Delaware
- [2] Concord
- Century I

GRAPES (French-American Hybrids)
- Aurora (Seibel 5279)
- Cascade (Seibel 13053)
- DeChaunac (Seibel 9549)
- Chancellor (Seibel 7053)

GRAPES (Vinifera)
- Pinot Chardonnay
- White Reisling

[1] **GRAPES** (Muscadine)
- Hunt
- Scuppernong
- * Carlos
- * Magnolia
- Thomas
- *Dearing
- Topsail

[1]Recommended for Eastern Virginia only.

[2]Not recommended for Eastern Virginia.

*Perfect flowered. Other varieties are pistillate and require pollinizers.

☐ **Earligrow.** A relatively new variety noted for disease resistance and dessert quality. Medium-large berries are a glossy, deep red color, and are among the best for eating fresh, for freezing and for using in jams and jellies.

☐ **Catskill.** A large but irregularly shaped berry, with red fruit, mildly subacid taste and good dessert quality. It freezes well.

☐ **Pocahontas.** It grows vigorously and produces a large fruit with bright red skin and flesh. It is slightly subacid, has good dessert quality and freezes well.

☐ **Surecrop.** Mildly subacid and a good dessert berry. Deep-red berries are large and irregularly shaped. It tolerates drought conditions.

☐ **Atlas.** A relatively new variety from North Carolina. It is a large firm berry that is somewhat wedge-shaped. Atlas is medium-red in color and of high quality, along with being tolerant to most strawberry diseases.

☐ **Redchief.** Very productive and a high quality dessert berry. It is medium to large and size and of deep-red color with a firm glossy surface. Redchief is very resistant to red *stele*.

☐ **Guardina.** Produces large, deep-red berries which are firm and uniform in size. Guardina has good dessert qualities, freezes well and is resistant to many common strawberry diseases.

☐ **Marlate.** It ripens a week or more after the usual late varieties and can help to extend the berry season. Seldom hurt by late frost, the fruit is large with good flavor. It freezes well.

☐ **Everbearing Strawberries.** They are not as good as regular varieties, but do yield longer.

☐ **Superfection.** A leading variety with an irregularly shaped fruit of medium size and firmness. It is acidic and of fair dessert quality.

☐ **Streamliner.** These fruits are larger than those of Superfection and more evenly shaped. They are soft and less acidic. Production is low, but flavor is pleasing.

□ **Ozark Beauty.** A relatively new everbearing variety. It is a good quality fruit, red, wedge-shaped and firm, and only slightly acidic. Ozark Beauty freezes well.

Planting

Strawberries bloom very early in spring. The blossoms are not hardy when frost lands. In areas where late frosts may be a hazard, select a slightly higher than usual planting site. Soil pH is important. Strawberries grow best in a 5.7 to 6.5 condition in sandy, loam soils, but they will grow in neutral (pH 7) soil that is well-drained and well supplied with humus. Do not plant strawberries on soil that has recently been sod. In such areas, grubs and ants may be a large problem.

Strawberry plants are set out early in spring, about three or four weeks before the average last frost date. Set the plants a foot apart and the rows about 3 feet apart. Set each plant so the base of the bud is at soil level (Fig. 13-1). Spread the roots carefully and firm the soil around them to prevent air pockets which may allow them to dry out.

From this point, fertilization and cultivation are pretty similar to other plants until time comes to train the plants.

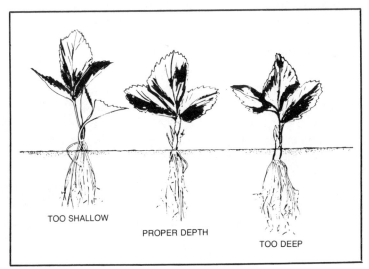

Fig. 13-1. Setting strawberry plants to correct depth.

Matted row systems allow the runners to go where they will, and this is popular with home gardeners. Mother plants here are set 2 feet apart in the row. Hill system plants are set as specified before—a foot apart. Runners are removed as they appear, and the plants will stool out with large crowns. This method provides easier cultivation, harvesting, and larger, higher quality berries. More plants are needed for the same area.

The *spaced row system* requires plants to be set 18 to 24 inches apart. Runner plants are set in place by hand, usually 6 to 12 inches apart. All late-forming runners are removed.

During the first season, remove all flower stems on the plants to strengthen them and allow for early and stronger runner production. Early formed runner plants will bear the best fruit the next year (Fig. 13-2).

Birds are the biggest pest problem with strawberries. You may find a need to cover the rows with tobacco cloth or plastic mesh to keep the plants from being eaten before they are ripe enough to pick.

GRAPES

Grape variety selection can determine the uses of the grapes. If jelly and jam is desired, then one kind is used; if wine is wanted, then another type is chosen.

American Bunch Grapes

Selected for the middle Atlantic states, many of these varieties are suitable elsewhere. A check with your local county agent is sensible to keep from wasting money.

Price, introduced by Virginia Polytechnic Institute and State University in 1972, is a medium-sized blue-black grape of good quality that ripens four weeks before Concord. It is less subject to black rot, mildew and skin cracking than many other varieties. The vine is of average vigor and productivity.

Seneca, an early yellow grape, has good flavor and a tender pulp. It keeps well, in cold storage, for up to two months after harvest. Vine vigor and productivity are only moderate and susceptible to black rot and mildew.

Fig. 13-2. Removing strawberry clusters.

Himrod is a relatively new golden yellow grape, almost seedless, with good flavor. Hardy, vigorous and productive, it is superior to its sister grape *Interlaken*.

Fredonia is a very popular early grape that ripens about 10 days before Concord. Berries and bunches are large, though the flavor is not as good as Concord. Fredonia is better adapted to warm climates than Concord.

Monticello is a medium-sized, blue-black slip skin grape that ripens 10 days before Concord. It is of average vigor, very productive and must be cluster-thinned to prevent overbearing. Monticello is high in sugars and good as a table grape, as well as for jams and jellies.

Delaware is a high quality red grape that ripens about a week before Concords. Susceptible to downy mildew, it has rather small clusters and berries. Vines are slow-growing. Delaware has a good balance of sweetness and acidity. It is a good white wine grape, often used in blends for American champagnes.

Concord is the most widely planted blue grape. The good quality fruit tends to ripen unevenly in warm climates.

Century I, another Virginia Tech introduction, is a non-slip skin grape that ripens with Concord. The crisp, meaty flesh has the sweet and fruity taste of the vinifera (wine grape) type. Clusters are large, with ovate reddish-black berries. Century I must be close-pruned and cluster-thinned to prevent overbearing of an extent that will damage the wood. Subject to black rot and powdery mildew, it requires disease control measures.

Steuben is a new blue-black variety that ripens about a week after Concord. Berries are medium-sized, with a sweet, spicy flavor. The berries store well and the vines are hardy, vigorous and productive.

French-American Hybrids

French-American hybrid grapes have been tested for use in the same areas where American bunch grapes do well.

Aurora (Seibel 5279) is an early pinkish-white grape of excellent flavor. Aurora will make a fine white table wine. The vine is vigorous and productive even in northern winter areas.

Cascade (Seibel 13053) is an early blue grape, hardy and productive, that produces a superior rose wine. It blends well with heavy-bodied dark-red wines.

DeChaunac (Seibel 9549) is an established commercial variety in Ontario, Canada and throughout the eastern United States. The vine is below average in vigor, but is winter hardy, productive and has very few disease problems. It ripens in early mid-season and will produce a red wine of consistently high quality.

Chancellor (Seibel 7053) ripens with the Concord in most areas and is hardy, vigorous and very productive. The grape is dark blue and will make a red wine of very high quality.

Vinifera

Vinifera, or *Vitis vinifera*, varieties are susceptible to fungus diseases and do not do well everywhere. In addition, they totally lack resistance to the grape root louse. In most cases, vinifera must be grafted to resistant rootstock and needs a rigorous spray program and protection in areas subject to fluctuating and low winter temperatures.

Pinot Chardonnay is one of the top vinifera for dry, white wines. It is moderate in hardiness, vigor and productivity. A medium-sized white grape, Pinot Chardonnay ripens three to five days ahead of the Concord.

Johannisberg (White) Riesling is vigorous, productive and moderately hardy. A white grape that whitens about a week after the Concord, it makes an excellent dry white wine if growing conditions are good.

Muscadine

Muscadine grapes are adapted only to warm areas—spots where it does not drop below 10 degrees F. all year round. The varieties make superb jams and jellies. Some are grown for exceptional wines. Most varieties have imperfect flowers and require pollination from either male or perfect-flowered varieties. *Carlos, Magnolia* and *Dearing* are perfect-flowered.

Hunt is an all-purpose black variety, with large berries that ripen evenly. It ripens early, too, and makes fine juice, jam, jelly and wine.

Scuppernong, a name commonly applied to all bronze colored muscadine grapes, is the oldest and best known variety. Berries are small, but grape quality is good with a distinctive flavor.

Carlos was introduced in 1970 from North Carolina and is a perfect-flowered bronze variety, ripening with Scuppernong, and similar in size and flavor. It makes an excellent white wine and is relatively cold hardy, disease resistant and productive.

Magnolia is a self-fertile white variety of large size and high quality. It is vigorous and very productive.

Thomas has reddish-black, medium to small high quality berries which are very sweet. It makes an excellent unfermented juice.

Dearing is a light-skinned perfect-flowered variety with very sweet medium-sized berries.

Topsail is the sweetest of all and is preferred by many people because of its high sugar content. Berries are medium-sized and greenish-bronze, with smooth skins.

Planting

Grapes require sun throughout most of the day, so the site needs to be selected with that in mind. The vines are deep-rooted, often as far as 8 feet down under good soil conditions, and they grow best in sandy loam conditions with a high humus content. Deep sands and heavy clays can be used if you provide for good drainage. Grapes tolerate a wide range of pH situations, but will do best if the pH range is 6.0 to 7.0.

Grape vines are usually set in early spring, some three to four weeks before the last frost is expected. Allow at least 8 feet between American bunch grape varieties and 10 feet between other kinds, except for the less vigorous vinifera. Roots are trimmed to about 6 inches long to encourage the growth of feeder roots near the trunk. Dig holes large enough so that the roots are not crowded, and set at about the same depth as the plants were set at the nursery. Prune to a single cane, and head it back to two buds.

Now mulch with organic material or black plastic, and keep fertile after spring growth begins. Use about 2 ounces of nitrate of soda per vine, spread 10 to 12 inches from the trunk. Repeat in six weeks. In the second year spread about four ounces of nitrate of soda around the trunk in a 4-foot circle, ending about 1 foot from the trunk. Increase to 8 ounces the third year. If potassium and phosphorous (potash) are needed, you can use a complete fertilizer instead. If, when the vines mature, average cane growth is 3 inches or less, you may need to fertilize. Competition from weeds and grass should be checked first, for in most cases fertilizing is not needed after the third year.

Pruning and Training of Vines

The pruning and training of grape vines is of great importance in overall productivity. For greatest production, your vines must be pruned and trained to a system, and the two most common are the *vertical trellis* and the *overhead arbor*.

The vertical trellis has many variations. The single trunk, four-arm *Kniffin* system is the most popular of these.

Most types of grapes will do well with this system. Posts are set 15 to 29 feet apart and must extend 5 feet above ground. Two wires are stretched between the posts, with the lower being 2½ feet off the ground and the upper being on top of the post. Set between the posts, the vine is trained to a single trunk with four semi-permanent arms, each cut back 6 to 10 inches in length. One arm is trained in each direction on the lower wires, and one in each direction on the upper wire (Fig. 13-3). During annual winter pruning, one cane is saved from those that grew near the base of each arm the preceding summer. Cut this cane back to about 10 buds.

The coming season's fruit will be borne on these buds or, actually, shoots developing from these buds. Select another cane on each arm, as close to the trunk as possible, and cut it back to short stubs of two buds. This is a *renewal spur* and should grow vigorously during spring, becoming the new fruiting cane for the next season. Cut back all other growth on the vine, leaving four fruiting canes of 10 buds each and four renewal canes of two buds each. Annual pruning consists of removing dead wood and tendrils that gird the arms and trunk.

The same pruning and training techniques are used for the arbor system, with the only difference being that you place the supporting wires overhead and parallel instead of horizontal. Arbor wires are commonly placed 6 to 7 feet above the ground (Fig. 13-4).

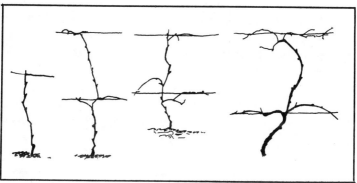

Fig. 13-3. Using the four-arm Kniffin systems to train grapes.

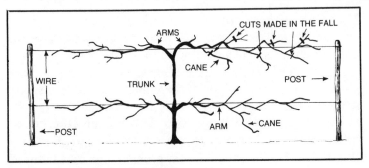

Fig. 13-4. Pruning muscadine grapes.

BRAMBLE FRUITS

Bramble fruits include the red, black and purple raspberries and erect and trailing blackberries. Both will usually yield a modest crop the second year after planting, and a full crop by the third season. Average plant life is six to eight years, but can be extended by careful gardening practices and good location.

Blackberries

Blackberry selection includes three erect types. *Black Satin* is thornless, very productive and hardy. It has large, firm fruit and is jet black when fully ripe, with an excellent flavor. Peak quality is two to three days after the berry turns black. *Darrow* is a large berry almost an inch long. Glossy black, it is mildly subacid and of good quality. *Dirksen* is also thornless, very productive and hardy. Somewhat smaller than Black Satin, it has an equally good taste when fully ripe.

The trailing blackberries are generally not as hardy as the erect types. They do better in areas with a bit more warmth during the Winter months.

Lucretia is probably the best of the trailing blackberries and is reasonably winter-hardy, vigorous and productive. Berries are sweet flavored and very large, often as much as 1½ inches long.

Boysenberry is not hardy and requires mild winters. Plants are very vigorous and productive, with large, flavorful berries. They are available thornless as well.

Lavaca is an offspring of the Boysenberry and is superior to its parent in production, size and resistance to cold and disease. The fruit is firmer, less acidic and of better overall quality.

Raspberries

Raspberries do better in cooler areas. However, the red raspberries tolerate heat reasonably well.

Sunrise is a good quality red raspberry. The berry is firm and finely textured, very tolerant to *anthracnose, leaf spot* and *cane blight*, and is hardy.

Latham is the standard red raspberry for the eastern United States. Plants are vigorous, productive and fairly tolerant of viral diseases. Berries are above average in size. The flavor is tart with good quality.

Pocahontas, a recent introduction from Virginia Tech, produces a large, firm medium red berry with a tart flavor. It is winter-hardy and productive.

Cherokee is another Virginia Tech introduction and is an everbearing variety especially adapted to Virginia's Piedmont area. Good quality berries are large and firm. It is winter-hardy and very productive.

Heritage is an everbearing red raspberry. It is pruned annually simply by mowing back all the tops.

Black raspberries are very susceptible to viral diseases and should not be grown next to resistant red varieties which may be carrying such diseases. Separate by at least 700 feet.

New Logan yields heavy crops of glossy black berries of good quality. Plants are drought-resistant and relatively tolerant to *mosaic* and other raspberry diseases.

Briston is a hardy, vigorous and highly productive variety. Large, firm and good quality berries can be hard to pick unless they are fully ripe.

Cumberland is the favored variety because it produces large, firm, attractive berries with fine flavor. Plants are vigorous and productive.

Purple raspberries are hybrids of red and black types. The berries are a purple color and usually larger than either parent variety. More tart than either red or black raspberries, they are best use in jams, jellies and pies and are superb for quick freezing. Plants are hardy, vigorous and very productive. *Sodus* is the best available.

Planting

Raspberries do best in deep, sandy loam with plenty of humus. Soil pH is not critical, but best results are had with a slightly acid soil, from about 5.8 to 6.5 pH. Do not site where tomatoes, potatoes or eggplant have been grown since those crops often carry *verticillium wilt* which can remain in the soil for many years. Bramble fruits are extremely susceptible to verticillium wilt. Plantings on such sites will almost always fail.

Plant early in the spring, two to four weeks before the last expected frost date. Allow 8 feet between rows, though erect growing varieties need only 3 feet. Erect growing blackberries and red and purple raspberries may be set as close as 3 feet apart in a row, with black raspberries set no less than 4 feet apart and trailing blackberries no less than 6 feet.

Most bramble fruits will arrive with a portion of the old cane attached. Once the plant is set out, cut off this old cane and burn it. This is a precaution against anthracnose infection. Set the plants so the crown is about 2 inches below the ground.

Pruning and Training

Trailing blackberries need some form of support, so they may grown to a trellis, trained along a fence or tied to stakes. Other brambles may be trained to supports or, with more severe pruning, grown as upright, self-supporting plants.

For a trellis for blackberries, set posts 15 to 20 feet apart. Place wires at the 3-foot and 5-foot levels. Tie erect varieties where the canes cross the wires. Canes of the trailing varieties are trained along the wires.

Canes of bramble fruits are biennial, but the crowns are perennial. After fruiting, the old canes die and new shoots spring from the crowns. Fruiting canes can be pruned any time after harvest and are cut off close to the base of the plant. Black raspberries should be summer-topped when the young shoots are about 2 feet high, with purple raspberries waiting until they reach 30 inches. Remove the top 3 to 4 inches of the shoots (Figs. 13-5 and 13-6).

Harvest bramble fruits as soon as they are fully ripe. They are very perishable.

BLUEBERRIES

Blueberries do well in areas where native blueberries, mountain laurel and rhododendrons do well. Flavor is best if nights during the ripening season are cool. Two or more varieties must be planted to assure cross-pollination.

Earliblue has large-sized, good quality berries. It is vigorous and productive. The berry is light blue, firm, resists cracking and is not hardy.

Ivanhoe is not hardy. But it has a large, light blue, firm berry of good quality and top flavor.

Blueray is very hardy and productive, with a large medium light blue fruit. It is very flavorful and resistant to cracking.

Bluecrop lacks vigor but is very hardy and drought-resistant. Fruit is large, light blue and firm.

Jersey is vigorous, hardy and produces heavy crops of large, light blue berries of good quality.

Berkeley has a very large, light blue berry that is exceptionally firm and resistant to cracking. The berry is medium in dessert quality.

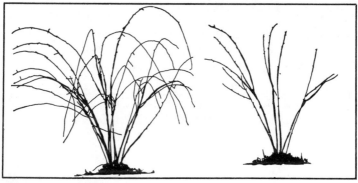

Fig. 13-5. Pruning black raspberries.

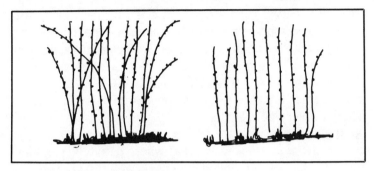

Fig. 13-6. Pruning red raspberries.

Herbert has a superior dessert quality. It has a very large, medium blue berry that is moderately firm and resistant to cracking.

Coville has good dessert quality, but is very tart until it is fully ripe. The berry is very large, deep blue, firm and resistant to cracking.

Planting

Blueberries are shallow rooted plants and will require irrigation, heavy mulch or a high water table. They also need full sunlight and good drainage as constantly wet roots will damage the plants. Acid soil, 4.0 to 5.2 pH, is best. If the soil is not acid enough, work in some pine needles, oak leaves or sulfur six months to a year before planting. For each full point the soil tests out above 4.5 pH, work in three-fourths of a pound of sulfur per 100 square feet. On heavy clay soils, work in about twice that much. Once you get the correct acidity in the soil, maintain it with an annual dressing of acid fertilizer such as ammonium sulfate or cottonseed meal.

Select two-year-old plants about 15 inches tall and plant in early spring, two to four weeks before the last expected frost. Plant every 4 feet in rows 6 feet apart. Plants are set just a little bit deeper than they were at the nursery. Trim off dead and damaged portions of the top.

Pruning

Up to the end of the third growing season, prune only low-spreading canes and dead and broken branches. Annual

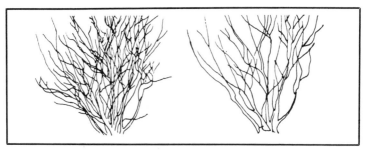

Fig. 13-7. Pruning blueberries.

pruning is needed after your plants begin bearing. Select six to eight canes of the most vigorous and erect stock. Remove all the rest. At about six years of age, the canes will begin to lose vigor. You will need to select, at dormant pruning, vigorous new shoots at the base of the plant and trim away the rest. Keep the number of canes at six or eight and trim off all the rest. Head back terminal growth so the plant stays at a convenient berry picking height (Fig. 13-7).

Birds can harvest blueberries before you do. You may wish to cover the plants with tobacco cloth, or you may want to use aluminum pie tins to scare off the birds. Suspend the tins above the bushes so they will twist and turn in any breeze, thus scaring off the birds.

Depending on variety, blueberries may bear the second year. Full production is not reached for about six years, at which time each plant should give you four to six quarts of berries.

Blueberries are not as perishable as blackberries and raspberries, so picking is needed only about once a week. The berries keep well, for several weeks, in cold storage.

Currants and *gooseberries* are alternate hosts of white pine blister rust, and thus they are restricted in planting in many areas of the country. At present, Virginia has 33 counties where permits are needed, and other states may be as badly restricted. I would suggest that if you are interested in either of these small fruits, get in touch with your local extension agent as to types allowed, whether permits are needed, and the distances from stands of white pine needed where allowed (1,500 feet here).

14

Keeping Food

All the time spent in growing your own food can be considered wasted if it goes bad before use. No matter how large the family, only so much garden produce can be eaten fresh. One family can only devour a certain amount of hamburger before the rest of the carcass rots. Thus, methods for canning, freezing, drying and pickling foods are essential to rural living, if you wish to come as close as possible to supplying all your own needs on a year round basis.

When preserving food, you are fighting the action of organisms such as bacteria, molds and yeasts that are always present in the air. The foods themselves will have enzymes that can cause nasty changes in color, flavor and texture of the fruits or vegetables.

CANNING EQUIPMENT

Each food requires the correct *canner*. The one that is right for tomatoes cannot be used on non-acid foods such as green beans or peas. For fruits, tomatoes and pickled vegetables you can use the cheapest canner available, the *boiling water bath* model. Acid foods are the only ones that can safely be processed in boiling water. For non-acid foods such as most common vegetables (and for yellow and orange tomato varieties), you will need a steam pressure canner to cut time to a reasonable length.

Getting a steam pressure canner ready for each session of canning requires a bit of care. Safe operation, because of the temperature and pressure, is essential, as is a high enough pressure, and temperature to make sure the foods are safely processed. For safe operation, at the start of the canning season and frequently during the season, draw a string through the *petcock* and safety valve openings to clean them. Check the pressure gauge against a known pressure source at least at the start of each season, and any time after the canner is handled roughly. Make sure a weighted gauge is cleaned thoroughly. A dial gauge can be checked against another dial. The checking can often be done by the dealer, or the canner manufacturer can supply details. Any gauge that is 5 pounds or more off requires replacement. If the gauge is 4 pounds or less off, tie a tag on the canner and use the following figures to correct for the pressure.

For a gauge that reads high, process at 11 pounds for 1 pound high on the reading, 12 pounds for 2 pounds high, and so on to 14 pounds for 4 pounds high. If the gauge reads low, process at 9 pounds for 1 pound low, 8 pounds for 2 pounds low, etc.

The canner must be completely clean. Wash the canner kettle well, but don't immerse the cover in water. Wipe it with a soapy cloth and then with a clean damp cloth. Dry it well.

Water bath canners require less care, as there are no dangers from steam and extremely high temperatures. A few precautions are in order to get the job done properly. Any large kettle or container can be used as a water bath canner, but make sure it is deep enough to allow 2 to 4 inches of space above the jars. This will provide for complete coverage of the jars by water and still allow room for brisk boiling (Fig. 14-1). The canner needs a tight fitting lid and a rack to hold the jars, so they don't touch each other or fall against the sides of the canner during processing. You can usually use a steam pressure canner, if it is large enough, as a water bath canner as well. Simply cover, but do not fasten the lid and leave the petcock wide open so that steam escapes instead of building up.

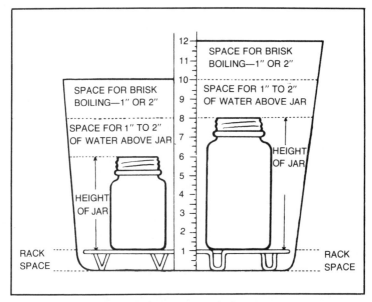

Fig. 14-1. Correct spacing for jars in a water bath canner.

Glass jars used for canning must be perfect. Toss out any jars that have nicks, cracks or chips. Make sure you use new closures each time. Select the correct size closure for the jars you are using. Wash all jars in hot, soapy water and rinse very well. If you use glass top jars, with rubber rings, use clean, new rings, and wash and rinse them well before use.

A few people may still use tin cans for storage these days, but I honestly can't remember seeing any in over a decade. There seems little point in going into the procedures needed for the cans. In general, glass jars are easier to use and do not require a special tool to seal, as do tin cans.

CANNING PROCEDURES

When selecting food for canning, pick the best. Look for young and tender vegetables, and can them while they remain fresh. Any food held for canning should be either refrigerated or kept in a dry, cool, airy place. Sort vegetables for size and ripeness before canning, since this assures a more even final product.

417

All fruits and vegetables must be washed thoroughly, even if they are to be pared. Dirt may contain much of the bacteria that is hardest to kill, so washing under running water, in small lots, is best. If you don't wish to use running water, wash very small batches in several changes of water. Lift the food out of the water each time a change is made, so that the dirt already washed off doesn't get back on the food. Rinse the pan well between washings. Do not let fruits or vegetables soak as they may lose flavor and nutritional value if they do. Handle as gently as possible to keep from bruising.

There are two methods of packing vegetables in canning jars. For a raw pack, you simply cut to the desired size and pack in the jars. Hot pack foods are preheated and packed while still hot. Most raw fruits and vegetables are packed as tightly as possible into the jars since they will shrink during the processing. There are a few, though, that must be packed loosely to allow for expansion: corn, lima beans and peas. Hot pack foods are packed fairly loosely and should be at, or very close to, boiling temperature when packed.

Make sure there is enough syrup, juice or water to fill in around the solid food in the jar and to cover the food. Food above water in a jar will tend to get dark with time. You will find you need from ½ to 1½ cups of liquid for a quart glass jar.

With very few exceptions, some head space at the top of the jar should be allowed. This head space will be covered as it comes up, with each food, as it is variable.

Glass jars have two main types of closures (Fig. 14-2). The metal screwband with the flat metal lid is probably the most popular type today. The flat metal lid has a sealing compound around its edges. Wipe the jar top clean after it is packed, and put the lid on with the sealing compound on the rim of the glass. Screw the metal rim down tight, by hand. Tightening by hand allows enough slack to let air escape during processing. Never tighten the rim more after you remove the jar upon completion of processing. Most people, in fact, take the rims off and reuse them on other jars being readied for processing. The metal rims may be reused as long as they are in good condition, but the sealing lids can be used only one time.

The porcelain-lined metal zinc cap is also used today, though not as extensively as it once was. This type of cap has a rubber shoulder ring, which is wetted and placed on the cleaned jar rim and pulled down on the shoulder of the jar. Do not stretch any more than is necessary to get the ring down on the shoulder. The jar is then filled and the edges cleaned again, along with the rubber ring. Screw the cap down firmly and then back it off a quarter turn. As soon as the jar is lifted from the canner, screw the lid down tight again to complete the seal. Obviously, you will need some sort of hand protection to screw down the hot cap on the hot jar. The porcelain-lined caps may be re-used as long as they are in good shape, but the rubber rings are used only once.

A third type of seal for glass jars exists, but is less often used these days. The jar will have a rubber ring and a glass cap. The ring fits on the jar, and the cap is tightened by a wire bail lever. These jars tend to be the most fragile and give the worst seal. I have used them for tomatoes only, but I think it is best to go with one of the newer kinds whenever possible. Ball and other companies make flat lid sealers with a dome in the middle that delates when processing.

Once the food is processed, the glass jars are removed and placed on racks for cooling. Cake racks do fine, and you should leave an inch or two of space between jars to allow air

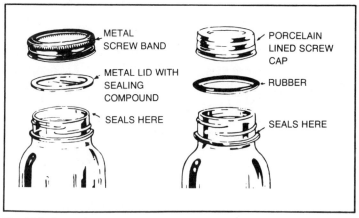

METAL SCREW BAND

METAL LID WITH SEALING COMPOUND

SEALS HERE

PORCELAIN LINED SCREW CAP

RUBBER

SEALS HERE

Fig. 14-2. Jar seal types.

flow to speed cooling. Any seals not made can be completed as the jars are removed from the canner. If any liquid has boiled out during processing, complete the seal anyway. Jars are cooled top side up and are not covered. The day after canning—or any time after the jar has cooled—you test the seal. Flat lid covered glass jars with the dome feature can be tested by eye when removed from the canner, but for those without the dome, press down on the center of the lid. If it stays down when pressed, the jar is sealed. If you find a leaky jar, you have two choices. You can use the food immediately, or you can re-process it. Metal bands can now be removed and reused. Wipe the jars clean and lable them with the date and the contents. If more than one batch was done in a day, also put the lot number on the number on the label. If one batch goes bad, this helps isolate the problem batch so you can discard the remainder.

If you have done the job correctly and the food is stored in a cool, dry place, your canned food will hold its eating quality for about a year. Food placed too close to warm pipes or in direct sunlight will lose edibility in just a few weeks or, at best, a few months. Too much dampness can corrode lids and cause leakage, while freezing will not necessarily spoil the food if the seal remains intact. Freezing will though, cause a change of taste. If your storage area is unheated, it is best to wrap the jars with paper or a blanker during really cold weather.

Unless procedures are followed exactly, a bit of spoilage can be expected. Always check canned food for bulging or leaking lids. After opening, look for signs of mold, spurting liquid as the jar is opened or an "off" odor. It is possible for food to spoil without any of these signs and the major problem here is *botulism*, the most virulent form of food poisoning known. The pressure canner must be in perfect operating order to avoid this risk. Still, boil home-canned vegetables before tasting—not just before eating, but before tasting, as this poison is really virulent. Heating will bring out any hidden odor of spoilage. Boiling vegetables—at a rolling boil—for 10 minutes (spinach and corn need to go at a rolling boil for 20 minutes) is a good idea. If the food looks spoiled, foams or has an "off" odor during heating, destroy it. Destroy is the operative word. Either burn the spoiled food or get rid of it in some manner that you can be sure it cannot be eaten by humans or animals.

CANNINGS FRUITS, TOMATOES AND PICKLED VEGETABLES

For a raw pack place cold, raw fruit into the jar and cover with boiling water, syrup or juice. Press tomatoes down in the jars so their own juice covers them. Do not add water.

For a hot pack, heat the fruit in syrup, water or in extracted juice before packing. Juicy fruits and tomatoes can usually be preheated without adding water, and you can then pack the food in the liquid that cooks out.

Sugar is often used to help canned fruit to hold its shape, color and, some claim, flavor. Sugar syrup is most often used for those who wish the addition. For a thin syrup, add 2 cups of sugar to 4 of water or juice to get a 5 cup batch. For a medium syrup, add 3 cups of sugar to 4 of water to get about 5½ cups of syrup. For a thick syrup, add 4¾ cups of sugar to 4 cups of water to get 6½ cups of syrup. Heat the sugar and water, or juice, together until the sugar dissolves completely, skimming as needed.

To extract juice, simply crush thoroughly ripened, juicy fruit and heat to simmering (about 185 to 210 degrees F.), using low heat. Strain the results through a jelly bag or linen toweling.

Sugar can also be added directly to fruit, though I can't see why anyone would want to. I guess it is due to the American sweet tooth. For hot packs, add about a half cup of sugar to each quart of fruit when raw. Then heat to simmering and, again, over low heat. Pack the fruit in the juice that cooks out. You can also use honey to replace the sugar, or at least about half of it.

Personally, I prefer to work without sugar, canning the fruit in its own juice or water. Fruit has fructose, which provides all the sugar anyone needs anyway. Adding more, for me, kills the taste of the fruit.

Once the jars are filled, they are placed in the hot water bath, which has already been brought to boiling, if you are using a hot pack, or has been heated if you are using a raw pack. Add boiling or hot water to bring the water an inch or two over the tops of the jars, but make sure the water does not strike the glass jars directly. Cover and bring back to a rolling boil. Once the water starts its rolling boil, start to count your processing time. Add boiling water during processing if it is needed to keep the jars covered.

Follow processing times carefully, making sure to never shorten them (Fig. 14-3). Altitude will affect processing time. The higher you get, the lower is the temperature at which water boils. Table 14-1 will indicate the changes in time needed for different altitudes and times.

How much food are you going to get? It varies with fruit size, quality, maturity and cut—whether you use the fruit whole or cut in halves, quarters, etc. Table 14-2 will give an indication of how many pounds it takes to get one quart of canned food.

Apples

Apples are pared, cored and cut into pieces. To prevent fruit darkening, drop them into water containing about 2 tablespoons each of salt and vinegar per gallon. Drain and then boil for five minutes in water or syrup. Pack hot fruit to within ½ inch of the top of the glass jar, and just cover with water. Process pint jars for 15 minutes in a boiling water bath and quart jars for 20 minutes.

Applesauce can be made sweetened or unsweetened. Heat the apples to 185 to 210 degrees F. and crush and stir, adding the flavorings you prefer. Pack hot applesauce to within ¼ inch of the tops of the jars and process in boiling water for 10 minutes (both pints and quarts).

Pickled Beets and Berries

Pickled beets are done by cutting off beet tops, leaving an inch of stem. The root is also left. Wash beets, cover them with water and boil until tender. Remove the skins and slice the beets into pickling syrup (2 cups of vinegar and 2 cups of sugar). Heat to a boil. Pack the beets in glass jars allowing ½

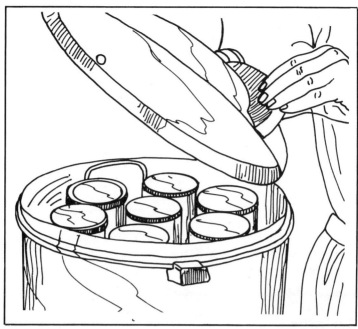

Fig. 14-3. Unsealing the canner after processing time is up and pressure has dropped to zero.

inch of head space, while adding ½ teaspoon of salt to pints and a teaspoon to quarts. Process in boiling water for 30 minutes, both pints and quarts.

Table 14-1. Changes in Processing Times Needed for Different Altitudes and Times.

INCREASE IN PROCESSING TIME IF THE TIME CALLED FOR IS—		
ALTITUDE	**20 MINUTES OR LESS**	**MORE THAN 20 MINUTES**
1,000 feet	1 minute	2 minutes
2,000 feet	2 minutes	4 minutes.
3,000 feet	3 minutes	6 minutes.
4,000 feet	4 minutes	8 minutes.
5,000 feet	5 minutes	10 minutes
6,000 feet	6 minutes	12 minutes
7,000 feet	7 minutes	14 minutes.
8,000 feet	8 minutes	16 minutes.
9,000 feet	9 minutes	18 minutes.
10,000 feet	10 minutes	20 minutes

Table 14-2. Pounds of Fruit Needed to Get One Quart of Canned Food.

	POUNDS
Apples	2½ to 3
Berries, except strawberries	1½ to 3 (1 to 2 quart boxes)
Cherries (canned unpitted)	2 to 2½
Peaches	2 to 3
Pears	2 to 3
Plums	1½ to 2½
Tomatoes	2½ to 3½

In 1 pound there are about 3 medium apples and pears; 4 medium peaches or tomatoes; 8 medium plums.

Berries (except strawberries) are washed, drained and packed in jars to ½ inch from the top. Shake the berries down while packing and cover with syrup or water, keeping the ½ inch head space. Process in boiling water, with pint jars needing 10 minutes and quart jars 15. For a hot pack, use only firm berries. Wash and drain well, and add a half cup of sugar to each quart of fruit (if you wish). Cover and bring to a boil, shaking the pan to keep the berries from sticking. Again, pack the berries allowing ½ inch of head space and process in boiling water, allowing 10 minutes for pints and 15 for quarts.

Cherries and Fruit Juices

Cherries are washed, and can be pitted if desired. For a raw pack, leave ½ inch of head space and shake the cherries down for a full pack. Cover with water or syrup, boiling, and keep the ½ inch space. Process pints for 20 minutes and quarts for 25 minutes in boiling water. For a hot pack, the addition of ½ cup of sugar is in the recipe, but not essential. If the cherries are not pitted, add some water while heating or they may stick to the pan. Cover and boil. Allow ½ inch of head space when packing and process in boiling water, giving pints 10 minutes and quarts 15 minutes.

Fruit juices are made with washed fruit, which is easier to handle if pitted (though this is not essential). Crush the fruit. Heat to simmering. Then strain through a cloth.

You can add sugar if you want, using about a cup to a gallon of homemade juice, If you add sugar, bring back to a simmer. Now fill the jars to within ½ inch of the top, and process in boiling water five minutes for both pints and quarts.

Peaches and Pears

Peaches are washed and the skins removed. The best way to peel peaches (and tomatoes)is to dip the fruit into boiling water for an instant, and to then stick it in cold water. The skins loosen nicely with this treatment. Cut peaches into halves and remove the pits. Slice whatever way you wish. You can now, if you want to keep the fruit from darkening, drop them into water containing 2 tablespoons each of salt and vinegar. Drain this water off before packing or heating. The raw pack requires ½ inch of head space after the fruit is covered with boiling water or syrup. Pint jars are processed in boiling water for 25 minutes, with quarts needing 30 minutes. The hot pack requires that peaches be heated in water or syrup. Leave ½ inch head space. Process in boiling water, 20 minutes for a pint and 25 minutes for a quart.

Pears are washed, peeled, cut into halves and cored. The rest is just like the procedure for peaches.

Plums and Rhubarb

Plums can be canned whole, but they must have their skins pricked after washing. Freestone varieties may be cut in half and pitted. Prepare the plums for the raw pack, and pack the fruit in glass jars leaving ½ inch of head space. Cover with boiling water or syrup and process, in boiling water, pint jars for 20 minutes and quarts for 25 minutes. The hot pack requires the same preparation, with the plums then prepared in a bit of water, with or without sugar, or in syrup, and packed to leave ½ inch of head space. Timing is the same as for raw packs.

Rhubarb is washed and cut into ½-inch pieces. This is one food that *needs* sugar, so add ½ cup to each quart and let it stand to draw out the juices. Rhubarb is always packed hot to within ½ inch of the top of the jar. Both pints and quarts take 10 minutes at a rolling boil.

Tomatoes

Tomatoes should be selected for ripeness and firmness. As with peaches, dipping first in boiling water and then in cold makes peeling much easier, but make the hot water dip at least 30 seconds long. Cut out stem ends and peel. Tomatoes can be left whole, or cut into halves or quarters. Pack to leave ½ inch of head space, pressing gently. Add ½ teaspoon of salt to pints and a teaspoon to quarts. Process in boiling water, with pints taking 35 minutes and quarts needing 45 minutes. Hot pack tomatoes are quartered, peeled and brought to a boil. Keep stirring to prevent sticking to the pan. Again, leave ½ inch head space, and add ½ teaspoon of salt to pints and a teaspoon to quarts. Process for 10 minutes, both pints and quarts.

Tomato juice is my next door neighbor's favorite drink, which is the reason he always plants at least 48 tomato vines. Use ripe and juicy tomatoes, washing them and removing the stem ends. Simmer until soft, stirring frequently. Strain them. Add a teaspoon of salt to each quart of juice and reheat to boiling at once. Fill jars with boiling hot juice, leaving ½ inch of head space. Process in boiling water, allowing 10 minutes for both pints and quarts.

CANNING LOW ACID VEGETABLES

Many vegetables cannot safely be processed in boiling water in a reasonable amount of time. Our ancestors did it, but it is not safe and never was. There is simply no point in taking chances with food poisoning when pressure canners are readily available, though often their cost may seem out of line. Depending on where you buy, a large pressure canner today will run from about $55 on up past $70. Too, using a pressure canner today cuts down on the use of gas or electricity at the kitchen range or the use of wood if you are using a wood range.

The basics, if you've already followed the cleaning and checking directions at the outset of this chapter, are not any more difficult than using the boiling water process for high acid vegetables. A raw pack requires cold, raw vegetables (except for corn, lima beans and peas) packed tightly into the jar and covered with boiling water. The hot pack means the vegetables are preheated in water or steam and are packed and covered with cooking liquid or boiling water. In most cases, cooking liquid is your best bet, since it will contain vitamins and minerals from the vegetables. Boiling water is used only when the cooking water is dark, gritty or too strongly flavored, or when there isn't enough cooking liquid.

Each pressure canner will be slightly different. Supplement these basics with the manufacturer's directions to make sure things are correct.

Put 2 to 3 inches of water in the bottom of the canner, making sure it is boiling (this saves time). The amount used will depend on the size of the canner. The filled glass jars are now set on the rack in the canner, leaving enough space for steam to flow around each jar. If the canner is large enough to take two tiers of jars, stagger them so there is space for steam flow. Always use a rack between rows of glass jars. Fasten the canner lid so that no steam can escape except through the vent. When the steam starts to escape from the vent, start timing for 10 minutes, which allows the air to be driven from the canner. Close the petcock or place the weighted gauge on the vent. Let the pressure rise to 10 pounds (giving a temperature of 240 degrees F.) and start counting processing time. Keep the pressure constant by regulating the heat under the canner. Do not open the petcock to lower pressure. You will find it easier to hold a constant pressure if the canner is kept from drafts.

Once the processing time is up, remove the canner from the heat immediately. Let the canner stand until the pressure drops to zero—do not rush things by running cold water over the canner. After the pressure has dropped to zero, give things another couple of minutes and then slowly open the petcock or lift off the weighted gauge. Unfasten the lid and tilt the side away from you and up to allow steam to escape. Remove the jars and set them to cool.

Processing times and pressures may need to be adjusted for altitudes. If you live 2000 feet above sea level on down, stay at 10 pounds for the times given. If you live between 2000 and 4000 feet, use 11 pounds of pressure. From 4000 to 6000 feet, use 12 pounds. From 6000 to 8000 feet, use 13 pounds, and from 8000 to 10,000 feet use 14 pounds. At 10,000 feet, you will need 15 pounds of pressure. You may, on weighted gauge styles, need to get a specially adapted gauge from the manufacturer of your canner. Again, the yield of vegetables canned from a particular amount of fresh, raw vegetables will vary with quality, condition, maturity and the variety of the vegetable, as well as with whether it is packed raw or hot.

Asparagus

Asparagus is washed and trimmed to get rid of tough ends and scale. Wash a second time after trimming and cut in 1-inch pieces. For a raw pack, pack as tightly as you can without crushing the vegetable and leave ½ inch of head space. Add ½ teaspoon of salt to pints and a teaspoon to quarts. Cover with boiling water, Keeping the ½ inch head space. Pint jars will need 25 minutes and quarts 30. For a hot pack, wash, trim and cut as for a raw pack. Then cover with boiling water and bring back to a boil for two to three minutes. Add salt as with the raw pack and cover with boiling hot cooking liquid or water. Leave ½ inch of head space. Pint jars will take 25 minutes; quarts take 30 minutes.

Lima Beans and Snap Beans

Lima beans should be young and tender for best results. Shell and wash the beans. Pack raw beans into clean jars, leaving an inch of head space on pints and 1½ inches on quarts. Do not shake or press down. Add ½ teaspoon of salt in pints and a teaspoon in quarts. Fill the jar to within ½ inch of the top with boiling water. Process pint jars for 40 minutes and quart jars for 50 minutes. For a hot pack, once the beans are shelled, cover them with boiling water and bring to a boil. Pack the hot beans to within an inch of the top of the jar. Add ½ teaspoon of salt to pints and a teaspoon to quarts. Cover with boiling water or cooking liquid and leave the 1 inch head space. Process for the same times as with cold packs.

Snap beans are washed and the ends are trimmed. Cut into 1 inch pieces (or feed through a frencher) and pack the raw beans tightly to within ½ inch of the top of the jar. Add salt, ½ teaspoon for pints and 1 teaspoon for quarts. Cover with boiling water, leaving ½ inch of head space. Process for 20 minutes in pints and 25 minutes in quart jars. For a hot pack, wash, trim and cut the beans. Then cover with boiling water and boil for five minutes. Pack the beans loosely to within ½ inch of the jar's top, and add salt as mentioned earlier. Cover with boiling hot cooking liquid, leaving the ½ inch head space. Pint jars take 20 minutes and quarts-take 25 minutes.

Beets and Carrots

Beets should be sorted for size. Cut the tops off, leaving an inch of stem and the root. Wash well and cover with boiling water until the skins slip off easily. Skin and trim. Leave baby beets whole, but cut medium and large beets in ½-inch cubes or slices. Very large slices should be halved or quartered. Pack the hot beets to within ½ inch of the top of the jar, and add ½ teaspoon of salt to pints and 1 teaspoon to quarts. Cover with boiling water, maintaining the ½ inch head space. Process pints for 30 minutes and quarts for 35 minutes.

Carrots are washed, scraped and then sliced or diced as you prefer. Leave an inch of head space when packing the raw carrots tightly in the jar. Again, add ½ teaspoon of salt to pints and a teaspoon to quarts. Fill the jar to within ½ inch of the top with boiling water. Process pint jars for 25 minutes and quart jars for 30 minutes. For a hot pack, once the carrots are sliced or diced, they are covered with boiling water and brought to a boil. Then add salt as mentioned earlier and cover with the boiling hot cooking liquid, keeping the ½ inch head space. Process pints for 25 minutes and quarts for 30 minutes.

Cream Style and Whole Kernel Corn

Cream style corn is made by husking the corn and getting all the silk off. Wash and then cut the corn off the cob at about the center of the kernel. Scrape the cobs. Pack corn to within 1½ inches of the top, but don't shake or press down. Add ½ teaspoon of salt to each jar and fill to within ½ inch of the top with boiling water. Process pint jars for 95 minutes. For a hot pack, prepare the corn as for a raw pack, and then add a pint of boiling water to each quart of corn. Heat to boiling, and pack corn in pint jars to within an inch of the jar's top. Add ½ teaspoon of salt. Process for 85 minutes. For both hot and raw packs with cream style corn, never use quart jars.

Whole kernel corn requires that corn be husked, silk removed and the corn washed. The corn is cut from the cob at about two-thirds the depth of the kernel, and packed to within an inch of the top of the jar. Don't shake or press down while packing the corn, and add ½ teaspoon of salt to pints and a teaspoon to quarts. Fill to ½ inch of the top of the jar with boiling water, and process pint jars for 55 minutes and quarts for 85 minutes. For hot packs, the corn is prepared as before. Then you add a pint of boiling water to each quart of corn. Bring back to a boil and pack in jars leaving an inch of space at the top. Cover with boiling hot liquid and maintain the cooking space. You can pack with corn right from the cooking and still keep the 1 inch of space. Add salt as mentioned, and process pints for 55 minutes and quarts for 85 minutes.

Peas

Fresh blackeye peas are shelled and washed. For the raw pack, the peas need 1½ inches of head space to start in pint jars and 2 inches in quarts. Add ½ teaspoon of salt to the pints and a teaspoon to the quarts. Cover with boiling water to within ½ inch of the top of the jar. Process pints for 35 minutes and quarts for 40 minutes. For a hot pack, the blackeye peas are shelled, washed and covered with boiling water. Bring to a rolling boil and pack the hot peas to within 1½ inches of the top of pint jars and 1½ inches for quart jars. Do not shake or press down. Add ½ teaspoon of salt to pints and a teaspoon to quarts. Cover with boiling water, leaving ½ inch of head space. Process pints for 35 minutes and quarts for 45 minutes.

Fresh green peas are shelled and washed. Pack the peas, without shaking or pressing down, to leave an inch of head space. Add ½ teaspoon of salt to pints and double that to quarts. Cover with boiling water to ½ inch below the top of the peas. Process both pints and quarts for 40 minutes. Hot pack peas are shelled, washed and then covered with boiling water. Bring to a boil and pack in jars loosely to within an inch of the top. Add salt as mentioned earlier and cover with boiling cooking liquid or water. Process pints and quarts for 40 minutes.

Potatoes

Potatoes canned whole should be no more than 2½ inches in diameter. Wash, pare and cook them for 10 minutes in boiling water. Drain and pack the hot potatoes to ½ inch of the top of the jars, adding ½ teaspoon of salt to pints and a whole teaspoon to quarts. Cover with boiling water, keeping the ½ inch head space. Pint jars will take 30 minutes processing time and quarts 40.

Cubed pumpkin is washed and the seeds removed. Pare and cut into 1-inch cubes. Add just enough water to cover the cubes and bring to a boil. Pack the hot cubes with ½ inch of head space, and add the usual amount of salt to pints and quarts. Cover with the hot cooking liquid, keeping the ½ inch head space. Pint jars will take 55 minutes, while the quarts require 95 minutes.

Strained pumpkin is prepared right to the cubed stage. The cubes are then steamed until they are tender, which will usually take about 25 to 30 minutes. Then run the cubes through a food mill or strainer. Simmer this until it is heated thoroughly, making sure to keep stirring so it won't stick to the pan. Pack the hot strained pumpkin to ½ inch of the top of the jar, adding no liquid or salt. Process pint jars for 75 minutes and quarts for 95 minutes.

Spinach and Squash

Spinach and other greens should be freshly picked and tender. Wash thoroughly and cut out tough stems and mid-ribs. Place about 2½ pounds of spinach in a cheesecloth bag and steam for around 10 minutes or until it is well wilted.

Pack the spinach loosely in the jar to ½ inch from the top. Add ¼ teaspoon of salt to pints and ½ teaspoon to quarts and cover with boiling water, keeping ½ inch headspace. Pint jars will take 70 minutes to process while quarts need 90 minutes.

Summer squash is washed but not pared. The ends must be trimmed, and the squash is then cut into ½ inch slices. Halve or quarter as needed to get pieces of a uniform size. Raw squash is packed tightly to an inch of the top of the jars and ½ teaspoon of salt is added to pints, with the quarts getting a teaspoon. Fill the jar to within ½ inch of the top with boiling water, and process pints for 25 minutes and quarts for 30 minutes. For a hot pack, prepare the squash as mentioned, adding ½ teaspoon of salt. Add just enough water to cover the slices and bring to a boil. Pack into jars leaving ½ inch of head space. Fill with boiling cooking liquid, keeping the ½ inch head space. Process pints for 30 minutes and quarts for 40 minutes. Winter squash is canned in the same manner, with the same times, as pumpkin.

Sweet Potatoes

Sweet potatoes can be done either as dry pack or wet pack. For a dry pack, the sweet potatoes are first washed and then sorted for size. Next, they are boiled or steamed until partially soft and then skinned. If the potatoes are large, they should be cut to provide a uniform size. The sweet potatoes are then packed to within an inch of the top of the jar, with gentle pressing to fill spaces. No salt or liquid is added, and the pints are processed for 65 minutes, while the quarts go for 95 minutes. For a wet pack, the process is as above until you get the potatoes packed. Then add ½ teaspoon of salt to pints and a teaspoon to quarts. Cover with boiling water or, if you wish, a medium syrup, leaving a 1-inch space at the top. Pint jars will take 55 minutes and quarts 90 minutes.

BENEFITS OF CANNING

In general, canning is a good way to process some foods for long term storage. To be honest, though, freezing sometimes offers better flavor retention and appearance. Still, in areas where power failures are likely during winter and at other times of the year, canning may well be your best bet. I have several times lost frozen food because of power failures several days long. In areas where such things are likely, I would advise anyone with large amounts of frozen foods to check the availability of dry ice for those times when power is out more than 36 hours. While some experts say food in a refrigerator is good for a day and food in a freezer is fine for at least 48 hours, I tend to throw out things if they show any signs of thawing. Everything in my refrigerator if the milk smells even the slightest bit sour.

Oven processing, or canning, is no good. Temperatures do not get high enough for safety, and jars may explode. Open kettle canning is no longer used for anything at all, as the temperatures do not get high enough to really retard spoilage for long periods of time.

Your canned fruit may float in the jars if the pack is too loose or the syrup is too heavy. However, this can also result if some air stayed in the tissues of the fruit after processing.

Foods can be canned without a bit of salt being added. The salt amounts listed for fruits and vegetables here are flavor suggestions only and have nothing to do with canning safety. If you or someone in your family is on a low sodium diet, simply eliminate the salt and can away.

To prevent darkening for those of you who do not wish to settle for the vinegar/salt solution, try instead adding about ¼ teaspoon of crystalline vitamin C (*ascorbic acid*) to each quart of fruit or vegetable being processed.

CANNING MEAT

Meat and poultry can be home-canned, along with vegetables and fruits. A steam-pressure canner is essential to the process. You need to start with good quality fresh or frozen meat. Make sure all meat and all work surfaces are clean. Preparation of the canner and jars is the same as for fruits and vegetables. Under no circumstances should processing times be shortened. It is imperative that the gauge be checked for accuracy since meat contains bacteria that may cause botulism. No short cuts are allowed here, unless illness is a preference of yours.

Generally, chilling meat to at least 40 degrees F. makes it easier to handle. Any meat that must be held more than a few days after slaughter should be frozen. Any frozen meat to be thawed for canning should be thawed under refrigeration at a temperature no higher than 40 degrees.

For greatest safety, cutting boards need special treatment when canning meats. Any wood utensils, in fact, need such treatment. First, scrub with hot soapy water and rinse with boiling water. Then disinfect the surfaces using a liquid chlorine disinfectant, mixed according to the directions on the container (liquid laundry bleaches are fine). Cover wooden surfaces with the solution and let them stand for about 15 minutes. Wash the solution off with boiling water.

Meat and poultry broths to add to canning are made by placing bony pieces in a saucepan and covering with cold water. Simmer until the meat is tender and pour the broth into another pan. When it cools, skim off the fat. Boiling broth is added to jars packed with precooked meat or poultry.

Meat is packed loosely in jars, since the jars may well lose liquid during processing if packed too tightly. Meat may be canned with a hot or a raw pack. Raw pack meat is usually heated to at least 170 degrees F. before processing in the canner to exhaust air from the jars; hot packed meat is precooked and held at 170 degrees F. while packing.

To exhaust air in raw packed meat jars, set open jars on a rack in a large pan of boiling water. Water level should be about 2 inches below the tops of the jars. Cover the pan. The water is kept at a slow boil until the center of the meat packed in the jars reads 170 degrees F.

Remove as much fat from meats as possible. Make sure the rims of the jars receive a good wiping to remove fat before the lids are put in place. Any fat on the rims may serve to prevent a seal and let the meat spoil.

Like vegetables, the yield you can expect from any particular piece of meat is approximate. You can expect to get about a quart of canned meat from the following: 3 to 3½ pounds of beef round; 5 to 5½ pounds of beef rump; 5 to 5½ pounds of pork loin; 3½ to 4½ pounds of chicken with bone in; 5½ to 6½ pounds of boned chicken.

Meat canning directions apply to *beef, veal, pork, lamb* and *mutton*, as well as *venison* and other meat from large game animals. Use tender meat for canning large pieces and less tender cuts for canning as stew meat or ground meat. Bony pieces can be canned for soup.

Meat is cut in jar length pieces, with the grain of the meat running the length of the jar. Jars are filled to within an inch of the top with one or more pieces of meat. The air is then exhausted, as described earlier, if a raw pack is to be used. This will take about 75 minutes with quart jars. Salt can be added, if you wish. Then the jars are set up and lids adjusted. Pints are processed for 75 minutes and quarts for 90 minutes. Hot pack processing requires that the meat be placed in a shallow pan, with just enough water added to keep it from sticking. The pan is covered and the meat cooked until done, over medium heat. Stir the meat occasionally so it will heat evenly. Pack hot meat loosely, leaving an inch of head space. Salt if desired, and cover meat with the boiling meat juice, adding boiling water if needed. Keep the head space at 1 inch, and process pint jars for 75 minutes and quart jars for 90 minutes.

Ground Meat

Ground meat in glass jars is done only in hot pack. Form the meat into patties thin enough to pack in the jars without breaking. Patties are then precooked in a slow oven (about 325 degrees F.) until medium done (almost no red at the center of a cut pattie). Skim fat off the drippings; no fat is used in canning. Pack the patties so that there is 1 inch of head space and cover with boiling meat juice, keeping the inch of head space. Process pint jars for 75 minutes and quarts for 90 minutes.

Sausage and Corned Beef

Sausage is not a great candidate for canning. It tends to change flavor when canned because of the spices and other seasonings used to make it. Sage should never be used in canned sausage since it will make the meat bitter. Use any good sausage recipe, going light on seasonings and onion, and shape, cook, pack and process just as you would patties of ground beef.

Corned beef is washed, drained and cut into pieces of strips that will fit into the jars. Cover the meat with water and bring to a boil. If broth is extremely salty, drain the meat. Boil again in fresh water. Pack while hot, leaving an inch of head space, and then cover the meat with boiling broth or water, keeping the same head space. Process pints for 75 minutes and quarts for 90 minutes.

Stew and Soup Stock

Meat and *vegetable stew* is done with a raw pack. Start with beef, lamb or veal cut in 1½-inch cubes. You will need 2 quarts. Add 2 quarts of pared potatoes in ½-inch cubes, and 2 quarts of carrots in ½-inch cubes. Next, 3 cups of celery cut into ¼-inch pieces are placed next to 7 cups of small, white onions (peeled). Fill the jars right to the top with the raw mixture, and add salt if you wish. Process pints for 60 minutes, with quarts needing 75 minutes.

Soup stock makes a good canning item. Make the meat stock or broth fairly thick. Cover bony pieces of meat or chicken with slightly salty water and simmer until the meat is tender. Skim off the fat and take out the bones, but leave the meat and sediment in the stock. Pour the boiling soup stock into jars, leaving an inch of headspace. Process pint jars for 20 minutes, quarts for 25.

Poultry

Poultry, duck, goose, guinea fowl, squab, turkey and small game birds can be canned in the same manner. Soup stock is made, and canned, just as it is with meat.

For a hot pack, with the bone in, first bone the breast. Saw the drumsticks off short and leave the bone in other meaty parts. Trim off any large lumps of far and place the raw meaty pieces in a pan, covering them with broth or water. Cover and heat, with occasional stirring, until medium done. If pink color is almost gone at the center, the poultry is ready. Pack poultry loosely, and place thighs and drumsticks with the skin next to the glass. Breasts are fitted into the center, and fill-in is done with small pieces. An inch of head space is needed, and salt can be added if desired.

Cover the poultry with boiling broth and maintain the inch of head space. Process pint jars for 65 minutes and quarts for 75 minutes. For a raw pack, bone the breast and cut the drumsticks off short. Follow the directions for hot pack, right up to packing with an inch of headspace. Cook at a slow boil to 170 degrees F. to exhaust air (about 75 minutes, but it is best to use a meat thermometer). Pint jars will need 65 minutes of processing, while quarts need 75 minutes.

JELLIES, JAMS AND PRESERVES

One of my oldest memories involves picking grapes at an aunt's arbor and a few days later having *jelly* or *jam* made from those grapes. For whatever reason, I have never had commercial jelly or jam that even approaches the quality in taste or texture of that prepared by my mother and aunt. Maybe it's the "good old days" syndrome, since I almost never eat sweets now, but somehow I really doubt it. The same syndrome operates now when I pluck a tomato from the garden and eat it without salt or anything else. No store bought tomato tastes as good as a homegrown tomato. And no store bought jelly or jam tastes as good as homemade. Making jellys, jams and preserves will provide you with a good way to use up fruits that are not good enough to can or freeze. If you use attractive jars for your jams and jellies, the products make fine gifts for friends at Christmas.

Some fruits make better jellies and jams than others, simply because the properties of the fruit make it work better when jellying time comes. Today, though, commercial pectin can be added so that almost any fruit will provide a good jelly, jam or preserve. Jelly is made from fruit juice, and the final product will be clear and firm enough to stand by itself when turned out of its container. Jam is made from crushed or ground fruit and is less firm than jelly. *Conserves* are jams made from a mixture of fruits, usually including a citrus fruit. *Marmalade* is a jelly with small pieces of fruit distributed evenly throughout. Preserves are whole pieces of fruit or large pieces (of larger fruits) in a thick syrup which may be slightly jellied. You need proper amounts of fruit, sugar, pectin and acid to make any jellied fruit product. It pays to use the most flavorful fruit possible since a large amount of sugar is used. The sugar dilutes the fruit flavor, as it provides proper consistency and good keeping quality (Figs. 14-4 through 14-15).

Pectin is found naturally in many fruits, and in amounts to make them jell quite easily. Underripe fruits have more pectin than do overripe fruits. Commercial pectins are made from apples or citrus fruits and are available as liquids or powders to be used with any fruit being jellied. Fruit pectins do not last from one season to the next, but fresh pectin should be stored in a cool, dry place to prevent loss of strength. Fruits somewhat low in acid, needed for gel formation and flavor, can sometimes use a bit of lemon juice or citric acid.

Sugar is needed to add keeping qualities and to sweeten the product. It also has a firming effect on the fruit, useful when you are making preserves. Either cane or beet sugar is fine.

Equipment and Containers

You will need an 8 to 10 quart kettle and some jelly bags or a fruit press. Jelly bags are made of several layers of closely woven cheesecloth, or sturdy unbleached *muslin*. Use a *colander* to support the jelly bag when you are straining pressed juice. A candy thermometer is of great help if you are making these fruit products without adding pectin.

Containers may vary for different products, with plenty of companies selling special jelly glasses. For jelly itself, when you wish to seal with paraffin, use a straight-sided container. Preserves and other products will need a jar with a lid, since the paraffin seal is too easily broken by these products. Again, get everything clean and keep it that way during processing.

For best results, remember that jellied fruit products do lose flavor over time, so make only enough to be used up in two, three or no more than four months. Start a small batch first and check the firmness. If all is well, keep on as you are.

Fig. 14-4. Place the strawberries in a wire basket and wash them.

Fig. 14-5. Place crushed berries in a double thickness of cheesecloth held in a colander over a bowl.

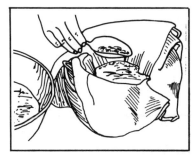

Fig. 14-6. Strain the juice through two thicknesses of damp cheesecloth without squeezing.

Fig. 14-7. Add 7½ cups of sugar to the juice and stir to dissolve the sugar.

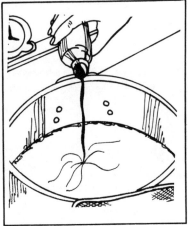

Fig. 14-8. Add a bottle of liquid pectin. Boil the mixture hard for one minute; then remove it from heat and skim off the foam quickly.

Fig. 14-9. Pour the jelly immediately into hot glasses.

Fig. 14-10. Cut the apples into small pieces.

Fig. 14-11. Add 1 cup of water per pound of apples.

Fig. 14-12. Strain pressed juice through two thicknesses of damp cheesecloth without squeezing.

Fig. 14-13. Measure 4 cups of the apple juice into a large kettle. Add 3 cups of sugar and 2 tablespoons of lemon juice.

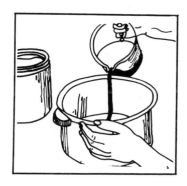

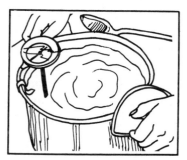

Fig. 14-14. Boil rapidly to 8 degrees F above the boiling point of water until the jelly mixture sheets from a spoon.

Fig. 14-15. Pour the jelly immediately into hot containers.

If the product is too soft or too firm and you are adding pectin, to get a softer product add ¼ to ½ cup more fruit or juice; for a firmer product, use ¼ to ½ cup less fruit or juice. In products without added pectin, shorten the cooking time to make it softer and lengthen the time to make it firmer.

Jelly jars have metal sealing lids with a sealing compound around the edges, just as do regular canning jars. Paraffin sealing requires no more than ⅛ inch of the wax layered on top of the product. Any air bubbles in the paraffin should be pricked because they will cause holes as the wax hardens, ruining the seal. Use a double boiler to melt the paraffin, since it can be kept hot without the wax reaching smoking temperature.

Pour the hot mixture—jellies—into glass containers that are also hot, bringing the jelly to within ½ inch of the top. Immediately cover with hot paraffin.

Fruit products in the jelly class should be left to stand overnight so the seal of the paraffin, and the gel of the product, are not broken. Label with name, date and lot number and store in a cool, dry place.

When making jelllies it is best to work with small lots, whether you are using added pectin or not. The recipes can give only approximate amounts of the fruit needed to produce the amount called for. Much depends on just how juicy a particular batch of fruit is, so keep extra on hand for those batches where the fruit lacks juice. All fruit should be washed in cold, running water and should not be left to stand in the water.

Generally, the fruit is placed in a damp jelly bag, or in a fruit press. You will get very clear jelly if you allow the juice to drop from the bag without pressing or squeezing. But you will get a great deal more juice if you press hard or twist the bag tightly. Pressed or squeezed juice should then be strained through another damp jelly bag. Do not squeeze this second time around.

Apple Jelly

Apple jelly without added pectin requires 4 cups of apple juice (about 3 pounds of apples and 3 cups of water), 2 tablespoons of strained lemon juice and 3 cups of sugar. For the juice, choose apples that are one-fourth underripe and then get your next three-fourths fully ripe. Use a tart apple for best results. Sort, wash and remove stem and blossom ends. Add water, cover and bring to a boil on high heat. Reduce heat and simmer for 25 minutes, or until apples are soft. Extract the juice.

Measure the apple juice into your kettle. Then add the lemon juice and sugar and stir well. Boil over high heat 8 degrees F. above the boiling point of water, and the jelly will start to sheet from your spoon. Remove from the heat as soon as it sheets and skim off the foam. Pour jelly right away into hot containers and seal. This will make about four or five 6-ounce glasses.

Blackberry Jelly

Blackberry jelly with liquid pectin requires 4 cups of blackberry juice (about 3 quart boxes), 7½ cups of sugar and one bottle of liquid pectin. Sort and wash fully ripe berries and remove any stems or caps. Crush the berries and extract the juice. Measure the juice into the kettle, stir in the sugar and place on high heat. Bring to a full rolling boil that can't be stirred down and add the pectin. Bring back to a full rolling boil and boil hard for one minute. Remove from heat. Skim off the foam and pour immediately into hot containers and seal. This will make 11 or 12 6-ounce glasses.

Blackberry jelly without added pectin requires the same 4 cups of blackberry juice (about 2¾ quart boxes of berries and ¾ cup of water), but only 3 cups of sugar. As with apples, select about one-fourth underripe and three-fourths ripe berries. Sort, wash and remove any stems or caps. Crush the berries, add water, cover and bring to a boil on high heat. Reduce heat and simmer for five minutes. Extract the juice. Measure the juice into the kettle, add sugar and stir well. Boil over high heat to 8 degrees F. above the boiling point of water until the jelly sheets on the spoon. Remove from heat and quickly skim off the foam. Pour right away into hot containers and seal. Yield is about five 6-ounce glasses.

Cherry Jelly

Cherry jelly with liquid pectin requires 3 cups of cherry juice (about 3 pounds or 2 quart boxes of sour cherries and ½ cup of water), 7 cups of sugar and a bottle of liquid pectin. Use fully ripe cherries that have been sorted and washed but not pitted. Crush and add water; then bring quickly to a boil. Reduce heat and simmer 10 minutes. Extract the juice. Measure juice into the kettle and stir in the sugar. Place it on high heat and stir constantly until the juice/sugar mix reaches a full rolling boil that can't be stirred down. Add pectin and heat again to a full rolling boil. Boil hard for a minute. Remove from heat and quickly skim off foam. Pour jelly into hot containers and seal. It makes 10 or 11 6-ounce glasses.

Grape Jelly

Grape jelly with liquid pectin takes 4 cups of grape juice (about 3½ pounds of Concord grapes and ½ cup of water), 7 cups of sugar and a half bottle of liquid pectin. Sort, wash and remove stems from fully ripe grapes. Crush grapes and add water. Bring to a boil on high heat; then reduce to a simmer for 10 minutes. Extract the juice. To keep tartrate crystals from forming in the jelly, let the juice stand overnight in a cool spot and then strain through two thicknesses of cheesecloth to remove crystals. Measure the juice into the kettle and stir in the sugar. On high heat, bring to a full rolling boil that can't be stirred down, add the pectin and return to a full boil, keeping it there for one minute. Remove from the heat, skim off the foam and pour jelly into hot containers as quickly as possible. Seal. It makes from 10 to a dozen 6-ounce glasses.

Grape jelly without added pectin takes 4 cups of grape juice (again, 3½ pounds of Concord grapes and ½ cup of water) and 3 cups of sugar. Select one-fourth underripe and three-fourths ripe grapes. Sort, wash and remove stems. Crush the grapes, add water, cover and bring to a fast boil. Reduce heat and simmer for 10 minutes. Extract the juice and let it stand in a cold place overnight. Remove crystals by straining through a double layer of cheesecloth. Measure juice into the kettle, add sugar and stir well. Boil over high heat until 8 degrees above the boiling point of water, or until mixture sheets on the spoon. Remove from heat, skim off foam and pour into hot containers. Seal and expect to have about five 6-ounce glasses.

Plum Jelly

Plum jelly without pectin needs 4 cups of plum juice (about 3½ pounds of plums and 1½ cups of water) plus 3 cups of sugar. Select one-fourth underripe and three-fourths ripe plums. Sort, wash and cut into pieces without peeling or pitting. Crush the fruit, add water, cover and boil quickly. Reduce the heat and simmer for 20 minutes or until the fruit is soft. Extract the juice. Measure the juice into the kettle, add sugar and stir well. Boil to 8 degrees F. above the boiling point of water or until the mixture sheets on your spoon. Remove it from heat, skim foam and pour into hot containers. Seal. Look for about five 6-ounce glasses.

Quince and Strawberry Jellies

Quince jelly without added pectin will call for 3¾ cups of quince juice (3½ pounds of quince and 7 cups of water), ¼ cup of lemon juice and 3 cups of sugar. Select the usual one-fourth underripe and three-fourths ripe quince. Sort, wash and remove blossom ends and stems. Do not pare or core. Slice quince very thin or cut into small cubes. Add water, cover and rapidly bring to a boil. Reduce heat and let simmer for 25 minutes. Extract the juice, and measure it into the kettle. Add lemon juice and sugar and stir well. Boil until it reaches 8 degrees above the boiling point of water, or until it sheets from the spoon. Remove from heat, skim foam and rapidly pour into heated containers. Seal, and you will get five or six 6-ounce glasses.

Strawberry jelly with liquid pectin follows the directions for blackberry jelly with liquid pectin.

Jams and marmalades are, to me, preferable to jellies and not really any harder to make. In fact, since most do not require juice extraction, the job is actually sometimes easier. They will often require pitting and peeling which jelly does not need, though.

Apple Marmalade

Apple marmalade without added pectin needs 8 cups of thinly sliced apples (about 3 pounds), one orange, 1½ cups of water, 5 cups of sugar and 2 tablespoons of lemon juice. Select tart apples. Wash, pare, quarter and core the apples and then slice them very thin. Quarter the orange, remove any seeds and slice thin. Heat water and sugar until the sugar dissolves. Add lemon juice and fruit. Boil rapidly, stirring constantly, until it reaches 9 degrees above the boiling point of water or until the mix gets thick. Remove from the heat and skim. Fill and seal containers (do not use paraffin seals). This makes about six ½ pint jars of apple marmalade.

Blackberry and Cherry Jams

Blackberry jam without added pectin needs 4 cups of crushed blackberries (about 2 quarts) and 4 cups of sugar. Sort and wash berries, removing any stems and caps. Crush the berries, and measure the mass into a kettle. Add sugar and stir well. Boil rapidly until 9 degrees F. above the boiling point of water, or until the mixture gets thick. Remove from the heat and skim. Fill and seal containers. The yield is about four ½-pint jars.

Cherry jam with liquid pectin needs about 4½ cups of finely ground or chopped pitted cherries (about 3 pounds or 2 quart boxes of sour cherries), 7 cups of sugar and one bottle of liquid pectin. Remove cherry stems and pits. Grind or chop the cherries until they are fine. Measure cherries into a kettle, add sugar and stir well. Bring rapidly to a full boil with bubbles all over the surface. Boil hard for one minute, stirring constantly. Remove from the heat, skim and fill and seal containers. The yield is nine ½-pint jars.

Peach Jams

Peach jam with liquid pectin requires about 4½ cups of crushed peaches (about 3½ pounds of peaches), ¼ cup of lemon juice, 7 cups of sugar and half a bottle of liquid pectin.

Select ripe peaches, sort them and wash them. Remove skins, stems and pits and crush the peaches. Measure the peaches into the kettle, add lemon juice and stir. Use high heat to bring to a boil, stirring constantly, until it reaches a full boil, with bubbles over the entire top. Boil hard for one minute, remove from the heat and stir in the pectin. Fill and seal the containers. You should get about eight ½ pint jars. *Ginger-peach jam* is made like peach jam with the addition of 1 or 2 ounces of finely chopped candied ginger added to the crushed peaches before you add the pectin.

Plum Jam

Plum jam with liquid pectin requires 4½ cups of crushed plums (about 2½ pounds), 7½ cups of sugar and a half bottle of liquid pectin. Use fully ripe plums, sort them, wash them, cut into pieces and remove the pits. If the pits cling tightly, simmering a few minutes in a small amount of water will make them easy to remove. Crush the plums and measure them into the kettle. Add the sugar and stir well. Use high heat to bring to a boil, while you keep stirring. Boil hard for one minute, still stirring, and then remove it from the heat and stir in the pectin. Skim. You get about eight ½ pint jars.

Strawberry Jam

Strawberry jam with liquid pectin requires 4 cups of crushed strawberries, 7 cups of sugar and a half bottle of liquid pectin. Sort and wash ripe strawberries, removing stems and caps. Crush the berries and measure them into the kettle. Add sugar and stir well. Place on high heat and bring to a full boil, with bubbles covering the surface. Boil for one minute, remove from the heat and stir in the pectin. Skim and then fill and seal the containers. Again, about eight ½ pint jars will be the result.

Preserves require top grade fruit at the firm, ripe stage. If you plan to leave the fruit whole, choose for uniform size and shape.

Damson Plum Preserves

Damson plum preserves take about 1½ cups of prepared Damson plums (3 pounds of ripe plums), 5½ cups of sugar and 1 cup of water. Use a pitting spoon to remove pits after sorting and washing the plums. Leave the plums whole. Dissolve the sugar in the water and bring to a boil. Add the plums and boil, with gentle stirring, to about 9 degrees F. above the boiling point of water, or until the fruit turns translucent and the syrup is thick. Remove from the heat, skim and fill the containers and seal. The result is about six ½ pint jars.

Strawberry Preserves

Strawberry preserves require 6 cups of prepared strawberries (about 2 quart boxes) and 4½ cups of sugar. Generally tart strawberries make the best preserves, so select large, firm tart berries. Wash, drain and remove the caps. Combine the prepared fruit and sugar in alternate layers and let the mixture stand for eight to 10 hours, or overnight, in the refrigerator or other cool place. Heat the fruit mixture to boiling, while stirring gently. Boil rapidly and up to 9 degrees F. above the boiling point of water, or until the syrup becomes somewhat thick (this usually takes 15 to 20 minutes). Remove from the heat, skim and fill and seal the containers. You get about four ½ pint jars.

PICKLING

Most of us are familiar with, and enjoy the various types of *pickles* made from *cucumbers*, but many other fruits and vegetables can also be used. Sour pickles generally use only spices and vinegar, though not always, while sweet pickles use some sugar. There are different types of pickles, beyond sweet and sour, once processing time comes.

Brined pickles are often called *fermented* pickles, and the curing process takes about three weeks. *Dilled cucumbers* and *sauerkraut* are in this group, and green tomatoes can also be cured this way.

Fresh-pack pickles are also known as quick processed pickles and include crosscut cucumber slices, whole cucumber dills, sweet *gherkins* and dilled green beans. These are brined for several hours, or overnight, and combined with boiling hot vinegar, spices and other seasonings. The flavor is tart and pungent, as you may imagine.

Fruit pickles are most often made from whole fruits, simmered in a spicy, sweet and sour sauce or syrup. Pears, peaches and watermelon rind are popular types.

Relishes are made from fruits and vegetables which are chopped, seasoned and cooked to the desired consistency. Used to accent the flavor of other foods, relishes include *piccalilli*, pepper-onion and corn relish.

When making the selection for any kind of pickling, choose tender vegetables and firm fruit. Pears and peaches may be slightly underripe when used for pickling. Use no fruits or vegetables that show any signs at all of mold. The mold will cause an off flavor, even though the spoilage organisms are destroyed by processing. Wash fruits or vegetables thoroughly, using a brush and washing only a few at a time, under running water. Make sure all blossoms are removed from cucumbers, as the blossoms are a source of *enzymes* that may soften the cucumbers during fermentation.

The salt used should be pure, granulated salt. Do not used iodized salt as it darkens the pickles. Uniodized table salt can be used, but the stuff used to prevent its caking will probably make the brine cloudy.

Vinegar for pickling is best—a high-grade cider type or white distilled vinegar with 4 to 6 percent acidity (40 to 60 grain). Do not use vinegar of unknown acidity. Cider vinegar may darken white or light-colored fruits and vegetables. Don't dilute vinegar to cut sourness. Add sugar instead. Sugar used can be either white or brown granulated, with the brown used to add color. Use fresh spices and herbs for best results with final flavors.

You will need to haul out your water-bath canner and, for fermenting or brining, a crock or a stone jar, an unchipped enamel pan or a large glass jar. You will need measuring spoons. You will need some kind of lid to fit inside the container on the vegetables being brined, too. Kitchen scales are needed to make sauerkraut along with glass jars and the appropriate lids. I would recommend that if you are pickling whole fruits or vegetables, use wide mouth jars for ease of insertion and later for ease in lifting out the pickles for eating.

All pickled products should be heat-treated after the jars are filled. This will kill any remaining spoilage organisms that may be picked up as the pickles are transferred from the kettle to the jars.

Brined Dill Pickles

Brined dill pickles (yield is 9 to 10 quarts) require 20 pounds (about ½ bushel) of cucumbers 3 to 6 inches long, ¾ cup of whole mixed pickling spice, two or three bunches of fresh or dried dill plant, 2½ cups of vinegar, 1¾ cups of salt and 2½ gallons of water. Cover the cucumbers with cold water and wash thoroughly with a vegetable brush. Drain or wipe dry. Place half the pickle spices and a layer of dill in a 5 gallon crock or jar. Fill the crock with cucumbers to within 3 or 4 inches of the top. Place a layer of dill and the rest of the spices on top of the cucumbers (add garlic if you wish), and then completely mix the salt, vinegar and water and pour it over the cucumbers. Cover with a lid fitting inside the crock. Use a weight to hold the lid down and to make sure the cucumbers stay under the brine. Cover the crock loosely with a clean cloth. Keep at room temperature, and each day check for scum formation. Remove any you find—it usually takes from three to five days for the formation to start. If necessary, make additional brine to keep the cucumbers covered well.

In about three weeks the cucumbers will have turned an olive green color and should have the desired flavor. White spots inside the cucumbers will disappear during processing. The original brine will probably be cloudy now, so if the cloudiness bothers you, use fresh brine when packing the pickles into jars. To make the fresh brine, use ½ cup of salt and 4 cups of vinegar to a gallon of water. Usually, the brine used for fermentation is preferable as it adds to flavor, but it should be strained before use for packing. Pack the pickles into clean, hot jars, adding some of the dill and garlic if you want. Do not pack them too tightly, and then cover with boiling brine to leave a head space of ½ inch. Process in boiling water for 15 minutes, and then remove and cool the jars.

Fresh-Pack Dill Pickles

Fresh-pack dill pickles to yield 7 quarts require 17 or 18 pounds of 3 to 5-inch long cucumbers, about 2 gallons of 5 percent brine (¾ cup of salt to a gallon of water), 6 cups of vinegar, ¾ cup of salt, ¼ cup of sugar, 9 cups of water, 2 tablespoons of whole mixed pickling spice, 2 teaspoons per quart jar of whole mustard seed, and a clove or two of garlic per jar (if desired), plus three heads of dill plant per jar and 1 tablespoon of dill seed per quart jar. Scrub the cucumbers and drain. Cover them with the 5 percent brine solution and let them sit overnight. Drain. Combine the vinegar, salt, sugar, water and pickling spices. Heat to a boil. Pack the cucumbers into clean, hot quart jars, seven to 10 per jar, and add the mustard seed, dill plant (or seed) and garlic to each jar. Cover with boiling liquid to leave ½ inch of head space. Process in boiling water for 20 minutes (processing time is counted as soon as the hot jars are placed in the boiling water).

Sweet Gherkins

Sweet gherkins for a yield of 7 to 8 pints will require 5 quarts (about 7 pounds) of cucumbers 1½ to 3 inches long, ½ cup of salt, 8 cups of sugar, 6 cups of vinegar, ¾ teaspoon of *turmeric*, 2 teaspoons of celery seed, 2 teaspoons of whole mixed pickling spices, eight 1-inch pieces of stick cinnamon and, as optionals, ½ teaspoon of *fennel* and 2 teaspoons of vanilla. Once the cucumbers are washed and drained, place them in a large container and cover them with boiling water. Six to eight hours later drain and cover once more with fresh, boiling water. The next morning, drain and again cover with boiling water. Six or eight hours later, drain, add salt and cover with fresh boiling water. The next morning, drain and prick the cucumbers in several places with a table fork. Make a syrup of 3 cups of the sugar and 3 cups of the vinegar. Add turmeric and spices. Heat to boiling and pour over the cucumbers (this will not totally cover the cucumbers at this point). Six to eight hours later drain the syrup into a pan. Add 2 cups of sugar and 2 cups of vinegar to the syrup, heat it to boiling and pour it back over the pickles.

On the fourth day, start by draining the syrup into a pan and adding 2 cups more sugar to it, along with 1 cup of vinegar. Heat to boiling and pour it over the pickles. Six to eight hours later, drain the syrup into its pan, add the last cup of sugar and the vanilla to the syrup and heat it to boiling. Pack the pickles into clean, hot pint jars and cover with the boiling syrup leaving ½ inch of head space. Process in boiling water for five minutes.

Crosscut Pickle Slices

Crosscut pickle slices will take about 6 pounds of medium sized cucumbers, 1½ cups (12-15 small white) sliced onions, two large garlic cloves, ⅓ cup of salt, 2 quarts of crushed ice, 4½ cups of sugar, 1½ teaspoons of turmeric, 1½ teaspoons of celery seed, 2 tablespoons of mustard seed and 3 cups of white vinegar. Wash, drain and slice the cucumbers and onions (Fig. 14-16). Leave the cucumbers unpeeled. Slices should be ⅛ to ¼ inch thick. Toss away the ends (onto your compost pile). Add onions and garlic to the cucumbers and then add salt, mixing thoroughly (Fig. 14-17). Cover with crushed ice and let the mixture stand for three hours. Combine sugar, spices and vinegar, heating just to boiling (Fig. 14-18). Remove the garlic cloves from the cucumbers and drain. Add the drained cucumber and onion slices to the mix and heat for five minutes. Pack the hot pickles loosely into clean, hot pint jars, leaving ½ inch of head space (Fig. 14-19). Process in boiling water for five minutes, again starting the count just as the hot jars go into the boiling water. You can reduce the sugar by ½ cup or so if you wish a more tart pickle. Yield will be 7 pints (Fig. 14-20).

Pickled Peaches and Pears

Pickled peaches for 7 quart yield requires about 16 pounds (11quarts) of peaches, 3 quarts of sugar, 2 quarts of vinegar, seven 2-inch pieces of stick cinnamon, 2 tablespoons of whole cloves and much less time than crosscut cucumber pickles. First combine the sugar, vinegar, stick cinnamon and cloves (tie the cloves in a clean cloth and remove them after cooking). Bring to a boil and simmer for

Fig. 14-16. Slice unpeeled cucumbers into ⅛ to ¼-inch crosswise slices.

30 minutes. Wash the peaches and remove the skins. Dip the peaches in boiling water for one minute, and then into cold, to make the job easier. Next immerse the peaches in cold water containing 2 tablespoons each of vinegar and salt to keep them from darkening. Drain this off just before adding the peaches to the boiling syrup. Add enough peaches to the syrup to make 3 to 4 quarts at a time, and heat for about five minutes. Pack the hot peaches into clean, hot jars. Continue to heat in syrup and pack into jars, meanwhile adding a piece of stick cinnamon and a few cloves to each jar. Cover the peaches with boiling syrup, leaving ½ inch of head space. Process in boiling water for 20 minutes.

Pickled pears require 8 pounds of pears (Seckel preferably), 2 quarts of sugar, 1 quart of white vinegar, 1 pint of water, eight 2-inch pieces of stick cinnamon, 2 tablespoons of whole cloves and 2 tablespoons of allspice. Combine the sugar, vinegar, water and stick cinnamon, adding the cloves

Fig. 14-17. Combine cucumber and onion slices with peeled garlic cloves. Add salt and mix thoroughly. Cover with crushed ice or ice cubes.

Fig. 14-18. Combine sugar, spices and vinegar; heat to boiling. Add drained cucumber and onion slices and heat five minutes.

and allspice tied in clean white cloth. Bring to a boil and simmer for 30 minutes. Wash the pears, peel, and remove the entire blossom end. Stems may be left on. Use the same 2 tablespoons each of 1 salt and vinegar in a gallon of water to prevent darkening. Drain and add the pears to the syrup. Let things simmer for about 25 minutes. Then pack the hot pears into clean, hot pint jars, and add one piece of cinnamon per jar. Cover with boiling liquid, leaving ½ inch of head space, and process in boiling water for 20 minutes. Processing time again starts as the hot jars are set in the boiling water. You get 7 or 8 pints.

Fig. 14-19. Pack loosely into clean, hot pint jars to ½ inch of the top of the jar.

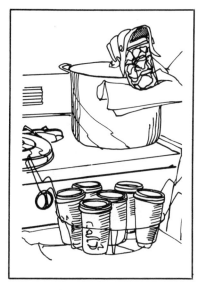

Fig. 14-20. Remove the jars and complete seals if necessary. Set the jars upright, several inches apart, on a wire rack or folded towel to cool.

Watermelon Pickles

Watermelon pickles require about 6 pounds of rind (or half a large melon), ¾ cup of salt, 3 quarts of water, 2 quarts of ice cubes or crushed ice, 9 cups of sugar, 3 cups of white vinegar, 3 more cups of water, 1 tablespoon of whole cloves, six 1-inch pieces of stick cinnamon and one lemon sliced very thin with the seeds removed. Pare the rind so that all pink is removed, and cut it into 1-inch cubes. Cover with the brine made by mixing the salt with 3 quarts of cold water, and add the ice cubes. Let stand for about six hours. Drain and rinse in cold water. Cover with cold water and cook until fork tender (about 10 minutes). Take care not to overcook. Drain again. Combine the sugar, vinegar, water and spices (tied in a clean white cloth). Boil for five minutes and pour over the watermelon. Add the lemon slices and let it stand overnight.

Next morning, heat the watermelon in the syrup to boiling and cook until the watermelon becomes translucent. Pack the hot pickles loosely in clean, hot pint jars, adding a stick of cinnamon to each from the spice bag. Leave ½ inch of head space. Process in boiling water for five minutes, starting from the time the hot jars are set in the boiling water. Yield is 4 to 5 pints.

Sauerkraut

Sauerkraut, enough to fill 16 to 18 quart jars, needs 50 pounds of cabbage and 1 pound of salt. Remove the outer leaves and any bad portions from the cabbage. Wash, drain and cut into halves or quarters, removing the core as you do. Use a shredder to cut the cabbage into strips about the thickness of a dime. In a large container, thoroughly mix 3 tablespoons of salt with 5 pounds of shredded cabbage. Let the salted cabbage stand for a few minutes so that it starts to wilt—the wilting allows you to pack it without bruising or breaking too many of the shreds. Pack the salted cabbage firmly and evenly into a large, clean crock or jar. Repeat the shredding, salting and packing until the cabbage is packed to within about 3 inches of the top of the container. Cover the cabbage with clean, thin cloth and tuck the edges down inside the crock. Cover the cloth with a plate or a round paraffined board that just fits inside the container to keep the cabbage from being exposed to the air. You can also use a plastic bag filled with water as a seal for the crock. Use two bags, actually, and the heaviest weight possible, one inside the other. Using water in a plastic bag lets you keep the weight of covering adjusted so that the brine always covers the cabbage.

Once gas bubbles begin to form, fermentation has started. The process takes five to six weeks, and is done best when room temperatures are around 68 to 72 degrees F. Once fermentation is done, heat the sauerkraut to simmering and pack the hot sauerkraut into clean, hot quart jars, leaving ½ inch of head space. Process in boiling water for 20 minutes (if you decide to use pint jars, process for 15 minutes). Again, processing time begins as soon as the hot jars are lowered into the boiling water.

Pepper-Onion Relish

Pepper-onion relish (five ½ pint jars) requires six to eight large finely chopped onions to give 1 quart. Next, finely chop four or five medium sweet red peppers to get a pint. Do the same with green peppers for the same amount. You now need a cup of sugar, a quart of vinegar and 4 teaspoons of salt.

Combine all the ingredients and bring them to a boil, cooking until slightly thickened (about 45 to 50 minutes), with an occasional twist of the stirring spoon. Pack the boiling hot relish into clean, hot ½ pint jars. This can now be stored in the refrigerator as is. If you wish to store without refrigeration, leave ½ inch of head space and process the covered jars in boiling water for five minutes from the time the hot jars enter the boiling water.

Piccallili

Piccallili, yielding 4 pints, requires a quart of green tomatoes, finely chopped (about 16 medium tomatoes), 1 cup of finely chopped sweet red peppers (two or three medium peppers), 1 cup of finely chopped green peppers, 1½ cups of finely chopped onions (two or three medium), chopped cabbage to make 5 cups (about 2 pounds), ⅓ cup of salt, 3 cups of vinegar, 2 cups of firmly packed brown sugar and 2 tablespoons of whole mixed pickling spices. Combine the vegetables and mix with the salt. Let that stand overnight. Drain and press in a clean, white cloth to remove all the liquid you can. Combine the vinegar and sugar, and place the spices loosely in a clean white cloth, tied with a string. Add that to the vinegar mixture and bring to a boil. Add the vegetables and bring to a boil once more. Turning it down to simmer for about 30 minutes, or until you see just enough liquid to moisten the vegetables. Remove the spice bag and pack the hot relish into clean, hot jars, leaving ½ inch of head space. Process in boiling water for five minutes, starting the timing from the instant the hot jars are set in the boiling water.

Corn Relish

Corn relish goes well with a number of main dishes and requires 2 quarts of whole kernel corn (16 to 20 medium size ears), 1 pint (4 to 5 medium) sweet red peppers, 1 pint of sweet green peppers (both kinds of peppers are diced), 1 quart of celery (one large bunch) chopped, and 1 cup of onions (8 to 10 small, or ¾ pound) chopped or sliced, 1½ cups of sugar, 1 quart of vinegar, 2 tablespoons of salt, 2 teaspoons of celery seed, 2 tablespoons of powdered dry mustard and 1 teaspoon of turmeric. Remove the husks and silk from the corn and cook the ears in boiling water for five minutes. Remove and stick them in cold water. Drain and slice the corn from the cob, but do not scrape the cob. Combine the peppers, celery, onions, sugar, vinegar, salt and celery seed. Cover the pan until the mixture comes to a boil, and then boil uncovered for five minutes, stirring once in a while. Mix the dry mustard and turmeric and blend with the liquid from the boiling mixture. Add that with the corn to the boiling mixture. Return to a boil and cook, with occasional stirring, for five more minutes. Pack loosely in pint jars leaving ½ inch of head space. Process in boiling water for 15 minutes, again starting your timing as soon as the hot jars go into the boiling water. Yield is about 7 pints.

There are a few more or less common problems that may crop up in making pickles. Shriveling is usually caused by overcooking or overprocessing, but it may also result from too strong a salt, vinegar or sugar solution at the start of the pickling process. Hollow pickles sometimes show up and are caused by poorly developed cucumbers, or cucumbers held too long before pickling. Too rapid fermentation will also cause hollowness, as will a too strong or too weak brine solution. Soft or slippery pickles generally come from microbe action causing spoilage, which may arise from too little salt or acid during pickling, or cucumbers not completely covered with brine during fermentation. Scum scattered through the brine, insufficient heat treatment, a leaking seal and moldy garlic or spices may also cause softness and slipperiness.

BASIC FOOD FREEZING TECHNIQUES

Home freezers are one of the biggest items for home gardeners to ever come along. Many foods respond better to freezing than to canning as far as retaining flavor goes, and often as far as texture and nutritive value, too. While many types of foods do well stored either way, one or two should not be frozen. Offhand, I can think of only tomatoes as responding better to canning than to freezing. Actually, a check shows that green onions, lettuce, radishes and most salad greens do not freeze well. Tomatoes, if cooked or made into juice, do fine.

Containers for frozen foods vary greatly in size, shape, rigidity and sealing methods. Rigid containers made of plastic in most cases are suitable for any kind of vegetable being frozen. No-water packed produce can be frozen in glass jars, but put liquid in and nine times out of 10 you will have a broken jar. Non rigid containers are usually of plastic, too, and are available in most stores that sell foods or any kind of food preservation materials. Select sizes to fit your family's needs trying, when possible, to get sizes to hold a single meal supply, or no more than two meals (unless the container is easily resealable and the material easily separated). Select rigid containers with flat tops and bottoms (and either square or rectangular as they save space). Make sure openings are as wide as the container if you wish to remove foods before they thaw.

Most of the rigid containers I have used have a type of snap-on top that does a good job of sealing. Plastic bags can be sealed in many ways, some just folded back and a rubber band slipped over the fold, while others get quite a lot fancier (and usually more expensive).

When packing food into containers, have it cold. This helps to retain natural color, flavor and texture of the food. Press air out of the unfilled part of bags when they are used. As with canning, allow head space because the food will expand as it freezes. If you are using a liquid pack, allow ½ inch of head space for wide top pint containers. One inch of the top is narrow. For quarts, allow 1 inch for wide tops and 1½ inches for narrow tops. For dry pack foods, allow ½ inch across the board for any kind of container up to a quart in size. A liquid pack includes fruit packed in juice, syrup or water, and crushed or pureed foods, as well as juices.

Keep sealing edges clean and seal carefully. The cold of the freezer will ruin taste and texture if it gets into the package. Label with food name, date of freezing and type of pack if you use more than one type for that food.

You can either stick a few packages at a time in the freezer, as they are done, or refrigerate them until you have a large load ready to go in. They should be frozen, in either case, as soon as possible after packing. All freezing should be done at 0 degrees F. or below. To keep from losing frozen foods or to-be-frozen foods, pack no more into the freezer than can be frozen in 24 hours. Usually this will mean no more than 2 to 3 pounds of food per cubic foot of freezer capacity. Leave a bit of space between packages to allow the cold air to circulate. After the packages are frozen, you can then move them close together to get more into the space (if you do lose power, a tightly packed freezer stays cold longer than a loosely packed or partially filled one). Most fruits and vegetables can be stored for 8 to 12 months at 0 degrees F., but citrus fruits and juices start loosening up on quality by the time six months have gone by.

If you do lose power and need dry ice to keep things cold, 25 pounds will hold a 10 cubic foot freezer for two or three days if partially full and for three to four days if completely loaded. In other words, 2.5 pounds of dry ice per cubic foot of freezer space will keep your food frozen for something like three days, after which you can hope the local utility is "on the ball," or you can get more dry ice. Do not ever handle dry ice with your bare hands, and do not place it directly on packages. The stuff is so cold it will burn you and may cause plastic packages to crack.

Foods may be refrozen if they have not totally lost all the ice crystals in them, or if they have been held at no more than 40 degrees F. for no more than a day or two. Foods that are refrozen won't taste as good as those that are only frozen once, but if the above is kept in mind, they will be safe to eat.

FREEZING FRUITS

Fruits when frozen hold their flavor well, but tend to take on a softer texture and may not retain color too well. Wash all fruits in cold water, doing only a small amount at a time to hold down bruising. Use a colander or a wire basket to drain washed fruits. Do not let the fruit stand in the water as it can lose flavor and taste that way.

Table 14-3 shows the different syrups for frozen fruits. You may prefer a sugar free method, but it is generally agreed that frozen fruit retains flavor and texture better if packed with sugar or with a syrup. For a sugar pack, cut the

Table 14-3. Syrups for Use in Freezing Fruits.

TYPE OF SYRUP	SUGAR CUPS	¹WATER CUPS	YIELD OF SYRUP CUPS
30-percent syrup	2	4	5
35-percent syrup	2½	4	5⅓
40-percent syrup	3	4	5½
50-percent syrup	4¾	4	6½
60-percent syrup	7	4	7¾
65-percent syrup	8¾	4	8⅔

¹ In general, up to one-fourth of the sugar may be replaced by corn syrup. A larger proportion of corn syrup may be used if a very bland, light-colored type is selected.

fruit into a bowl or shallow pan and sprinkle the needed quantity of sugar over the fruit. Mix with a large spoon until juices are drawn out and the sugar dissolves. If you place a small piece of waxed paper on top of the fruit, in the container, it will help to hold the fruit in the juice until the pack freezes.

Unsweetened packs can be covered with water containing some vitamin C, or simply place it in the packs. It can be packed dry or held until juices form and then be packed in the juices, in which case the wax paper treatment is a good idea. Usually ⅛ teaspoon per quart will do the job of keeping the fruit from darkening. Table 14-4 gives an idea of about how much fruit you can expect to put in your freezer from the fresh volume or weight.

Sliced Apples

Sliced apples can be packed in syrup, sugar or unsweetened, but most people seem to prefer the syrup pack if the apples are to be used in uncooked desserts. Treat to prevent darkening. Wash, peel and core, and slice medium apples into twelfths, larger ones into sixteenths. Use a 40 percent syrup for a syrup pack, along with ½ teaspoon of vitamin C in crystalline form. Slice the apples right into the cold syrup in the container, starting with ½ cup of syrup in each container. Press fruit down and add enough syrup to cover, leaving the correct amount of head space. For a sugar

461

pack, place apples in a solution of 2 tablespoons of salt to a gallon of water (to prevent darkening). Hold them in this no more than 20 minutes and drain. Place slices in a single layer in a steamer and steam 1½ to 2 minutes. Cool in cold water and drain. Over each quart of apple slices sprinkle ½ cup of sugar and stir. Pack into containers and press down, leaving the correct head space. For an unsweetened pack for apple slices, just do the same as for the sugar pack and omit the sugar.

Table 14-4. Approximate Yield of Frozen Fruits from Fresh Ones.

FRUIT	FRESH, AS PURCHASED OR PICKED	FROZEN
Apples	1 bu. (48 lb.)	32 to 40 pt.
	1 box (44 lb.)	29 to 35 pt.
	1¼ to 1½ lb.	1 pt.
Apricots	1 bu. (48 lb.)	60 to 72 pt.
	1 crate (22 lb.)	28 to 33 pt.
	⅔ to 4/5 lb.	1 pt.
Berries[1]	1 crate (24 qt.)	32 to 36 pt.
	1⅓ to 1½ pt.	1 pt.
Cantaloupes	1 dozen (28 lb.)	22 pt.
	1 to 1¼ lb.	1 pt.
Cherries, sweet or sour	1 bu. (56 lb.)	36 to 44 pt.
	1¼ to 1½ lb.	1 pt.
Cranberries	1 box (25 lb.)	50 pt.
	1 peck (8 lb.)	16 pt.
	½ lb.	1 pt.
Currants	2 qt. (3 lb.)	4 pt.
	¾ lb.	1 pt.
Peaches	1 bu. (48 lb.)	32 to 48 pt.
	1 lug box (20 lb.)	13 to 20 pt.
	1 to 1½ lb.	1 pt.
Pears	1 bu. (50 lb.)	40 to 50 pt.
	1 western box (46 lb.)	37 to 46 pt.
	1 to 1¼ lb.	1 pt.
Pineapple	5 lb.	4 pt.
Plums and prunes	1 bu. (56 lb.)	38 to 56 pt.
	1 crate (20 lb.)	13 to 20 pt.
	1 to 1½ lb.	1 pt.
Raspberries	1 crate (24 pt.)	24 pt.
	1 pt.	1 pt.
Rhubarb	15 lb.	15 to 22 pt.
	⅔ to 1 lb.	1 pt.
Strawberries	1 crate (24 qt.)	38 pt.
	⅔ qt.	1 pt.

[1]Includes blackberries, blueberries, boysenberries, dewberries, elderberries, gooseberries, huckleberries, loganberries, and youngberries.

Various Berries

Blackberries, boysenberries, dewberries and loganberries are often packed whole. Use of the syrup pack is preferred if the berries are to be served uncooked, while the sugar pack or unsweetened pack is fine for berries to be cooked in pies, etc. Make sure the berries chosen are firm and fully ripe, as green berries will give an off-flavor. Wash, remove stems and leaves and drain. Pack the berries into containers and cover with cold 40 percent syrup—for less sweet berries, you may wish to use 50 percent syrup. Leave head space, seal and freeze. For the sugar pack, take 1 quart of berries, add ¾ cup of sugar, and turn the berries over and over until most of the sugar is dissolved. Fill containers, leaving head space and freeze. The unsweetened pack requires that you simply place the washed and drained berries in the container, seal and freeze.

Blueberries packed whole should go to the syrup pack for any being served uncooked. Select berries fully ripe and close to the same size. Sort, wash and drain. If you wish, the berries can be steamed for one minute to tenderize the skins. Then pack the berries in containers and pour, cold, 40 percent syrup over them, leaving enough head space. Seal and freeze. For the unsweetened pack, the berries are merely put into the container, sealed and frozen.

Sour Cherries and Grapes

Sour cherries again find the syrup pack considered best for anything served uncooked. The syrup pack is preferred for sour cherries to be made into pies. Cherries are packed in containers and a 60 or 65 percent syrup is used to cover them, leaving head space. Seal and freeze. For a sugar pack, add ¾ cup of sugar to each quart of cherries, and mix until the sugar is dissolved. Pack, leaving head space, and freeze.

Grapes can also be frozen and are usually done in a syrup pack, though they can be done unsweetened. Wash and stem, and cut seeded grapes in half and remove the seeds. For an unsweetened pack, just pack into the container, leaving head space, and freeze. For a syrup pack, pack into containers and cover with cold 40 percent syrup. Leave head space. Seal and freeze.

Peaches and Pears

Peaches in halves and slices tend to hold taste better if packed in syrup, but a water pack can also be used. Select firm, ripe peaches with no green at all on the skins. Sort, wash, pit and peel. The flavor will stay better, as will the texture, if you can peel the peaches without using the boiling water dip. Add ½ a teaspoon of crystalline vitamin C to retain color, and put the peaches directly into cold, 40 percent syrup, starting with ½ cup in the containers. Press fruit down and add syrup to cover, leaving the correct head space. Seal and freeze. For a sugar pack, add 2/3 cup of sugar to each quart of prepared peaches, after sprinkling ¼ teaspoon vitamin C in ¼ cup of cold water over each quart of peaches. Mix well, pack into containers, and freeze after sealing. For a water pack, the peaches are packed in the containers and covered with cold water containing 1 teaspoon of crystalline vitamin C for each quart of water. Leave head space. Seal and freeze.

Pears should be well ripened but still firm. Wash, peel and cut into halves or quarters. Remove cores. Heat the pears in boiling 40 percent syrup for two minutes. Drain and cool before packing. Pack into containers and cover with cold 40 percent syrup. For better color, add ¾ teaspoon of crystalline vitamin C to each quart of syrup. Leave head space, seal and freeze.

Raspberries and Strawberries

Raspberries frozen whole are sorted and washed carefully and then drained well. The berries are placed in the containers for the syrup pack, and 40 percent syrup is poured over them. Leave head space, seal and freeze. For the sugar pack, add ¾ cup of sugar to a quart of berries and mix carefully. Pack into the containers, leaving head space, seal and freeze. For the unsweetened pack, simply put the berries in the container, leave head space, seal and freeze.

Strawberries should be firm and ripe, with a slightly tart flavor. Slice large berries. Wash, drain well and remove caps. Place the berries in containers, cover with 50 percent syrup, leave head space, seal and freeze. For a sugar pack, add ¾ of a cup of sugar to each quart of strawberries, mix well and place in containers leaving head space. Seal and freeze. For the unsweetened pack, just pack into containers leaving head space, seal and freeze. For this pack, you will retain color better if the berries are covered with water which contains a teaspoon of crystalline vitamin C per quart of water.

FREEZING VEGETABLES

Vegetables require heating, or *blanching*, before being frozen (with the exception of green peppers) as this helps them to hold quality better during storage. The heating slows up the action of the enzymes which causes a loss of flavor and color. Once the vegetables have been sorted, washed and drained, and cut to size if wanted, they are immersed in boiling water. You can buy a specially made blancher, with a blanching basket and cover that makes the job easy. The first time I did the job, I used a metal colander and an old spaghetti pot. That worked well, though the colander often did not hold as much as I wished to freeze. For each pound of prepared vegetable, you need at least a gallon of boiling water in the blancher. Once the vegetables are lowered into the boiling water, you start the time count, making sure the heat is kept high for the time given for the particular vegetable. Add a minute to the blanching time if you live above 5,000 feet. Once the vegetables have been heated, quick cooling is needed. Just sit the blanching basket in a large amount of cold (60 degrees F. or colder) water. It takes the same amount of time to cool the vegetable as it does to heat it.

Vegetables can also be heated in steamers. This is recommended for broccoli, pumpkin and sweet potatoes, as well as for winter squash. The steamer should have its vegetable rack high enough from the bottom of the kettle to allow 2 inches of water to be added.

As always, the amount of finished frozen vegetables you get from a particular amount of just-picked vegetables is variable depending on quality, condition, maturity, variety and the way you trim and cut the vegetable. Table 14-5 gives an approximation for many vegetables.

Asparagus

Asparagus for freezing is best selected when young, and the stalks are tender. Sort according to stalk thickness. Wash well, and cut or snap off any tough parts of the stalks. Leave spears in lengths to fit the packages or cut into 2-inch lengths, as you prefer. Heat, or blanch, according to stalk thickness. Small stalks take two minutes; medium stalks take three minutes; and large stalks take four minutes. Cool and drain. Pack into containers leaving *no* head space. When packing spears into wide mouth containers, alternate tips and spear ends. Seal and freeze.

Lima and Green Beans

Lima beans should be green, but should be picked before they reach the mealy stage. Shell and sort according to size. Heat in boiling water, giving small beans two minutes, medium beans three minutes and large beans four minutes. Cool in cold water, and pack into containers leaving ½ inch of head space. Seal and freeze.

Green beans (also wax beans) are picked young and tender. Go for the stringless kind that snap easily when broken. Remove the ends. Cut into 2-inch pieces, or french (slice lengthwise). Heat in boiling water for three minutes and cool promptly. Pack leaving ½ inch of head space, seal and freeze.

Beets and Broccoli

Beets are best frozen when they are no more than 3 inches across. Wash and sort according to size. Trim the tops but leave about ½ inch of the stems. Cook in boiling water until tender—small beets will take 25 or 30 minutes and medium sized beets will need about 50 minutes—and then cool quickly in cold water. Peel and cut into slices or cubes. Pack leaving ½ inch of head space. Seal and freeze.

Table 14-5. Approximate Yield of Frozen Vegetables from Fresh Ones.

VEGETABLE	FRESH, AS PURCHASED OR PICKED	FROZEN
Asparagus	1 crate (12 2 lb. bunches)	15 to 22 pt.
	1 to 1½ lb.	1 pt.
Beans, lima (in pods)	1 bu. (32 lb.)	12 to 16 pt.
	2 to 2½ lb.	1 pt.
Beans, snap, green, and	1 bu. (30 lb.)	30 to 45 pt.
wax	⅔ to 1 lb.	1 pt.
Beet greens	15 lb.	10 to 15 pt.
	1 to 1½ lb.	1 pt.
Beets (without tops)	1 bu. (52 lb.)	35 to 42 pt.
	1¼ to 1½ lb.	1 pt.
Broccoli	1 crate (25 lb.)	24 pt.
	1 lb.	1 pt.
Brussels sprouts	4 quart boxes	6 pt.
	1 lb.	1 pt.
Carrots (without tops)	1 bu. (50 lb.)	32 to 40 pt.
	1¼ to 1½ lb.	1 pt.
Cauliflower	2 medium heads	3 pt.
	1⅓ lb.	1 pt.
Chard	1 bu. (12 lb.)	8 to 12 pt.
	1 to 1½ lb.	1 pt.
Collards	1 bu. (12 lb.)	8 to 12 pt.
	1 to 1½ lb.	1 pt.
Corn, sweet (in husks)	1 bu. (35 lb.)	14 to 17 pt.
	2 to 2½ lb.	1 pt.
Kale	1 bu. (18 lb.)	12 to 18 pt.
	1 to 1½ lb.	1 pt.
Mustard greens	1 bu. (12 lb.)	8 to 12 pt.
	1 to 1½ lb.	1 pt.
Peas	1 bu. (30 lb.)	12 to 15 pt.
	2 to 2½ lb.	1 pt.
Peppers, sweet	⅔ lb. (3 peppers)	1 pt.
Pumpkin	3 lb.	2 pt.
Spinach	1 bu. (18 lb.)	12 to 18 pt.
	1 to 1½ lb.	1 pt.
Squash, summer	1 bu. (40 lb.)	32 to 40 pt.
	1 to 1¼ lb.	1 pt.
Squash, winter	3 lb.	2 pt.
Sweetpotatoes	⅔ lb.	1 pt.

Broccoli for freezing should be compact, dark green heads with stalks free of woodiness. Wash and peel the stalks. Trim as needed. If insects are a problem, soak the broccoli for half an hour in a solution of 4 teaspoons of salt in a gallon of cold water. Split lengthwise so pieces at the flower end are no more than 1½ inches across. Heat in steam for five minutes or boiling water for three minutes. Cool right away and drain. Pack leaving no head space.

Brussels Sprouts and Carrots

Brussels sprouts should be firm and compact. Check to make sure they are free of insects. Remove the coarse outer leaves and wash well. Sort into small, medium and large. Heat small heads for three minutes in boiling water, medium heads for four minutes and large heads for five minutes. Cool, drain and pack leaving no head space. Seal and freeze.

Carrots should be tender and mild flavored. Remove the tops, wash and peel or scrape. Leave small carrots whole, but cut others into ¼-inch cubes, thin slices or long strips. Small whole carrots are blanched for five minutes; diced or sliced carrots require two minutes and strips need two minutes. Cool, drain and pack leaving ½ inch of head space. Seal and freeze.

Cauliflower and Corn

Cauliflower should be snowy white, firm and tender for freezing. Break or cut into pieces about an inch across, and wash well. If needed, to remove insects, soak for half an hour in a solution of 4 teaspoons of salt to a gallon of water. Drain. Heat in boiling water, with 4 teaspoons of salt per gallon, for three minutes. Cool, drain and pack leaving no head space. Seal and freeze.

Sweet corn can be frozen several ways. Choose ears with plump, tender kernels and thin, sweet milk. If the milk stage has gotten to where it is thick and starchy, it is best to do the corn cream-style. Husk the ears, remove silk and wash the corn. Heat the ears in boiling water for four minutes. Cool and drain. For whole kernel corn, cut the kernels from the cob at about two-thirds of kernel depth.

For cream style corn, cut the corn from the cobs at about the center of the kernel. Scrape the cobs with the back of a knife to remove the juice and heart of the kernel. Pack into containers leaving ½ inch of head space. Seal and freeze. For corn-on-the cob, select the corn just as you would for the other types. Husk, remove silk, wash and sort ears for size. Heat in boiling water for seven minutes for small ears (1¼ inches or less in diameter), nine minutes for large ears (up to

1½ inches), or 11 minutes for large ears. Cool and drain. Pack ears in bags. Seal and freeze.

Peas

Blackeye peas should be shelled and you should toss out any that are hard. Heat in boiling water for two minutes. Cool and drain, and pack into containers leaving ½ inch of head space. Seal and freeze.

Green peas are chosen when bright green, plump and firm. Don't use immature or tough peas in any case. Shell and place in boiling water for 1½ minutes. Cool and drain. Pack with ½ inch of head space. Seal and freeze.

Peppers

Sweet or hot peppers are best frozen without heating, especially if they are to be used in uncooked foods. Heated peppers pack more easily and are fine for cooked foods. Choose firm, thick walled peppers that are crisp. Wash, cut out stems, cut in half and remove the seeds. If you wish, they can then be cut into ½-inch strips. Heat in boiling water three minutes for halved peppers and two minutes for sliced pappers. Cool, drain and pack. If the peppers have been heated, leave ½ inch of head space. Seal and freeze.

Squash

Summer and winter Squash require slightly different selection procedures. Summer squash is selected when young and tender, washed and cut into ½-inch slices. Heat in boiling water for three minutes. Cool and drain. Pack into containers leaving ½ inch of head space, seal and freeze. Winter squash is selected for firmness and maturity, washed, cut into pieces and the seeds are removed. Cook until soft in boiling water, steam or a pressure cooker. Remove the pulp from the rind and mash. Place the pan in cold water to cool, pack leaving ½ inch of head space. Seal and freeze.

Tomatoes and Turnips

Tomatoes are frozen only as juice or stewed. For juice, wash and trim firm, ripe tomatoes and cut into quarters. Simmer five to 10 minutes and press through a sieve. If you want, add a teaspoon of salt to each quart of juice. Pour into containers, leaving head space. Seal and freeze. For stewed tomatoes, remove the stem ends, peel and quarter firm, ripe tomatoes. Cover and cook until tender (10 to 20 minutes). Cool the pan and contents in cold water. Pack, leaving head space. Seal and freeze.

Turnips should be small to medium and firm. Select those that are tender and have a mild flavor. Wash, peel and cut into ½-inch cubes. Heat in boiling water for two minutes. Cool, drain, seal and freeze, making sure there is ½ inch of head space.

As you can see, freezing foods requires less time and usually less effort than does canning. The investment in equipment is probably about the same, since the freezer adds to costs. With the cost of pressure canners today, you can sometimes buy a used freezer for the same amount. Too, the containers tend to be a bit cheaper than are canning jars. If the top quality rigid containers are used, they will generally outlast glass jars since there is no worry about chipping and cracking. Table 14-6 provides some cooking times for frozen foods.

TYPES OF FREEZERS

Frozen foods, though, do have an added cost, and that is the cost of running the freezer over the year. Today, two types of freezers are found on the market. The *upright* freezer offers the greatest convenience in loading and in removing packages and takes up less floor space, but the *chest style* freezer offers more food storage for the same cubic foot capacity and is better for storing large packages. If you are selecting a new freezer, check the listed operating cost estimates. Self-defrosting freezers always cost more to run than do manual defrost models, and uprights cost more than chest styles. If you can locate the freezer in a cool area, operating cost will also be lower (don't keep it in an area that gets below about 40 degrees F. or the unit may freeze up on you).

Freezer size depends on just how much of your food you plan to store over the year. The basic freezer recommendation for those with small gardens is about 6 cubic feet per person in your family (a cubic foot of freezer will hold about

Table 14-6. Timetable for Cooking Vegetables in a Small Amount of Water.

VEGETABLE	TIME TO ALLOW AFTER WATER RETURNS TO BOIL[2] MINUTES	VEGETABLE	TIME TO ALLOW AFTER WATER RETURNS TO BOIL[2] MINUTES
Asparagus	5-10	Chard	8-10
Beans, lima:		Corn:	
Large type	6-10	Whole-kernel	3-5
Baby type	15-20	On-the-cob	3-4
Beans, snap, green, or wax:		Kale	8-12
1-inch pieces	12-18	Kohlrabi	8-10
Julienne	5-10	Mustard greens	8-15
Beans, soybeans, green	10-20	Peas, green	5-10
Beet greens	6-12	Spinach	5-10
Broccoli	5-8	Squash, summer	4-6
Brussels sprouts	4-9	Turnip greens	10-12
Carrots	5-10	Turnips	15-20
Cauliflower	5-8		8-12

[1]Use ½ cup of lightly salted water for each pint of vegetable with these exceptions: Lima beans, 1 cup; corn-on-the-cob, water to cover.
[2]Time required at sea level; slightly longer time is required at higher altitudes.

35 pounds of food). For those who have larger gardens and who plan to store large quantities of meat, that figure can be doubled. Still, the small the freezer possible, the lower the operating costs.

DRYING FOODS

The final method of food preservation is the oldest one around—drying. The removal of most of the water from foods is simple and inexpensive, but the processes of canning and freezing do an overall better job of holding nutritional values, taste, texture and flavor in foods. Certain foods respond better to drying than do others. For home drying, apples, herbs, dry beans and peas, corn, sweet potatoes, green beans and onions are your best bet.

Food selected for drying should be top quality and fresh, just ripe enough for eating. Wash well before drying. To dry foods in most areas of the country, you will need to use either your oven or a dehydrator. You do no more than 4 to 6 pounds of prepared food at a time. The process can take from four to 12 hours, depending on size, moisture content and other factors. Use trays to allow air circulation from the bottom as well as the top. Trays can be made at home of wood slats and screening in sizes to fit your oven. Preheat the oven to 140 degrees F. If your oven doesn't go this low, place it on the lowest setting and use an oven thermometer to keep a check, propping the door open a bit when it gets too warm. Foods will need to be turned every half hour or 45 minutes. The drier they get, the more important the turning becomes as they then tend to scorch more easily. Vegetables should be blanched, just as for freezing, before being dried.

Herbs

Herbs should be especially suitable for home drying. Select tender, young herbs and wash thoroughly, leaving the leaves on the stems. Shake off excess water and dry on paper towels until water evaporates. Spread on drying trays no more than an inch deep. As you dry, at 140 degrees, check the herbs. When they feel crisp and dry, strip the leaves from the stems, crumbling them coarse or fine as needed. Place in jars, cap and put in a cool, dark place. If the jars show signs of interior moisture after 24 hours, you will need to repeat the drying process. Herbs can also be dried by tying the stems together and hanging them from a rafter in a warm, well aired room, or in a warm, dry attic.

Fruit Leathers

Fruit leathers can be of most any type of fruit, but seem to work best with apricots, apples, grapes, berries, oranges, pears, peaches, tomatoes, plums and a few others. Grapeuit, lemon and rhubarb do not work as well. Select ripe or slightly overripe fruit, and remove any stones or pits. Seeds of berries and grapes need not be removed. You can peel the fruit if you want, or leave it as is. Cut the fruit into chunks and place it in a blender or use a food chopper. To light colored fruit, add a tablespoon of lemon or lime juice for each quart of fruit. Chop or blend until a thick puree is formed. Add 2 tablespoons of sugar per quart of orange pulp. Line a cookie sheet with waxed paper, and pour the puree into the sheet in a layer about ¼ inch deep. Tilt the tray to get it spread evenly. Set the oven at 140 degrees and place the sheets in the oven, leaving the oven cracked open about 2 or 3 inches. Fruit leather takes four to six hours to dry. When it is properly dried, the leather will be still sticky to the touch but will peel easily from the waxed paper. If it peels back an inch at the edges readily, the process is finished. Now you simply roll the paper and all up and store the fruit leather. It will keep for years in the freezer, for several months in the refrigerator, and will last for as much as six months at room temperature (70 degrees or below).

Such drying of foods tends to require a great deal of energy for the results. It takes about four kilowatt hours of electricity to dry a pound of apples which adds, at this moment and in this place, about 21 cents to the cost of the apples per pound. In other areas, it will add more. I dry herbs by hanging and let the rest go unless I feel a need for fruit leather to be used on hikes or camping trips. It is handy for that, as a fair amount is light, easily carried and tasty. Otherwise, my preference is for freezing or canning.

15

Afterword

As you note in reading through this book, a lot of hands-on information is presented. That is because rural life tends to be a hands-on way to get along. You can't afford to hire the jobs done, so you need to do them, after learning how, yourself.

THE IMPORTANCE OF SAFETY

There are a lot of things that are not covered and cannot be covered. No book can teach you how to milk a cow or help a ewe live through lambing when difficulties are present. You may learn the basics of running a chain saw and felling trees from a book, but it takes practice to fell them where you wish and when you wish.

I may have overemphasized safety aspects in some areas, but it seems to me that being a bit leery of one's tools is a basically sound idea when some of those tools can cause major injury. Farming is not a safe enterprise, and never has been. When living in a rural area, one comes rapidly to see that there are a great many dangers seldom thought about. Not many urbanites get yanked into a hay baler or fall off a tractor and get mangled by a brush cutting machine being towed behind. Still, it is not all danger.

ADVANTAGES OF COUNTRY LIVING

The clearness of country skies in most areas is another benefit of living in a rural area. There is no smog and little pollution of other kinds. Star gazing is almost mandatory since the stars are so bright.

Country recreations tend to be simple in some ways and very complex in others. Around my area, there are many bluegrass festivals each year and a number of country music concerts with most of the big name stars. A short drive (under 25 miles) will bring me to a city of about 130,000 people where there are plays, concerts and museums of several kinds. Most rural areas are now close enough to city culture for the hillbillies among us to take part in almost all the cultural activities possible.

At one time or another, I have lived in several large cities, including Manhattan, and I have visited a string of others. But over the last eight or nine years, my living has been rural, in three states (New York, Wisconsin and now Virginia), and the idea of living again in a city makes my skin crawl. At the moment, I have 4,200 feet of dirt road between me and the nearest neighbor on one side. On the other side, I have yet to clock the distance, but it is at least two miles. Days when five cars pass this place count as heavy traffic times. Parties can be as loud or as quiet as I wish, with no fear of anyone pounding on the door saying we're disturbing others. About the only objection to the road is the effort needed to keep my new pickup anywhere near clean. And there is a certain amount of difficulty in going down the road in winter when snow and ice are on the ground.

The choice of a rural area is up to you , as is the distance from other people. The enjoyment of rural living is ready and waiting for anyone willing to work a bit.

Appendix

A

Horse Breed Associations

When writing to any of these associations, give them a reasonable length of time in which to reply. It may be wise to include a self-addressed stamped business envelope in your request for information. Some of the associations are quite small and have small budgets. While they may have material you desire, they are being stretched a bit financially to send it out. The larger associations often have a publications list covering their breed, with most such publications going for a modest price for the information contained.

Appaloosas
Appaloosa Horse Club
P. O. Box 8403
Moscow, ID 83483
Colorado Ranger Horse Association
John Morris, President
7023 Eden Mill Road
Woodbine, MD 21794

Arabians
International Arabian Horse Association
P. O. Box 4502
Burbank, CA 91503

Draft Breeds

American Shire Horse Association
14410 High Bridge Road
Monroe, WA 98272

American Suffolk Horse Association
672 Polk Boulevard
Des Moines, IA 50312

Belgian Draft Horse Corporation of America
P.O. Box 335
Wabash, IN 46992

Cyldesdale Breeders Association of the United States
Route 1, Box 131
Pecatonica, IL 61063

Percheron Horse Association of America
Route 1
Belmont, OH 43718

Morgans

American Morgan Horse Association, Inc.
Oneida City Airport Industrial Park
P.O. Box 1
Westmoreland, NY 13940

Pintos

American Paint Horse Association
P.O. Box 18519
Fort Worth, TX 76118

Pinto Horse Association of America, Inc.
7525 Mission Gorge Road
Suite C
San Diego, CA 92120

Quarter Horses

American Quarter Horse Association
Amarillo, TX 79168

Standard Quarter Horse Association
4390 Fenton Street
Denver, CO 80212

Racking Horses

Racking Horse Breeders Association of America
Helena, AL 35080

Appendix

B

Solar Heating Systems Firms

I have tried both to avoid systems pieces makers and to get at least one maker or distributor for complete systems for each state. In cases where I missed, you can contact your county agricultural agent or a government agency to determine the name and address of the state group handling solar energy problems, systems manufacturers and so on in your state.

Acorn Structures
P.O. Box 250
Concord, MA 01742

Addison Products
Addison, MI 49220

Advanced Energy Technology
121 Albright
Los Gatos, CA 95030

Airtex Corporation
2900 N. Western Avenue
Chicago, IL 60618

Altenergy
P. O. Box 695
Ben Lomond, CA 94043

American Helio Thermal Corporation
2625 S. Santa Fe Drive
Denver, CO 80223

American Solar Heat Corporation
7 National Pl.
Danbury, CT 06810

American Solarize, Inc.
P. O. Box 15
Martinsville, NJ 07960

American Solar Systems
415 Branch Street
Arroyo Grande, CA 93420

Aqua Solar, Inc.
1234 Zacchini Avenue
Sarasota, FL 33577

A to Z Solar Products
200 E. 26th Street
Minneapolis, MN 55404

Carolina Solar Equipment Company
P.O. Box 2068
Salisbury, NC 28144

Climatrol Corporation
Woodbridge Avenue
Edison, NJ 08812

Colorado Sunworks Corporation
P.O. Box 455
Boulder, CO 80306

Contemporary Systems, Inc.
68 Charlonne St.
Jaffrey, NH 03452

Daystar Corporation
90 Cambridge Street
Burlington, MA 01803

Decker Manufacturing
Impac Corporation Division
312 Blondeau
Keokuk, IA 52632

Dumont Industries
Main Street
Monmouth, ME 04259

E&K Service Co.
16824 74th Avenue N.E.
Bothell, WA 98011

Energex Corporation
2302 E. Magnolia Street
Phoenix, AZ 85040

Energy Alternatives, Inc.
1006 East D Street
Moscow, ID 83843

Ethone Inc., Sunworks Division
P.O. Box 1004
New Haven, CT 06475

Florida Solar Power, Inc.
P.O. Box 5846
Tallahassee, FL 32401

Garden Way
P.O. Box 66
Charlotte, VT 05445

Grumman Corporation, Energy Systems Division
4175 Veterans Memorial Highway
Ronkonkoma, NY 11779

Helios Corporation
2120 Angus Road
Charlottesville, VA 22901

Heliotherm, Inc.
W. Lenni Road
Lenni, PA 19052

Helio Thermics, Inc.
110 Laurens Road
Greenville, SC 29601

Independent Living, Inc.
2300 Peachtree Rd.
Doraville, GA 30340

International Solar Industries, Inc.
3107 Memorial Parkway N.W.
Huntsville, AL 35801

Intertechnology-Solar Corporation of America
100 Main Street
Warrenton, VA 22186

Jensen Solar
P.O. Box 166
Goldsboro, NC 27530

Kastek Corporation
P.O. Box 8881
Portland, OR 97208

Kentucky Solar Energies
Route 1, Box 278
Frankfort, KY 40601

K-Line Corporation
911 Penn Avenue, N.E.
Albuquerque, NM 87110

KTA Corporation
12300 Washington Avenue
Rockville, MD 20852

Midwest Solar Corporation
2359 Grissom Drive
St. Louis, MO 63141

Mor-Flo Industries
18450 S. Miles Road
Cleveland, Ohio 44128

National Energy Systems Corporation
P.O. Box 1176
Birmingham, AL 35201

Natural Energy Systems, Inc.
1117 E. Carpenter Drive
Palatine, IL 60067

Northwest Solar Systems
7700 12th N.E.
Tacoma, WA 98421

P.C.A.
11031 Wye Drive
San Antonio, TX 75141

SEECO
3305 Metairie Road
Metairie, LA 70001

Solar America, Inc.
9001 Arbor Street
Omaha, NE 68124

Solaray Corporation
2414 Makiki Heights Drive
Honolulu, HI 96822

Solaray Inc.
324 S. Kidd Street
Whitewater, WI 53190

Solar Enterprises Inc.
2816 W. Division
Arlington, TX 76012

Solarequip
P.O. Box 21447
Phoenix, AZ 85014

Solargizer Corporation
220 Mulberry Street
Stillwater, MN 55082

Solar Products, Inc.
12 Hylestead Street
Providence, RI 02905

Solar Sun, Inc.
235 W. 12th Street
Cincinnati, OH 45210

Solar Technology, Inc.
3927 Oakcliff Industrial Ct.
Atlanta, GA 30340

Solar Utilities of Nebraska
P.O. Box 387
Gothenbrug, NE 69138

Soltrax, Inc.
720 Rankin Road, N.E.
Albuquerque, NM 87107

State Industries, Inc.
Cumberland Street
Ashland, TN 37105

Sundog Solar
3800 N. Virginia Street
Reno, NV 89506

Sunhouse Inc.
6 Southgate Drive
Nashua, NH 03060

Sun Saver Corporation
P.O. Box 276
North Liberty, IA 52317

Sunwall, Inc.
P.O. Box 9723
Pittsburgh, PA 15229

Thomason Solar Homes
6802 Walker Mill Road N.W.
Washington, D.C. 20027

Virginia Solar Components
Route 3, Highway 29 S.
Rustburg, VA 24588

Appendix

C

Plans for Outbuildings

Because outbuildings go up about like houses do and require the same tools and skills, I have not included a special section on their construction. Still, a few plans may be of help to you in getting things started.

Figure C-1 is from JET Manufacturing and shows the basics of erecting one of their small barns. These wood structures serve extremely well as tool storage and garden storage buildings. Figure C-2 is a poultry building, essentially meant as a brooding house, but adaptable to other uses. Figure C-3 is a general barn which may use either a gambrel or other kind of roof system. It can be adapted to either cattle or horses, and may serve for one of each. Figure C-4 is a larger general barn with a gambrel roof.

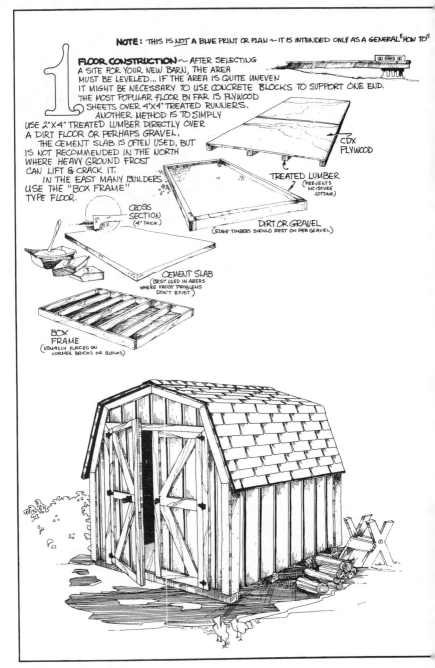

NOTE: THIS IS <u>NOT</u> A BLUE PRINT OR PLAN ~ IT IS INTENDED ONLY AS A GENERAL "HOW TO"

FLOOR CONSTRUCTION ~ AFTER SELECTING A SITE FOR YOUR NEW BARN, THE AREA MUST BE LEVELED... IF THE AREA IS QUITE UNEVEN IT MIGHT BE NECESSARY TO USE CONCRETE BLOCKS TO SUPPORT ONE END. THE MOST POPULAR FLOOR BY FAR IS PLYWOOD SHEETS OVER 4"X4" TREATED RUNNERS.

ANOTHER METHOD IS TO SIMPLY USE 2"X4" TREATED LUMBER DIRECTLY OVER A DIRT FLOOR OR PERHAPS GRAVEL.

THE CEMENT SLAB IS OFTEN USED, BUT IS NOT RECOMMENDED IN THE NORTH WHERE HEAVY GROUND FROST CAN LIFT & CRACK IT.

IN THE EAST MANY BUILDERS USE THE "BOX FRAME" TYPE FLOOR.

CDX PLYWOOD

TREATED LUMBER (PREVENTS MOISTURE ROTTING)

CROSS SECTION (4" THICK)

DIRT OR GRAVEL (EDGE TIMBERS SHOULD REST ON PEA GRAVEL)

CEMENT SLAB (BEST USED IN AREAS WHERE FROST PROBLEMS DON'T EXIST.)

BOX FRAME (USUALLY PLACED ON CORNER BRICKS OR BLOCKS)

Fig. C-1. Plan for a kit barn.

484

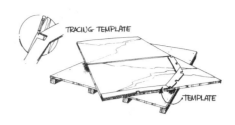

TRACING TEMPLATE

TEMPLATE

FRONT WALL AND BACK WALL CONSTRUCTION

2.

THE COMPLETED FLOOR SURFACE PROVIDES A GREAT WORK AREA TO BUILD THE FRONT & BACK WALLS.

EACH KIT CONTAINS A TEMPLATE...TO BE TRACED... ASSURING ALL ROOF CUTS WILL BE ACCURATE, AND BLOCKING WILL BE FIT INTO THEIR PROPER POSITIONS. EACH BLOCKING PIECE IS PRE-CUT TO ITS REQUIRED ANGLE...AND NUMBERED TO COINCIDE WITH THE PLAN BOOKLET.

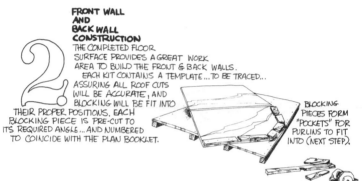

BLOCKING PIECES FORM "POCKETS" FOR PURLINS TO FIT INTO (NEXT STEP).

TRIM PIECES...PRE-CUT & NUMBERED ARE ALSO NAILED INTO PLACE AT THIS TIME. EVEN THE DOOR TRIM IS INSTALLED NOW.

HERE'S A NEAT TRICK!

THE DOOR TRIM STOCK IS 6" WIDE AND GROOVED DOWN THE MIDDLE... AFTER THE FRONT WALL IS COMPLETED...WITH ALL DOOR TRIM IN PLACE... SIMPLY CUT THE DOOR TRIM, IN THE GROOVE, AND INSTALL THE HINGES AS YOU CUT~IN OTHER WORDS~ CUT 18" OR SO AND INSTALL A HINGE...CUT AGAIN AND INSTALL HINGE, ETC. WHEN YOU COMPLETELY CUT THE GROOVES, YOU HAVE A SET OF DOUBLE HUNG DOORS PERFECTLY ALIGNED...AND IT WAS ALL DONE LYING FLAT & IN ONE STEP.

CUTTING DOORS

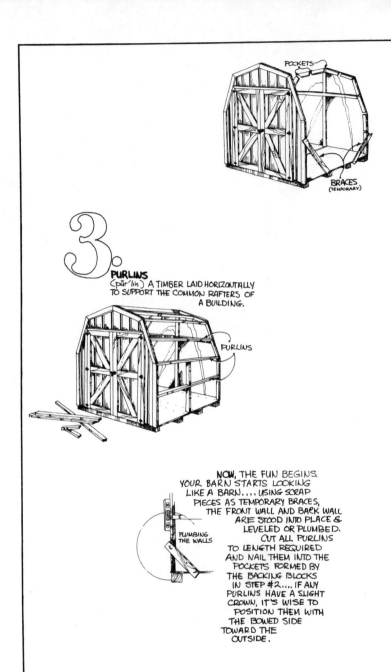

POCKETS

BRACES
(TEMPORARY)

3.

PURLINS
(pūr'lin) A TIMBER LAID HORIZONTALLY
TO SUPPORT THE COMMON RAFTERS OF
A BUILDING.

PURLINS

PLUMBING
THE WALLS

NOW, THE FUN BEGINS,
YOUR BARN STARTS LOOKING
LIKE A BARN.... USING SCRAP
PIECES AS TEMPORARY BRACES,
THE FRONT WALL AND BACK WALL
ARE STOOD INTO PLACE &
LEVELED OR PLUMBED.
CUT ALL PURLINS
TO LENGTH REQUIRED
AND NAIL THEM INTO THE
POCKETS FORMED BY
THE BACKING BLOCKS
IN STEP #2.... IF ANY
PURLINS HAVE A SLIGHT
CROWN, IT'S WISE TO
POSITION THEM WITH
THE BOWED SIDE
TOWARD THE
OUTSIDE.

Fig. C-1. Plan for a kit barn con't from pg. 485

4. SHEATHING

COVERING YOUR NEW STRUCTURE WITH SHEETING AND CAP SHINGLING THE RIDGE FINISHES IT OFF.... BUT.

SIDING:
THERE ARE A LOT OF CHOICES FOR COVERING YOUR BARN. COMPOSITION BOARD (GROOVED) AND ROUGH SAWN ARE MOST USED.

OPTIONAL KITS ARE AVAILABLE TO EXTEND YOUR BARN TO 12', 16' EVEN LONGER IF YOU WANT.

MOST BUILDERS LIKE TO PAINT THEIR BARNS TO MATCH OR TO CONTRAST WITH ITS SURROUNDINGS... RED IS BY FAR THE MOST POPULAR COLOR.... WITH WHITE TRIM, RED SIDING AND THE OPTION OF BLACK SHINGLES MAKES A <u>REALLY</u> GREAT LIL' BARN!

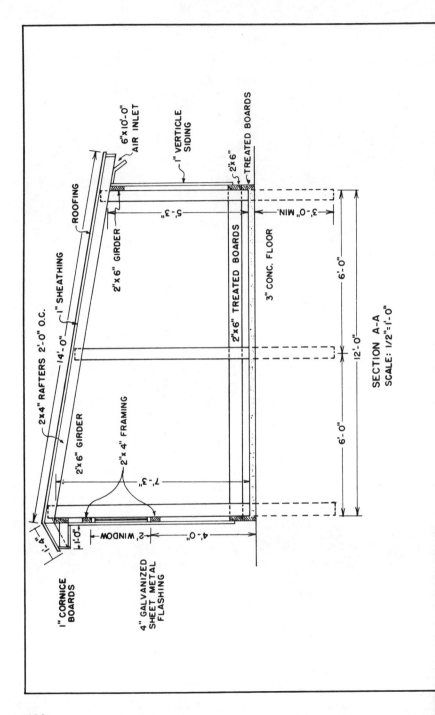

SECTION A-A
SCALE: 1/2"=1'-0"

2"x4" RAFTERS 2'-0" O.C.

ROOFING

6"x10'-0"
AIR INLET

1" VERTICLE
SIDING

1" SHEATHING

14'-0"

2" x 6" GIRDER

5'-3"

2"x 6"

TREATED BOARDS

2"x6" TREATED BOARDS

3" CONC. FLOOR

3'-0" MIN.

6'-0"

12'-0"

2'x 6" GIRDER

2"x 4" FRAMING

6'-0"

7'-3"

1" CORNICE
BOARDS

1'-0"

1'-4"

2' WINDOW

4'-0"

4" GALVANIZED
SHEET METAL
FLASHING

BILL OF MATERIALS

3 PCS. 11' POLES, 4" TOP DIAMETER, TREATED
6 PCS. 10' POLES, 4" TOP DIAMETER, TREATED
8 PCS. 2"x 6"x12', TREATED BOARDS
3 PCS. 2"x 6"x12' BOARDS
6 PCS. 2'x 4'x 14' RAFTERS
6 PCS. 2"x 4"x 10' DOOR FRAMING & BRACES, WINDOWS, & FRONT OVERHANG
4 PCS. 2"x 4"x 12' DOOR FRAMING & WINDOW FRAMING
24 PCS. 1"x 6"x 14', T & G SIDING
14 PCS. 1"x 6"x 12', T & G SIDING
12 PCS. 1"x 6"x 10', T & G SIDING
6 PCS. 1'x 6"x 12' CORNICE
2 PCS. 1"x 6'x 14' CORNICE
35 PCS. 1"x 6"x 12' SHEATHING
6 EACH, 6" STRAP HINGE
6 EACH, SCREEN DOOR HOOK AND EYE
2 EACH, 6" 'T' HINGES
9 FEET - 4' WIDE, 6-8 MIL PLASTIC
1 1/6 CU. YDS. CONCRETE 6 BAG MIX
15 LBS. 20D NAILS
12 LBS. 8D NAILS
1 LB. FLAT HEAD NAILS FOR PLASTIC
3 SHEETS 16'x 64" METAL ROOFING
1 RIDGE CAP
350-400 ROOFING NAILS - BUY NAIL FROM SAME DEALER AS ROOFING

Fig. C-2. Plan for a poultry brooding house.

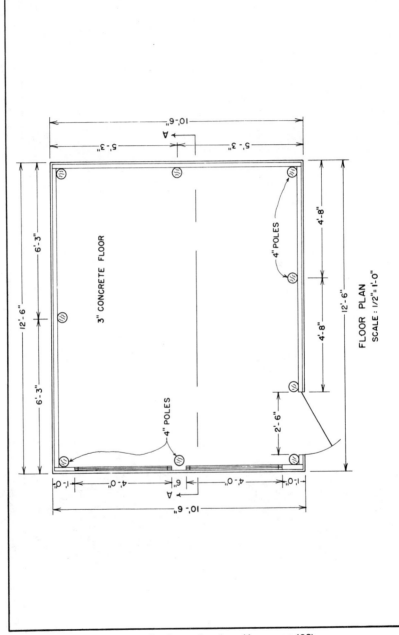

Fig. C-2. Plan for a poultry brooding house (continued from page 489).

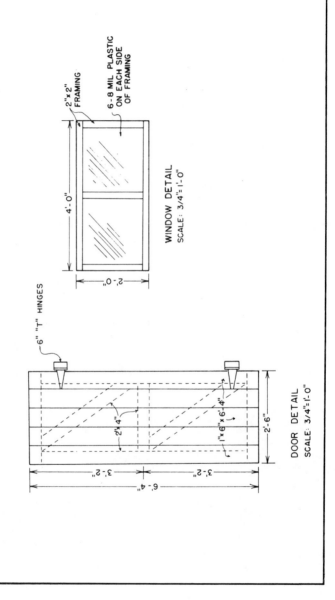

2"x 2" FRAMING

6-8 MIL PLASTIC ON EACH SIDE OF FRAMING

4'-0"

2'-0"

WINDOW DETAIL
SCALE: 3/4"=1'-0"

6" "T" HINGES

2"x 4"

1"x 6"x 6'-4"

2'-6"

3'-2"

3'-2"

6'-4"

DOOR DETAIL
SCALE: 3/4"=1'-0"

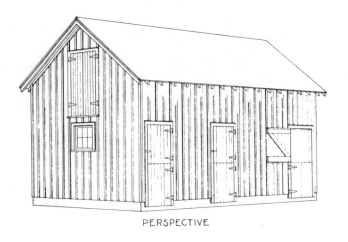

PERSPECTIVE

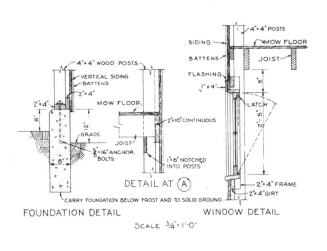

4"x 4" WOOD POSTS
VERTICAL SIDING
BATTENS
2"x 4"
MOW FLOOR
2"x 4"
8"
12"
GRADE
JOIST
⅝"x16" ANCHOR
BOLTS
8"
2"x10" CONTINUOUS
JOIST
1"x 6" NOTCHED
INTO POSTS

DETAIL AT Ⓐ

CARRY FOUNDATION BELOW FROST AND TO SOLID GROUND.

FOUNDATION DETAIL

SCALE ¾" = 1'-0"

4"x 4" POSTS
SIDING
MOW FLOOR
BATTENS
JOIST
FLASHING
1"x 4"
8"
LATCH
2'-5"
WINDOW DETAIL
2"x 4" FRAME
2"x 4" GIRT

Fig. C-3. Plan for a general barn.

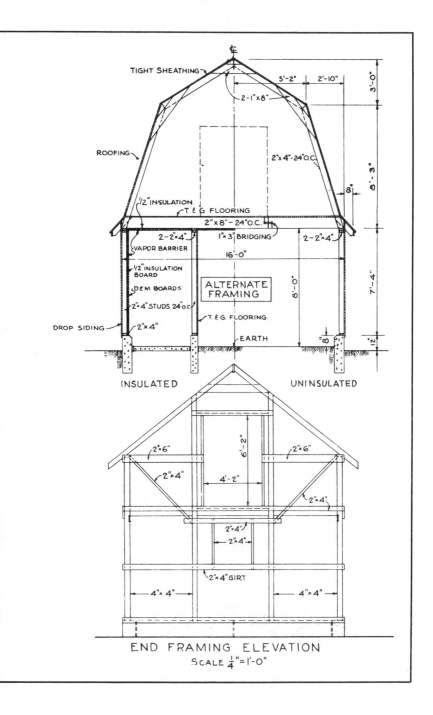

TIGHT SHEATHING

2-1"x 8"

ROOFING

5'-2" 2'-10"

3'-0"

2"x 4"-24"O.C.

8"

6'-3"

½"INSULATION
T. & G. FLOORING
2"x 8"- 24"O.C.
1"x 3" BRIDGING
2-2"x 4"
2 - 2"x 4"
VAPOR BARRIER
16'-0"
7'-4"

½"INSULATION
BOARD
DEM BOARDS
2"x 4" STUDS 24"o.c.
8'-0"

ALTERNATE
FRAMING

DROP SIDING
2"x 4"
T. & G. FLOORING
EARTH
8"
12"

INSULATED   UNINSULATED

2"x 6"   2"x 6"

2"x 4"   2"x 4"
6'-2"

4'-2"

2"x 4"

2"x 4"
2"x 4" GIRT

4"x 4"   4"x 4"

END FRAMING ELEVATION
SCALE ¼"= 1'-0"

493

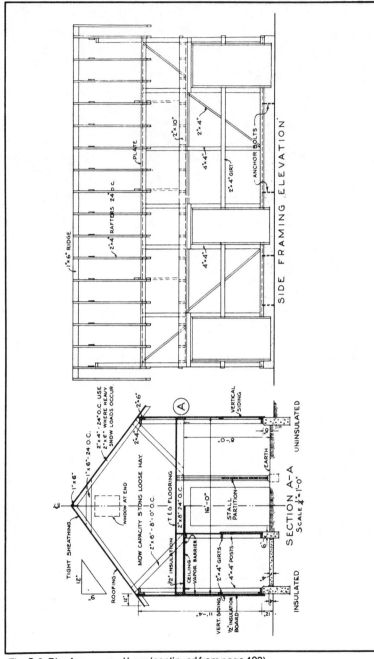

Fig. C-3. Plan for a general barn (continued from page 493).

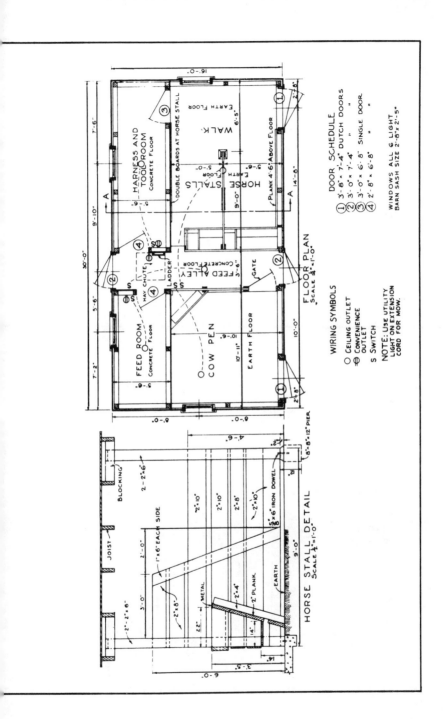

FLOOR PLAN
Scale ¼"=1'-0"

DOOR SCHEDULE
① 3'-8" × 7'-4" DUTCH DOORS
② 3'-0" × 7'-4" "   "
③ 3'-0" × 6'-8" SINGLE DOOR
④ 2'-8" × 6'-8"   "   "

WINDOWS ALL 6 LIGHT
BARN SASH SIZE 2'-8"× 2'-5"

WIRING SYMBOLS
○ CEILING OUTLET
⊕ CONVENIENCE OUTLET
S SWITCH

NOTE: USE UTILITY
LIGHT ON EXTENSION
CORD FOR MOW.

HORSE STALL DETAIL
Scale ½"=1'-0"

HARNESS AND TOOLROOM
CONCRETE FLOOR

HORSE STALLS
EARTH FLOOR

FEED ROOM
CONCRETE FLOOR

COW PEN
EARTH FLOOR

FEED ALLEY
CONCRETE FLOOR

WALK
EARTH FLOOR

495

CONCRETE 1:2½: 4 MIX CEMENT 113 BAGS

Item	Pcs.	Size	Length
Sills ——	pcs. 8	–2"×6"	–10'–0"
Sills ——	3	2"×6"	16'–0"
Sills ——	4	2×6"	14'–0"
Sills ——	2	2"×6"	12'–0"
Plates	16	2"×6"	10'–0"
Plates	4	2"×6"	14'–0"
Plates	4	"×6"	16'–0"
Joists	21	2"×10"	12'–0"
Joists	21	2"×10"	14'–0"
Joists	21	2"×10"	10'–0"
Lookouts	14	2"×4"	12'–0"
Rafter Braces ——	40	2"×6"	14'–0"
Rafter Braces ——	40	2"×6"	10'–0"
Collars ——	20	2"×6"	12'–0"
Cleats ——	21	2"×8"	12'–0"
Braces ——	5	2"×6"	16'–0"
Rafters ——	42	2"×6"	14'–0"

Sand 12 cu. yds.   Stone 17.25 cu. yds.

Item	Qty.	Size	Length
Partition Stalls	pcs. 41	2"×6"	14'–0"
Partition Stalls	11	2"6×"	12'–0"
Interior Planking	140	Sq. Ft.	
Siding	2460	Bd. Ft.	
Sheathing	2630	Bd. Ft.	
Roofing	23	Squares	
Flooring	1600	Sq. Ft.	
T&G Ceiling	600	Sq. Ft.	
Ventilator	1	20" Metal	
Bolts	14	⅝" × 18"	
Flashing (over doors and windows)			
Ridgeboards	pcs. 1	2" × 10"	14'–0"
Ridgeboards	pcs. 2	1"×8"	16'–0"
Windows	12 S.S.	9 Lts 10"/12" Gl.	
Gates	3	4'–0" × 5'–0"	
Doors	4	5'–2"×8'–2"	
Doors	5	4'–4"×8'–2"	

Item	Qty	Size	Length		Item	Qty	Size	Length
Rafters	42	2"×6"	12'—0"		Doors	1	3'—0" × 7'—0"	
Ribbons	8	1"×6"	10'—0"		Doors	1	4'—4"×5'—0"	
Studs	95	2"×6"	12'—0"		Doors	2	4'—2"×10'—2"	
Studs	24	2"×6"	16'—0"		Window Sills	pcs. 4	2"×8"	12'—0"
Studs	31	2"×6"	14'—0"		Window Plates	4	2"×6"	12'—0"
Studs	6	2"×4"	12'—0"		Window Shields	4	1"×10"	12'—0"
Posts	2	6"×6"	14'—0"		Dowels	4	5/8"×6"	
Posts	2	6"×6"	10'—0"		Verge Rafter	4	1"×6"	16'—0"
Girders	24	2"×12"	14'—0"		Hay Lift Rafter	2	2"×6"	12'—0"
Corner Boards	8	1"×4"	12'—0"		Door Trim	10	1"×4"	16'—0"
Track Planks	6	2"×10"	14'—0"		Window Trim	12	1"×4"	12'—0"
Track Planks	3	2"×6"	14'—0"		Window Keeper	3	1"×6"	12'—0"
Manager	25	1"×12"	12'—0"		Bridging	350	Lin Ft.	
Manager	11	2"×4"	12'—0"		Headers	5	2"×6"	12'—0"
Manager	1	2"×2"	10'—0"		Headers	6	2"×6"	12'—0"
Slats	3	1"×4"	8'—0"		Headers	3	2"×6"	16'—0"
Lookout Trim	6	1"×4"	14'—0"		Nails, Paint, Hardware, hayhock etc.			

Fig. C-4. Plan for a larger general barn with a gambrel roof.

497

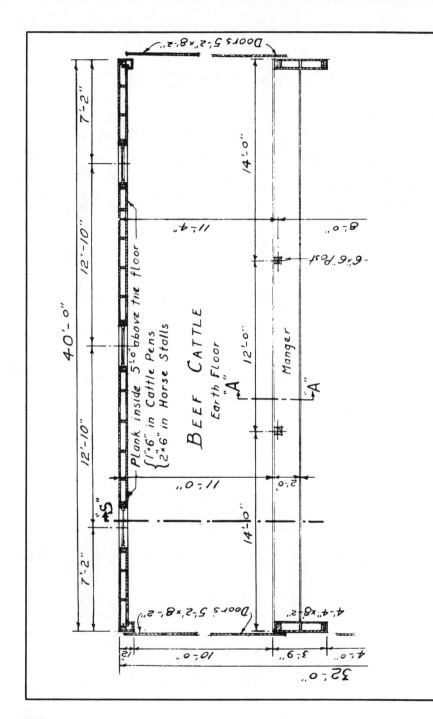

Doors 5'-2"x8'-2".

40'-0"

7'-2"   12'-10"   12'-10"   7'-2"

Plank inside 5'-0 above the floor
{ 1"x6" in Cattle Pens
{ 2"x6" in Horse Stalls

14'-0"

11'-4"

8'-0"

6"x6" Post

BEEF CATTLE
Earth Floor
"A"

12'-0"

Manger

"A"

11'-0"

2'-0"

14'-0"

"S"

Doors 5'-2"x8'-2".

4'-4"x8'-2".

1'-2"   10'-0"   3'-9"   4'-0"

32'-0"

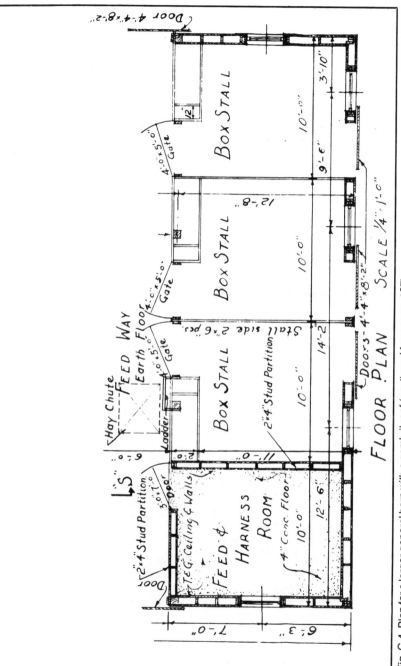

Fig. C-4. Plan for a larger general barn with a gambril roof (continued from page 497).

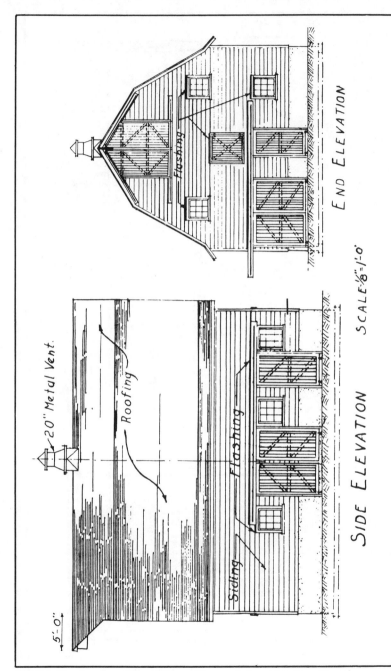

Fig. C-4. Plan for a larger general barn with a gambril roof (continued from page 499).

500

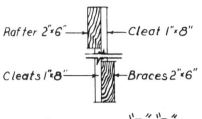

Rafter 2"×6" — Cleat 1"×8"

Cleats 1"×8" — Braces 2"×6"

SECTION "B"-"B"
SCALE - 1½" = 1'-0"

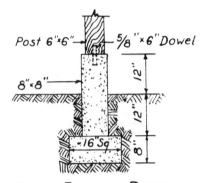

Post 6"×6" — ⅝"×6" Dowel

8"×8"

12"

12"

16" Sq

8"

POST FOOTING DETAIL
SCALE - ¾" = 1'-0"

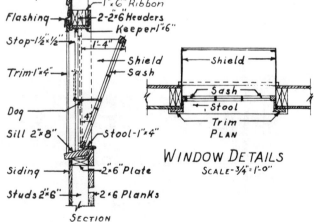

Siding — 2"×6" Studs
1"×6" Ribbon
Flashing — 2-2"×6" Headers
Keeper 1"×6"
Stop - 1½"×½"
1'-4"
Shield
Trim - 1"×4" — Sash

Dog

Sill 2"×8" — Stool - 1"×4"

Siding — 2"×6" Plate

Studs 2"×6" — 2"×6" Planks

SECTION

Shield

Sash

Stool

Trim
PLAN

WINDOW DETAILS
SCALE - ¾" = 1'-0"

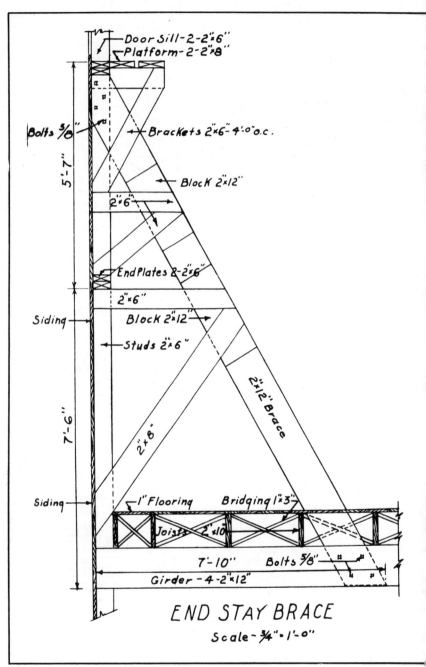

Fig. C-4. Plan for a larger general barn with a gambril roof (continued from page 501).

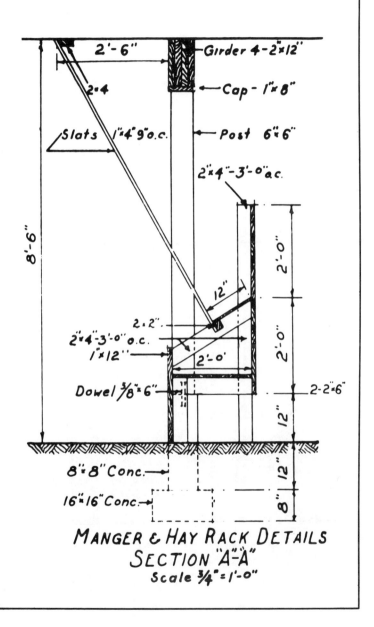

2'-6"

Girder 4-2"×12"

2·4

Cap - 1"×8"

Slats   1"×4" 9" o.c.

Post   6"×6"

2"×4"-3'-0" a.c.

8'-6"

12"

2·2"

2"×4"-3'-0" o.c.

1"×12"

2'-0"

Dowel ⅜"×6"

2-2"×6"

2'-0"

2'-0"

12"

8"×8" Conc.

12"

16"×16" Conc.

8"

MANGER & HAY RACK DETAILS
SECTION "A-A"
Scale ¾"=1'-0"

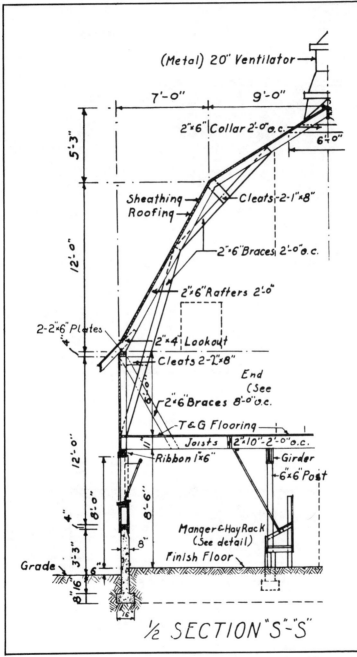

(Metal) 20" Ventilator

7'-0"   9'-0"

2"×6" Collar 2'-0" o.c.

6"-0"

5'-3"

Sheathing
Roofing

Cleats 2-1"×8"

2"×6" Braces 2'-0" o.c.

12'-0"

2"×6" Rafters 2'-0"

2-2"×6" Plates

2"×4" Lookout

Cleats 2-2"×8"

4"

End
(See

2"×6" Braces 8'-0" o.c.

T & G Flooring

Joists 2"×10"-2'-0" o.c.

Ribbon 1"×6"

Girder

6"×6" Post

12'-0"

Manger & Hay Rack
(See detail)

8'-0"

8'-6"

Finish Floor

Grade

3'-3"

8"

6"

8"16"

16

½ SECTION "S"-"S"

Fig. C-4. Plan for a larger general barn with a gambril roof (continued from page 503).

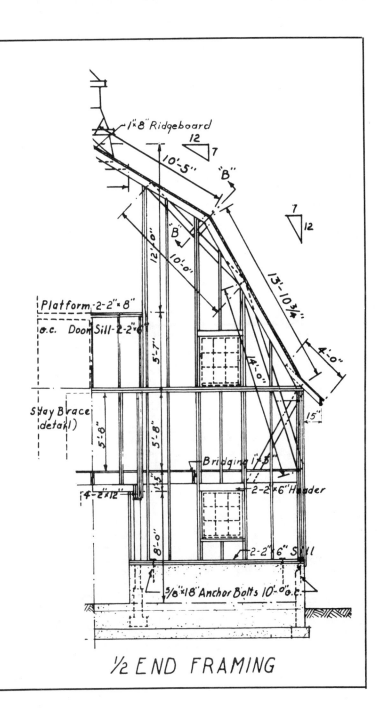

½ END FRAMING

Index